MINOR WORKS, ALTERATIONS, REPAIRS AND MAINTENANCE

SPON'S
CONTRACTORS' HANDBOOK

MINOR WORKS, ALTERATIONS, REPAIRS AND MAINTENANCE

1990

Edited by
SPAIN and PARTNERS
Consulting Quantity Surveyors

LONDON
E. & F.N. SPON

First published in 1986 by
E. & F.N. Spon Ltd
11 New Fetter Lane, London EC4P 4EE

Second edition 1988
Third edition 1990

©1986, 1988, 1990 E. & F.N. Spon

Printed in Great Britain by St Edmundsbury Press
Bury St Edmunds, Suffolk

ISBN 0 419 15020 X
ISSN 0 950 1967

British Library Cataloguing in Publication Data

Spon's contractors' handbook: prices, costs
    and estimates for jobs from £50-£30,000.
    Minor works, alterations, repairs and
    maintenance. – 3rd edn [1990] –
    1. Buildings – Maintenance – Estimates –
    Great Britain – Handbooks, manuals, etc.
    2. Buildings – Repair and reconstruction
    – Estimates – Great Britain –
    Handbooks, manuals, etc.
    692'.5   TH3311

    ISBN 0 – 419 – 15020 – X

CONTENTS

CONTENTS

PREFACE

This is the third edition of Spon's Contractors' Handbook - Minor Works, Alterations, Repairs and Maintenance. As before the book has been written for the contractor carrying out small works who is either considering starting his own business or has already commenced trading but requires both technical and commercial support sides of his business. The generic term 'Builder' or 'Contractor' has been used in the text and this applies to the operative carrying out the work which covers more than one trade in this context. The unit rates are intended to apply to work varying from small domestic work to contracts up to £30,000 in value.

The book has two main sections. The first ten chapters deal with problems of taxation, insurance, book-keeping, etc., and contain advice that would normally be available from professional advisers such as accountants, solicitors, insurance brokers and management consultants. This advice is set out in an easy-to-read style with many examples. It is not intended that these chapters should replace the need for professional advice when the occasion warrants it but are meant to complement this need and hopefully save money in consultation fees.

The remaining chapters deal with the technical aspects of minor works, alterations, repairs and maintenance particularly in relation to the costs of carrying out the work. It cannot be stressed too strongly that despite claims made on their behalf, price books should not be used as a literal source of information for preparing quotations. The item descriptions are based upon the requirements of SMM6 (The Standard Method of Building Works - 6th Edition) but do not comply with it in every case. SMM7 was published in January 1988 and will gradually replace SMM6. A comparative index has been set out on page ix showing the relationship of the relevant trade and and work sections of SMM6 and 7.

There are many items affecting the value of building works. The speed and skill of individual workmen, the price paid for materials, the co-operation of the occupier of the premises are only a few factors which can directly affect the profitability of a job. The rates in Chapter 12 should be used as a basis only for preparing an estimate or quotation.

These comments do not detract from the real value of the information in this chapter. Aproximately 4000 item descriptions and unit rates are given which are based on 15000 separate pieces of data

PREFACE

providing a wealth of detailed cost information. The approximate estimating section should prove useful in providing information of the costs of packages of work without the need for a detailed build up.

All the costing information contained in this book is based upon the price of material at April 1989 and the wages award on 26 June 1989. All the advice and comments made in Chapters 1 to 10 on the commercial side of the business are based on current legislation and professional help should be sought if changes are made.

There are now many women working in the construction industry. The pronoun 'he' used throughout this book applies to both men and women.

The editors have received a great deal of help from many sources in the research and the preparation of this book and would like to acknowledge the assistance given with grateful thanks.

In particular our thanks are again due to John Thirlwell for the major part he played in the preparation of the early chapters dealing with the commercial side of business.

The editors would welcome constructive criticism of the book together with suggestions for improving its scope and contents.

While every effort is made to ensure the accuracy of the information given in this publication, neither the editors nor the publishers in any way accept liability of any kind resulting from the use made by any person of such information.

Bryan J.D. Spain, FInstCES MACostE
Leonard B. Morley, DipQS FRICS MInstCES MACostE

Spain and Partners
Consulting Quantity Surveyors
Unit 9
SMM Business Park
Dock Road
Birkenhead
Merseyside L41 1DT

F CONCRETE WORK

E   IN SITU CONCRETE/LARGE PRECAST
    CONCRETE

In situ concrete

E10 In situ concrete

E11 Gun applied concrete

Labours/sundries

E40 Designed joints in in situ concrete

E41 Worked finishes/Cutting to in situ
    concrete

E42 Accessories cast into in situ concrete

P22 Sealant joints

J31 Liquid applied waterproof roof
    coatings

J32 Sprayed vapour barriers

J33 In situ glass reinforced plastics

damp proof membranes

J30 Liquid applied tanking/damp proof
    membranes

J40 Flexible sheet tanking/damp proof
    membranes

surface sealers

M60 Painting/Clear finishing

holes and chases for services

P31 Holes/Chases/Covers/Supports for
    services

Reinforcement

E30 Reinforcement for in situ concrete

E31 Post tensioned reinforcement for in
    situ concrete

Formwork

E20 Formwork for in situ concrete

Precast concrete
  small units

F31 Precast concrete sills/lintels/
    copings/features

H14 Concrete rooflights/pavement lights

large units

E50 Precast concrete large units

H40 Glass reinforced cement cladding/
    features

H50 Precast concrete slab cladding/
    features

F   CONCRETE WORK cont'd

R	PLUMBING AND MECHANICAL ENGINEERING INSTALLATIONS	R	DISPOSAL SYSTEMS
		S	PIPED SUPPLY SYSTEMS
		T	MECHANICAL HEATING/COOLING REFRIGERATION SYSTEMS
		U	VENTILATION/AIR CONDITIONING SYSTEMS
		X	TRANSPORT SYSTEMS
		Y	MECHANICAL AND ELECTRICAL SERVICES MEASUREMENT

Classification of work

a. rainwater installation — R10 Rainwater pipework/gutters

b. sanitary installation (including traps) — R11 Foul drainage above ground

c. cold water installation
- S10 Cold water
- S13 Pressurised water
- S14 Irrigation
- S15 Fountains/Water features
- S20 Treated/Deionised/Distilled water
- S21 Swimming pool water treatment

d. firefighting installation
- S60 Fire hose reels
- S61 Dry risers
- S62 Wet risers
- S63 Sprinklers
- S64 Deluge
- S65 Fire hydrants
- S70 Gas fire fighting
- S71 Foam fire fighting

e. heated, hot water installations etc.
- S11 Hot water
- S12 Hot and cold water (small scale)
- S51 Steam

R   PLUMBING AND MECHANICAL
     ENGINEERING INSTALLATIONS cont'd

R   PLUMBING AND MECHANICAL
     ENGINEERING INSTALLATIONS cont'd

	U10 General supply/extract
	U11 Toilet extract
	U12 Kitchen extract
	U13 Car parking extract
	U14 Smoke extract/Smoke control
	U15 Safety cabinet/Fume cupboard extract
	U16 Fume extract
	U17 Anaesthetic gas extract
	U20 Dust collection
	U30 Low-velocity air conditioning
	U31 VAV air conditioning
	U32 Dual-duct air conditioning
	U33 Multi-zone air conditioning
	U40 Induction air conditioning
	U41 Fan-coil air conditioning
	U42 Terminal re-heat air conditioning
	U43 Terminal heat pump air conditioning
	U50 Hybrid system air conditioning
	U60 Free standing air conditioning units
	U61 Windows/Wall air conditioning units
	U70 Air curtains
	Y24 Trace heating
	Y25 Cleaning and chemical treatment
t. automatic control installation	Y53 Control components-mechanical
u. special equipment eg kitchen equipment	N12 Catering equipment
v. other specialist installations	
	X10 Lifts
	X11 Escalators
	X12 Moving pavements
	X20 Hoists
	X21 Cranes
	X22 Travelling cradles
	X23 Goods distribution/Mechanized warehousing
	X30 Mechanical document conveying
	X31 Pneumatic document conveying
	X32 Automatic document filing and retrieval

PLUMBING AND MECHANICAL
ENGINEERING INSTALLATIONS cont'd

S ELECTRICAL INSTALLATIONS

V ELECTRICAL SUPPLY/POWER LIGHTING SYSTEMS

W COMMUNICATIONS/SECURITY/CONTROL SYSTEMS

Y MECHANICAL AND ELECTRICAL MEASUREMEN SERVICES

Classification of work

a. incoming services

V11 HV supply/distribution/public utilit supply

V12 LV supply/public utility supply

b. standby equipment

V32 Uninterrupted power supply

V40 Emergency lighting

c. mains installation excluding final sub circuits

V20 LV distribution

d. power installation

V22 General LV power

e. lighting installation

V21 General lighting

V41 Street/Area/Flood lighting

V42 Studio/Auditorium/Arena lighting

V90 General lighting and power (small scale)

W21 Projection

W22 Advertising display

f. electric heating installation

V50 Electric underfloor heating

V51 Local electric heating units

g. electric appliances

-

h. electrical work associated with plumbing and mechanical engineering installations

Y53 Control components - mechanical

j. telephone installations

W10 Telecommunications

k. clock installation

W23 Clocks

S   ELECTRICAL INSTALLATIONS cont'd

T   FLOOR WALL AND CEILING FINISHINGS cont'd

FEDERATION OF MASTER BUILDERS

National President: *R. W. Moore, B.Eng.*
Director General: *W. S. Hilton*

Gordon Fisher House
33 John Street
London WC1N 2BB
Telephone: 01-242 7583

Estimating is not an exact science; if it were then there would be almost no competitive element in tendering for work. It is more like the art of navigation: a great deal of detailed and scientific knowledge is required but, near the end of the journey, human judgement is necessary.

Yet some specific knowledge is required on which to base estimates and, for many builders doing minor works, this is usually supplied by a "price book" giving rates for measured work. There are a number of these and they have been around for many years. Yet most were of little specific assistance in the minor works area.

The advent of Spon's handbook, dealing precisely with the rates required on minor works of alteration, repairs and maintenance, was therefore warmly welcomed by builders in my Federation and throughout the industry.

Of course the builder still requires to exercise judgement, based on previous experience and the current state of the market, but — like a good compass and chart to the navigator — the Spon's handbook gives a valuable base for successful estimating.

W. S. Hilton
Director General

SPAIN AND PARTNERS

* Editors of Spon's Contractors' Handbooks for

    Painting and Decorating
    Plumbing and Domestic Heating
    Minor works, Alterations, Repairs and Maintenance
    Roofing
    Electrical Installation
    Floor Wall and Ceiling Finishes

* Authors of CESMM 2 Explained

    A complete guide for engineers, surveyors and students

* Authors of Home Improvement Price Guide

* Consultants to public and private clients on building
  and civil engineering projects

* Advisers on preparation and negotiation of contractual
  claims including recovery of outstanding monies

Unit 9
SMM Business Park
Dock Road   Tel: 051-652 6711
Birkenhead   Telex: 629270 SMM BH
Merseyside L41 1DT   Facsimile: 051-652 2377

SPON'S CONTRACTORS' HANDBOOKS

Edited by **Spain and Partners**

Prices, Costs and Estimates for jobs from £50 up to £30,000

Spon's Contractors' Handbook: Minor Works, Alterations, Repairs and Maintenance
3rd Edition (1990)
Paperback 0 419 15020 X £16.95 408pp

Spon's Contractors' Handbook: Roofing
2nd Edition (1990)
Paperback 0 419 15030 7 £15.95 248pp

Spon's Contractors' Handbook: Floor, Wall and Ceiling Finishings
2nd Edition (1990)
Paperback 0 419 15080 3 £16.95 280pp

Spon's Contractors' Handbook: Painting and Decorating
3rd Edition (1990)
Paperback 0 419 15040 4 £14.95 216pp

Spon's Contractors' Handbook: Plumbing and Domestic Heating
2nd Edition (1989)
Paperback 0 419 14720 9 £13.95 282pp

Spon's Contractors' Handbook: Electrical Installation
(1989)
Paperback 0 419 14740 3 £15.95 340pp

E & F N SPON
11 New Fetter Lane, London EC4P 4EE

SPON'S CONTRACTORS' HANDBOOKS

ORDER FORM

Please send me:–

_____ copy/ies of **Spon's Contractors' Handbook: Minor Works, Alterations, Repairs and Maintenance** @ £16.95

_____ copy/ies of **Spon's Contractors' Handbook: Roofing** @ £15.95

_____ copy/ies of **Spon's Contractors' Handbook: Floor, Wall and Ceiling Finishings** @ £16.95

_____ copy/ies of **Spon's Contractors' Handbook: Painting and Decorating** @ £14.95

_____ copy/ies of **Spon's Contractors' Handbook: Plumbing and Domestic Heating** @ £13.95
(1989 Edition)

_____ copy/ies of **Spon's Contractors' Handbook: Electrical Installation** @ £15.95
(1989 Edition)

Please tick as appropriate

☐ I enclose a cheque/PO for £ _____ payable to E & FN Spon Ltd

☐ Please charge to ☐ Access ☐ Visa ☐ AmEx ☐ Diners Club

Card Number_____ Expiry Date_____

☐ I enclose an official order, please send invoice with books

Name_____

Address_____

_____ Postcode_____

Signature_____

Return to: The Promotion Department, E & FN Spon, Freepost, KE7 748, London EC4B 4JB.

Chapter 1: Starting Up In Business

Before committing himself by giving up his job, the would-be business man should consider carefully whether he has the skills and also the temperament to survive in the highly competitive self-employed market. At the very least he needs:-

Enthusiasm - to work long hours not only at his trade but getting new contracts; buying stock of the right quality at the best price; planning work schedules and, often in the evenings and at weekends, entering up the books, making up and sending out bills and dealing with VAT, PAYE, 715's, etc.

Determination - to overcome the difficulties and set-backs (many wholly unexpected) that will surely arise.

Self-confidence - to act effectively on his own without the help of superiors to make decisions and take responsibility; the companionship of workmates and the support of a regular wage and paid holidays.

Where appropriate the whole project should be talked over with the family at a very early stage and their support enlisted. Many small businesses depend substantially for their success on the family member at home who answers the phone, takes messages and sometimes does the book work.

Before starting up the following should also be considered:-

1. Finance - what funds will be needed and at what points of time for such items as premises, plant, transport, tools, initial stocks of materials etc. and to pay wages, overheads and the proprietors' living expenses until the cash from work done begins to flow in. How is the price of work done to be calculated?
   All of this needs a proper "business plan" and if the bank or other sources of finance are to be tapped such a plan is essential. Fortunately help in its preparation is available from a number of agencies sponsored by government, local authorities and industry usually at little or no cost. (See check list item 5 below.)

2. Testing the market - talk to as many traders already operating in the same field as possible. Try to identify if the need is in the industrial, commercial, local government or domestic field. Talk to likely customers and clients and consider whether it is possible to improve on what they are being offered at present in terms of price, quality, speed, convenience, follow-up, etc.

3. Experience and training - an objective appraisal having been made of the likely market for the goods or services, the extent to which one is equipped to satisfy its requirements should be

1

considered. Gaps in experience might be filled by a change of present duties or of employer, whilst some lack of skills can probably be overcome by taking a training course.

With the preliminary work done, the businessman should have a general idea of the finance required for start up and be satisfied that there is a market for his product or service. He now needs to consider what will be the best format for his business; should he go it alone as a sole trader, take one or more partners, or set up a limited company?

Each has its advantages and drawbacks and although it is not usually crucial to survival, the businessman should try to choose the one best suited to his situation. Some of the points to consider are given below:-

1. Sole trader - the least complex structure and one which gives the businessman most freedom of action and decision. He does not have the onerous legal requirements of a limited company, nor does he have to consider the views and wishes of a partner. On the other hand, the sole trader has no-one who is as fully committed to the success of the enterprise as he is himself with whom to discuss his problems or assume part of the financial and managerial burden.

2. Partnership - one of the important advantages of a partnership is the sharing of the initial financial burden. Funds to buy plant, vehicles, stock, etc. are not easy to accumulate and borrowing from banks is costly so the prospect of a partner who will put up his share of the money can be very attractive. A well chosen partner can also be a great help in the day-to-day running of the business since he has (or should have) an equal interest in ensuring that new contracts are obtained and that work is done on time and to the required standard.

However, many partnerships founder because of disagreements between the partners. Inequality of work sharing, and of monies put in to the business, disagreement about pricing work and whether or not to expand or diversify are a few common areas of conflict. The choice of the right business partner is therefore crucial to the success of the undertaking. A friend or relative may make a good partner but that relationship alone is not a sound basis for going into business with him. A partner should be efficient at his work, easy to get on with, hard working, fully committed to the success of the enterprise and above all honest.

Honesty is of particular importance because partners are liable for the partnership debts on a "joint and several" basis. This means that if the firm should fail to meet its financial obligations each one of the partners individually may be proceeded against by a creditor for the whole of the debt. This liability extends to the income tax due on the partnership profits. For example if three partners, A, B and C each owe £5000 in income tax and A and B, having no funds or realisable assets, are unable to pay their shares the Inland Revenue will look to C for the whole

£15,000 due.

A sole trader might consider taking a partner:-

(a) To provide additional finance (unlike banks, etc. no
interest need be paid on 'capital introduced' by the
partners).

(b) To provide complementary skills - whether trade, financial,
marketing, etc.

(c) To cope with expansion or develop a new project.

(d) To provide cover whilst he is absent - on business, on
holiday or through sickness.

Some features are common to sole traders and partnerships:-

(a) Both pay income tax for a year of assessment based normally
on the profits of the accountancy period ended in the
previous year. There is usually therefore a longer time
between earning the profits and paying tax on them than
there is for a limited company.

(b) Sole traders and partners pay Class 2 and Class 4 National
Insurance contributions which total substantially less than
the Class 1 contributions made by employers and employees in
the case of company directors (it should be said that the
benefits are correspondingly less, too).

(c) For tax purposes trading losses may be set off against other
income (including wife's earnings) and losses incurred in
early years of trading may be carried back and set off
against income received before going into business.

3. Limited companies - a limited company is a legal entity in its
own right, separate from the individuals who own it (the shareholders) and those who run it (the directors). It can sue and be
sued in its own name and as the title implies the liability of the
investors in it is limited to the amount they have subscribed for
shares. It is regulated by complex and detailed rules which are
contained in the 747 sections and 25 schedules of the Companies Act
1985. It pays corporation tax on its profits; this falls due 9
months after the end of its accounting period. The directors are
employees of the company and pay tax under PAYE and they and the
company pay Class 1 National Insurance contributions.
Some additional points about limited companies are:-

(a) In practice the limitation of liability is often materially
reduced because banks and other lenders insist on personal

3

guarantees from the directors (usually a legal charge over any property owned).

(b) The limited company is a very useful and flexible instrument for the introduction of funds by non-active investors and for giving a stake in the business to family members or successful managers.

(c) Keeping up with the legal requirements is more costly in proprietors' time and professional fees.

(d) The tax regime of corporation tax and PAYE in general involves more paperwork and earlier payment than self-employment. However successful businesses can more readily avoid the higher rates of income tax if they are limited companies.

(e) Better pension provisions are available to directors than under the self-employed arrangements, but the Finance Act 1989 will propose higher contributions for the self-employed which will lessen the gap between them (see pages 56, 57 and 58).

The limited company format should be considered where:-

(a) Funds are available from individuals and concerns who do not wish to be involved in the daily running of the business and who prefer a share of the profits to interest on a loan.

(b) The trade is in a field where there is a high risk of legal claims for damages etc., and the protection of limited liability is very desirable.

(c) The profits of a sole trader are rising above £22,000 (in a partnership - above £22,000 for each partner). Higher rate tax at 40% will soon be payable and may be avoided by changing to a limited company.

(d) The normal practice in the trade is to be "limited". Those wishing to enter the field may have little choice but to be "limited" themselves.

(e) Wider family ownership is sought or senior staff incentives are required.

4. Co-operatives - a new form of business entity, the "co-operative" has arisen in recent years, which might suit some groups of traders. Before entering into such an arrangement however advice must be sought from experienced advisers. Advice and local contacts can be provided by the National Co-operative Development Agency. Phone London: 01-839-2988 or Manchester: 061-833-9379.

5. Conclusion - unless there are compelling reasons for trading through a limited company it is easier and cheaper to start up as a sole trader or in a small partnership because they both give important taxation and cash-flow advantages in the initial years. Also, it is relatively easy to change to a limited company if desired. However professional advice should be sought <u>before</u> any decision to incorporate an existing business is made because bad timing of the change could be costly.

Check list for business start-up

Preliminary work should include seeing as many of the following advisers, business contacts and officials as appropriate:-

1. The Small Firms Service - a confidential service run by the Government and operated by experienced and independent businessmen covering all aspects of business - finance, technical, marketing, advertising, grants, taxation, etc. Contact the service early - the advice given will help with the rest of the preliminary work and many of the publications mentioned below are available there. Small Firms Offices cover the whole of the country and the first three counselling sessions are free.

Point of contact: dial 100 and ask for Freephone Enterprise.

2. Department of Employment

(a) For advice about the Enterprise Allowance grant of £40 per week payable for 12 months after start-up to those who are unemployed or are made redundant and who can raise or borrow £1000. Ask for their pamphlet "Be Your Own Boss".

(b) For information about courses for new and existing businessmen - on start-up, management, marketing, craft and technical skills etc. Ask for their pamphlet "Your Guide to our Employment, Training and Enterprise Programmes" - These courses are FREE. Anyone starting in business for the first time is strongly advised to take up a 7 day "B.E.P." course BEFORE commencing to trade.

(c) For advice on recruitment and training if it is intended to employ people.

Once again the Government is making major changes in its arrangements for help to existing and would-be traders. It is setting up locally based Training and Enterprise Councils - to be known as TEC's - who will be responsible for most of the counselling, support and training for small businesses. Future editions of this publication will keep its readers up-to-date with developments in this field.

Point of contact: local telephone directory for address of local Jobcentre. At the Jobcentre ask for "Business Start-up Training".

3. Potential customers and trade contacts - many who go self-employed in the construction industry already have experience as employees. Use these contacts to check the market, establish the sort of work which is available and the current contract rates. In the domestic market check on the competition for prices, standards of work and service provided, customer complaints and types of advertising.

Try to get firm promises of work before the start-up date.

4. Potential suppliers - canvas local suppliers for the best prices, credit terms, minimum order, discounts offered and delivery times. Remember cash is the life-blood of business and a supplier who gives 30 days credit and delivers small quantities at 24/48 hours notice may be a better buy than one with lower prices but who operates on cash-and-carry terms only. Do not over stock, carry only what is needed for current requirements - this is important - do not tie-up scarce and expensive money in stock which may not be used for weeks or even months.

5. Banks - for information about a business current account and financial services available. Find out about the types of loan required; from an overdraft for working capital to medium and long term loans including the Government's Loan Guarantee Scheme for the purchase of plant and machinery, alterations to premises, etc. See the Small Firms Service first for information about the best approach and to find out what the Bank Manager will need. Shop around several banks and branches if you are not satisfied at first, managers vary widely in their views of what is a viable business proposition.

Point of contact: the local bank manager.

6. H.M. Inspector of Taxes - make a preliminary visit to the local tax office enquiry counter for their publications:-

IR 14/15 Construction Industry Tax Deduction Scheme
IR28   "Starting in Business", and, if needed,
IR40   "Conditions for getting a sub-contractor's tax certificate".
IR53   "PAYE for employers" (if you intend to employ someone).

The onus is on the taxpayer to notify the Inland Revenue that he is in business, failure to do so may result in the imposition of interest and penalties. Either send a letter or use the form provided in the middle of the "Starting in Business" booklet.

Point of contact: telephone directory for address.

7. VAT Office - registration for VAT is required if the taxable turnover (including zero-rated items) exceeds £23,600 in the past 4 quarters or £8,000 in the last quarter, or it is expected that the £23,600 level will be exceeded in the next 12 months. (These figures apply from 15.3.89.) Failure to register within 30 days of the end of the quarter in which the above limits are exceeded is an offence punishable by the imposition of financial penalties.

The VAT office also carries a number of useful publications; among them are:-

```
700      "The VAT Guide".
700/1    "Should I be Registered for VAT".
700/12   "Filling in Your VAT Return".
700/21   "Keeping Records and Accounts".
708/2    "Application of VAT to the Construction Industry".
731      "Cash Accounting".
732      "Annual Accounting".
742      "Land and Property".
```

Notes on the application of VAT to the Construction Industry are in Chapter 4 together with information about the new "Cash accounting scheme" and the proposal to introduce annual VAT returns.

Point of contact: telephone directory for address.

8. DSS Office - Class 2 contributions may be paid either in cash or by direct debit through a bank account. Call at the local office to make the necessary arrangements. Class 4 contributions which are also payable by the self-employed are collected along with the income tax by the Inland Revenue and no special action by the businessman is required.

Ask at the DSS office for the following publications:-

```
NI 41   "N.I. guide for the self-employed".
NI 27A  "People with small earnings from self-employment".
NI 35   "N.I. for Company Directors".
NI 255  "Direct debit - the easy way to pay".
```

and for employers

```
NP 15   "Employers guide to N.I.C".
NI 227  "Employers guide to Statutory Sick Pay".
```
Point of contact: telephone directory for address.

9. Local authorities - authorities vary in the provisions made for small businesses, but all have been asked to simplify and cut delays in planning applications. In "Assisted Areas" and "Enterprise Zones" rent free periods and reductions in rates may be available on certain industrial and commercial properties. As a preliminary to either purchasing or renting business premises the

following booklets will be very helpful. "A Step by Step Guide to
Planning Permission for Small Businesses" and "Business Leases and
Security of Tenure" both are issued by the Department of Employment
and are available at council offices, Citizens Advice Bureaux and
Small Firms Service Offices.

Some authorities run training schemes in conjunction with local
industry and educational establishments.

Point of contact: usually the planning department - ask for the
Industrial Development or Economic Development Officer.

10. Department of Trade and Industry - for information and advice
about grants available and application forms etc. (see Chapter 2
for details).

Point of contact: through the Small Firms Service: Freephone
Enterprise, or phone 01-215-4021 and ask for the address and phone
number of the nearest D.T.I. office.

11. Accountant - the services of a qualified accountant are
essential from the beginning if a limited company format is to be
used, the legal requirements start immediately and must be properly
complied with if later trouble is to be avoided. For all types of
business the accountant will give advice on book-keeping, taxation,
finance, etc., and will prepare the annual accounts.

It is worth spending some time finding an accountant who has
other clients in the same line of business and is able to give
sound advice particularly on taxation and business finance and is
not so overworked that damaging delays in producing accounts are
likely to arise. Ask other traders whether they can recommend
their own accountant; preferably visit more than one firm of
accountants, ask about the fees they charge and how much the
production of annual accounts and agreement with the Inland Revenue
is likely to cost and how long the work will take. A good
accountant is worth every penny of his fees but do not hesitate to
change him if his service is unsatisfactory.

12. Solicitor - many businesses operate without the services of a
solicitor but there are a number of occasions when legal advice
should be sought. In particular no-one should sign the lease of
premises without asking a solicitor what they are committing
themselves to because it is not unusual for a business to be put
into financial difficulty through unnoticed liabilities in its
lease. Either an accountant or solicitor will help with drawing up
a partnership agreement which all partnerships should have.

A solicitor will also help to explain complex contract terms and
prepare draft contracts if the type of business being entered into
requires them.

13. Insurance broker - policies are available to cover many aspects
of business: a few of these are:-

Employer's liability - compulsory if the business has employees.

Starting Up In Business

Public liability - essential in the construction industry.
Motor vehicles.
Theft of stock, plant, money, etc.
Fire and storm damage.
Personal accident and loss of profits.

Brokers are independent advisers who will obtain competitive
quotations on your behalf. See more than one broker before making
a decision - their advice is normally given free and without
obligation. See also Chapter 8.
Point of contact: telephone directory or write for a list of

local members to:- The British Insurance Brokers Association
                   Consumer Relations Department
                   BIBA House
                   14 Bevis Marks
                   London
                   EC3A 7NT
                   Phone 01-623 9043

or contact:-   The Association of British Insurers
                   Aldermary House
                   Queen Street
                   London
                   EC4N 1TT
                   Phone 01-248 4477

who will supply FREE a package of very useful Advice Files
specially designed for the Small Business.

14. The Health and Safety Executive - the Executive operates the
legislation covering everyone engaged in work activities. Concerns
should obtain the following free literature:-

    HSE 16   The Law on Health and Safety at Work.
    HSE2   Outline - Health and Safety at Work etc. Act.
    IND(G)14(L) Compliance with health and safety legislation at
                work.
    HSE4   Short guide to Employer's Liability (Compulsory
                Insurance) Act 1969.

The Executive has just issued a very useful set of "Construction
Health Hazard Information Sheets" covering such topics as handling
cement, lead and solvents; safety in the use of ladders,
scaffolding, hoists, cranes, flammable liquids and compressed
gases etc. A pack of these may be obtained FREE from:-

Starting Up In Business

The Health & Safety Executive
Sir Robert Jones Workshops
5/9 Grain Industrial Estate
Harlow Street
Liverpool
L8 4UH

Finally:-

1. The Business Names Act 1985 - this requires any business carried on
in a name other than that of the owner to disclose details of his name
and address. How this is done is described in a pamphlet issued by
the Companies Registration Office and obtainable on request from
offices of the Small Firms Service.

2. Expenditure incurred before trading starts - there is income tax
and corporation tax relief for revenue (i.e. not capital) expenditure
incurred for the purposes of the trade during the five years before
the trade commenced. All such expenses, e.g. business travelling
costs, postage and stationery, advertising, etc., should be properly
recorded and invoices retained for later production to the accountant.
The rent, rates, heat and light of business premises occupied in the
setting-up period would also qualify. Capital expenditure incurred
before trading begins (for example on plant and vehicles) is treated
as if incurred on the first-day of trading.

3. Advertising - this will be necessary at least for those entering
the domestic part of the industry. Advice on the best media to use
and on the content of advertising is available though the Small Firms
Service.

With the foregoing contacts made, the would-be businessman should
be a great deal better informed about his new venture and better
equipped to make it a success. Among other things he should know:-

1. Whether he is really suited to self-employment at all.

2. What business format - sole trader, partnership, limited company
   - will be best for him.

3. What training (if any) he needs and where it can be obtained.

4. Where his market is and how best it can be reached.

5. What money he needs (a) for capital items and (b) for running
   and living expenses and where it is coming from.

6. At what level his prices must be set.

7. What is required of him by the authorities.

8. What business insurances are needed.

Chapter 2: Finance And Grants

In Chapter 1 on Starting Up in Business the need for a business plan was explained. This would include a cash flow forecast (Chapter 5) which would indicate what funds would be needed to cover long term capital investment and the working capital (i.e. running costs) for start up and the first 12 months of trading. The immediate problem is to determine how the business is to be financed. The potential businessman may well find that his first ideas require too much money and have to be reduced in scale. For example too much is being locked up in capital equipment, or the proposed premises are too expensive so there will be little or nothing available for the proprietor to live on for some months. The first task therefore is to make whatever economies are needed in the plan and then to review the various sources from which the necessary funds might be obtained.

The proprietor and his family

Finance, like charity, begins at home and the would-be businessman should make a realistic assesment of his net worth including the value of his house after deducting any mortgage(s) outstanding on it, his savings, any car or van owned and any sums which his family are prepared to contribute and deduct any private borrowing which will come due for payment in the next 24 months. The whole of these funds may not of course be available (for instance, money which has been loaned to a friend or relative who is known to be unable to repay at the present time) and it may not be desirable either that it should all be put at risk on a business venture. Establish therefore (a) how much cash it is proposed to invest in the business and (b) whether the family home will be made available as security for any business borrowings.

Whilst it may be wise not to pledge too much of the family assets it has to be remembered that the bank will be looking closely at the degree to which the proprietor has committed himself to the venture and will not be impressed by an applicant for a loan who is prepared to risk only a small fraction of his own resources.

Having decided how much of his own funds to contribute, the businessman can now see what the shortfall is and consider how best to fill it.

Partners and directors

Where the gap is large and particularly when it is due to the need for heavy investment in fixed assets such as premises and capital equipment, consideration should be given to taking in partners or starting a limited company, with others also subscribing capital. In this country, unlike the USA, there is a strong aversion to allowing financial backers to have a share in a new venture. But a concern which is adequately funded from the start stands a much better chance of survival than one which is not.

13

Finance And Grants

Banks

The first outside source of money to which most businessmen turn is the bank and a book could be written solely on the do's and don't's of approaching a bank manager. Here are a few tips:-

(a) Have a proper business plan to present to him including a cash flow forecast (12 months is usual) also an opening statement of affairs, projected profit and loss accounts and balance sheets for two years and a written statement describing the whole business venture. Use conservative estimates which tend to understate rather than overstate the forecast sales and profits.

(b) Know the figures in detail - don't leave it to an accountant or Small Firms consultant to explain them for you. The bank manager is interested in the businessman not his advisers and will be impressed if he has a sound grasp of the financing of his business.

(c) Understand the difference between short and long term borrowing; know how much is needed of each and be ready to explain how the business will be able to repay the bank its money.

(d) Ask about the Government Loan Guarantee Scheme if there is a shortage of security for loans. Under this scheme the Government guarantees 70% of the loan up to £100,000 (now up to 85% for loans to businesses in the Inner City Task Force Areas) but in return exacts a premium (presently 2½%) on the normal rate of bank interest, making it rather expensive money. Repayment is over a period from 2 to 7 years.

   All the major banks participate in the scheme and vet applications for the Government. If the bank's local and regional managers accept an application it usually goes through quickly and easily.

   The approach is to the local bank manager and as with any other application a full business plan will be needed.

(e) Be prepared to take the business plan to a number of banks if a satisfactory response is not received at first: persistence sometimes pays off.

Other financial institutions

For well established businesses, usually limited companies, wishing to expand and for some well conceived start-ups, there are a number of financial institutions in the "venture capital" market who will provide a flexible package of equity and loan capital in the range of £25,000 to seven figures. Usually the deal entails the institution having a minority interest in the voting share capital and a seat on the board of the company; arrangements for the eventual purchase of

14

the shares held by the finance company by the private shareholders are
normally also incorporated in the scheme.

Contact points for information and advice are bank managers,
accountants and the Small Firms Service.

The Business Expansion Scheme

If the outside investor in the business is an individual he will
probably wish to invest within the terms of the Business Expansion
Scheme which enables him to get tax relief at his highest rate(s) on
the amount of his investment.

The rules are complex and professional advice is essential; some of
the main provisions are:-

(a) The shares must be new ones (i.e. not previously issued to
anyone) and be part of the ordinary share capital.

(b) The minimum direct investment is £500 and the maximum £40,000.

(c) The investor must not be a close relative of those who control
the business.

(d) Any one subscriber must not hold more than 30% of the issued
ordinary share capital but more than one individual may
subscribe for shares in the same company.

(e) The shares must be held for a minimum of 5 years to qualify for
full relief.

Government Grants

In recent years the Government has frequently changed the nature and
amounts of the grants it is prepared to make to industry. The Regional
Development Grant, which was a corner stone of the old system has been
withdrawn, which is a matter for regret since it was of help to new
businesses creating jobs and/or spending money on capital assets. The
new package of assistance, known collectively as the "Enterprise
Initiative" seems to be aimed more at the already established business
which wants to expand or to make its existing operations more
efficient and cost effective.

Details of the new arrangements are given below but first,
particulars of grants which are continuing to be given:-

1 Regional Selective Assistance Grants
These are to help manufacturing and service projects which
create or safeguard employment, have some identifiable regional
or national benefit and which are in the "Assisted Areas". The
location and extent of these "Assisted Areas" is given in the
booklet about these grants.

Finance And Grants

There are three types of assistance:-

(a) <u>Project Grant</u> Based on the fixed capital cost of project and on the number of jobs it is expected to create or safeguard. Only the minimum amount of money necessary for the project to proceed will be awarded.

(b) <u>Training Grant</u> The cost of training young people up to 25 years of age with new technology skills essential to a particular project may be met up to 80% of the total.

(c) <u>Exchange Risk Guarantees</u> Where a concern is entitled to a loan from the European Coal and Steel Community the Government will, for an annual service charge, cover the exchange risks. Most small building firm projects are unlikely to meet the criteria for acceptance under the scheme though they might benefit indirectly by getting construction contracts from large industrial concerns who are themselves grant-aided.

Any concern which wishes to seek such a grant must bear in mind the essential qualification that support will only be considered if it can be shown that without the grant the project could not be undertaken, or at least not on the scale proposed. No commitment to any expenditure must therefore be made <u>before</u> the grant has been applied for and an offer of assistance received by the Department of Trade and Industry. Any such expenditure or binding agreement to spend will be taken as evidence that the project <u>could</u> go ahead without a grant and the application will fail. Addresses for enquiries and application forms of all grants are given at the end of this section.

2   <u>The Enterprise Initiative</u> This is the title given to the new package of grants currently being introduced, they comprise the following types of assistance:-

(a) <u>The Consultancy Initiatives</u> This is help by way of <u>advice</u> to individuals, partnerships and companies of fewer than 500 employees in one or more of the following areas:-

            Marketing
            Design
            Quality
            Manufacturing systems
            Business planning
            Financial and information systems

At the request of the business the DTI arranges for one of its Enterprise Counsellors to visit the business premises and carry out a "Business Review", spending up to 2 days in doing so. This part of the scheme is free to the business. The Counsellor is looking for any areas where improvements can be made or constructive advice would be helpful; the DTI booklet says he "will keep an eye out for untapped resources, inefficient work systems and unrealised potential".

16

His findings will be discussed with the businessman and he may
recommend more detailed and specialised help to be sought from a
consultant who is expert in one of the above fields. If the
businessman agrees the DTI will find a consultant and put him in
touch with the business. Together the consultant and the
businessman will decide what, specifically, is to be looked at
and how many man-days it will involve.
If the business is not in an Assisted Area or an Urban Programme
Area the DTI will pay one half of the cost of between 5 and 15
man-days of consultancy. In Assisted Areas and Urban Programme
Areas the Department will pay two thirds of such cost. Two
aspects of the scheme are helpful to the construction industry:
it has a nationwide application and is not limited to the
Assisted Areas, also it is available to any type of business not
solely to manufacturers and the like. Any business in need of
help in any of the fields covered by the scheme has nothing to
lose by asking for the free two day "Business Review".

(b) Regional Enterprise Grants
These are available to individuals, partnerships and
companies with fewer than 25 employees for projects which will
take place in a Development Area or South Yorkshire.
Assistance is available for INVESTMENT projects in "most
manufacturing and some service sectors". Costs eligible for
grant include plant and machinery (new or second-hand),
buildings, purchase of land, site preparation and vehicles used
solely on site. The grant is 15% of such expenditure up to a
maximum of £15,000. Less likely to apply to most construction
industry work is the other type of grant for INNOVATION projects
which lead to the development and introduction of new products
and processes. The grant is a more generous 50% of eligible
costs up to a maximum of £25,000.
In both types of project the DTI needs to be satisfied that
the business and the project are viable and will ask for a
business plan which includes:
  - A brief description of the business and its key personnel.
  - How the business is expected to develop over the next 2 or
    3 years and what are the market opportunities.
  - How the project and the business will be financed.
The business plan and a copy of the latest accounts of the
business should accompany the grant application form.
As with the Regional Selective Grant no contracts should be
signed or work commenced on the project before the grant has
been approved otherwise the application is almost certain to
fail.

It appears that the ordinary contractor or sub-contractor undertaking
domestic or commercial construction work is most likely to be helped
by:-
The Enterprise Allowance Scheme (See Chapter 1 Check list Item 2) - on
start-up.

Finance And Grants

The Government Loan Guarantee Scheme (See above under "Banks")
- on start-up and for expansion.
The Consultancy Initiatives
- not only when in trouble but to bring added efficiency and new
  ideas to expansion and diversification plans. The initial review
  is free so take advantage of it <u>early</u> in any planning, before
  irrevocable decisions have been taken.
The above are all available nationwide but in Development Areas there
are also the Regional Enterprise Investment Project grants.

Information and Application Forms

Regional Selective Assistance.
    Grants up to £25,000 application forms RSA13
    Grants over £25,000 application forms RSA1.
The Consultancy Initiatives (all types).
    Application form EI 1
Regional Enterprise Grants
    Application forms EI 5

Points of Contact

Ring 0800-500-200 and ask for their booklet "The Enterprise
Initiative" plus any application forms required. Full details of DTI
adresses and phone numbers are given in the booklet.

Or ring the Small Firms Service free on "Freephone Enterprise" and ask
about grants. They have copies of the DTI booklet and application
forms and a counsellor will advise on eligibility etc., and assist
with the making of any application.

The Royal Jubilee and Prince's Trusts

The trusts, through the Youth Business Initiative, provide bursaries
of not more than £1,000 per individual to selected applicants who are
unemployed and aged 25 or under. Grants may be used for tools and
equipment, transport, fees, insurance, instruction and training, but
not to provide working capital, nor for rent and rates, new materials
or stock.
    They operate through a local representative whose name and address
may be ascertained by contacting:-

                        The Prince's Trust
                        Drapers Hall
                        London
                        EC2N 2DG
                        Telephone: 01-920 0861

Finance And Grants

Local Government assistance

In some areas local authorities make modest grants towards setting up new businesses in addition to offering rate and possibly rent free periods; job creation is often a key factor in securing their interest.

Ask the industrial development officer of the appropriate local authority.

Applying for Finance from Banks or other Investors - What to avoid

All proposals are probed for weaknesses and ones that are not accepted often show some of the following failings:-

(a) The proposer's enthusiasm for the idea is not backed by proper research to establish that there is a market for the product or service.

(b) Inadequate financing by the owner, who is either introducing insufficient funds himself or has inadequate security for the level of bank borrowing being sought.

Both situations leave the backer with what he regards as an unacceptable financial risk.

(c) The proposals are poorly presented; vital information is missing; the scheme does not come across as a credible venture and there is little or no understanding of what is most important to the backer - how and when he will get a return on his investment and the repayment of his capital.

(d) A poor track record. Anyone taking a new venture to a backer for funds, and who already has problems in his present business, has an extra hurdle to get over - convincing the financier that what has happened before will not happen again. Similarly backers will be wary of putting their money into an ambitious venture proposed by someone with little or no business experience.

(e) Lack of expertise. In most business ventures in the construction industry there is no shortage of technical know-how. The proposers are usually keen and capable tradesmen but they have little or no experience in marketing, business finance and commercial management and frequently their business plan does not include bringing in these skills from outside. Sometimes the individual proves to be exceptionally gifted and combines these new skills with his old ones very effectively. The danger then becomes over reliance on one person. Financiers do not like to invest in concerns where the illness or death of one individual is likely to put the whole venture, and with it

19

their money, into jeopardy even if the business has him well insured.

How to present the case

Financial backers are always on the lookout for sound well researched projects run by well organised and highly motivated entrepreneurs but much depends on how the scheme is presented. The business plan should therefore be typed and of attractive appearance. The narrative and figures should supply clear information on at least the following matters:-

(a) Who the proprietors are.

(b) What is the exact nature of their proposal.

(c) What business experience they have in this and other fields.

(d) How it is proposed to make up for any gaps in their experience and/or training.

(e) What market research has been done, by whom and with what result. Are the forecast sales figures in line with the market forecasts?

(f) Who the main competitors are and how this product/service will differ from and be better than existing ones.

(g) What the start-up costs are and the extent to which alternatives (eg renting or leasing property and plant instead of purchase) have been considered.

(h) What capital the proprietors propose to invest and what return they expect for themselves by way of salaries, dividends etc.

(i) What outside capital is being sought: what the security for it is: what return the investor can expect on his money and over what period it is expected any repayment of capital can be made.

(j) Any plans for expansion; product development; diversification etc.

Professional help will be needed in preparing the business plan and this is usually given by the firm's accountant; however new starters and those for whom cash is short should go to the Small Firms Service. One of their financial counsellors will advise on its preparation and probably at less cost.

Chapter 3: The Construction Industry Deduction Scheme (714's)

The Construction Industry Deduction Scheme

The Construction Industry Tax Deduction Scheme is known universally as the "714" Scheme, after the number of the official form around which the whole system revolves.

The Revenue first tried to counter the widespread tax evasion by sub-contractors working on the "Lump" in 1971 but that scheme created almost as many headaches for the tax authorities as they had had before. The present regulations were introduced by the Finance (No.2) Act 1975 and have remained substantially unaltered ever since. Evasion still exists but on a reduced scale and with the computerisation of the handling of documents within the department (this was up-dated as recently as March 1986), rigorous policing by the districts responsible for the issue of the 714 exemption certificates and heavy penalties for offenders, the pressure to comply is very strong indeed.

It is this background of evasion which explains why the Revenue is so strict in applying the conditions under which they will issue an exemption certificate.

The scheme operates whenever a 'Contractor' makes a payment to a 'Sub-contractor'.

If the Sub-contractor does not hold a valid tax certificate (714I, 714P, 714C or 714S) issued to him by the Inland Revenue then the Contractor must deduct tax (at 25%) from the whole of any payment made to him (excluding the cost of any materials). If however he holds such a certificate the payment may be made in full without deducting tax (in the case of a 714S there is a weekly limit after which tax is deductible).

A business is not obliged by law to seek an exemption certificate, it can legally work in the construction industry without one; but as a matter of practice many main Contractors are reluctant to undertake the additional paper work required when tax has to be deducted and accounted for to the Revenue and will give work to a Sub-contractor with a 714 certificate in preference to one without.

Those already working in the industry will know their position in relation to the scheme so these notes are addressed primarily to tradesmen just starting up on their own account.

First the businessman should visit his local income tax enquiry office and obtain copies of the Revenue booklet IR 14/15 and leaflet IR 40 which explain the conditions under which the Revenue will issue a 714 certificate. In the notes which follow where a matter is detailed or complex, reference is made to the relevant paragraphs of these two publications.

To whom does the Scheme apply?

The scheme covers "construction operations" for which a payment is made between a "Contractor" and a "Sub-contractor". All these terms

21

The Construction Industry Deduction Scheme (714's)

are clearly defined in the regulations.

(a) "Construction operations". This covers anything done to a temporary or permanent building, structure or civil engineering project or installation. It includes site preparation, construction, alteration, repair, dismantling and demolition, but not canteen facilities, security and other non-construction work. Where a contract relates to a mixture of jobs then if any one of the jobs comes within the scheme then <u>all</u> payments under the contract fall within the scheme.

For instance if a contract provides only for the delivery of road making materials to a site this would not be within the scheme, but if it also covers the forming of the roadway then all payments under it would come within the scheme (see the example at end of this chapter).

For detailed information see IR 14/15 paragraphs 36-40 and appendices A and B.

(b) "Contractor". This means any person carrying out "construction operations" as defined above plus local authorities, development corporations, new town commissions, housing associations and trusts and certain non-construction businesses which spend on average more than £250,000 p.a. on construction operations, for example large department stores, banks, etc. It includes, among others, speculative builders and certain labour agencies. (See IR 14/15 paragraphs 15-20).

c) "Sub-contractor". Any business which does "construction operations" for a "Contractor" is a "Sub-contractor" under the scheme, whether it is run by an individual, a partnership or as a limited company.

No part of the scheme applies however to employees; their emoluments should be taxed in the normal way under PAYE. (IR 14/15 paragraphs 25-34).

It will be seen that where a firm is doing work - say for a bank or brewery which is within the scheme, and that firm engages other businesses to do some of the work, it will be operating on that job both as a "Contractor" and a "Sub-contractor".

A small business that does work only for the general public, including small commercial concerns, is outside the scheme and does not need a 714 certificate to trade. If, however, it engages other Contractors to do jobs for it, the business would have to register under the scheme as a Contractor and deduct tax from any payments made to a Sub-contractor who did not produce a valid 714 certificate.

Obtaining a 714 certificate

There is a special application form which may be obtained from tax

The Construction Industry Deduction Scheme (714's)

offices and a number of conditions have to be met before the Revenue will issue a certificate.

In general terms these are:-

(a) The applicant must be working as a Sub-contractor in the United Kingdom in the construction industry.

(b) The business must be run from proper premises with the usual business facilities and records must be kept and a business bank account operated.

(c) The applicant must have been employed or self-employed in the United Kingdom for a continuous period of 3 years in the 6 years before the date of application. Short breaks in employment will not be taken into account unless they exceed 6 months in total (but see (e) below).

(d) The applicant must have a satisfactory tax and NIC record. (The Inland Revenue will check the NI contribution position with the DSS).

(e) School leavers who can show that in the 6 years up to the date of application they were in full-time education or training, for a continuous period of 3 years, or in full-time education or training for part of the 3 years and unemployed or in self employment for the rest, may apply for a special certificate (714S).

(f) Those who satisfy all the conditions except (c) above also may obtain a special certificate (714S) if they can arrange for a bank to guarantee the tax payable on the amounts received in full. (Leaflet IR 40 sets out the conditions in detail.)

Difficulties usually arise through long term unemployment beyond the limits referred to in (c). Representations have been and still are being made to the Revenue by a number of bodies to have this condition relaxed, but with no success to date. Anyone in this position who wishes to trade as a Sub-contractor should nevertheless make a personal application to his tax district because circumstances vary and the inspector might be able to exercise some discretion in a particular case, though it has to be said that usually very little leeway is allowed.

There is also a "Catch 22" situation which sometimes arises. The tradesman finds he is unable to get work unless he can produce a 714 certificate whilst the inspector tells him that he is unable to issue him with such a certificate until he has a contract to start on. Anyone in this situation should obtain from the contractor a clear statement of intent to the effect that on the issue of the 714 that a contract will be given.

The Construction Industry Deduction Scheme (714's)

Anyone applying for the 714S certificate will find that the inspector will put a limit on the amount which can be paid without deduction of tax (usually £150 per week) and that any excess over that figure paid in any week has to suffer the tax deduction. Also, in the case of those who require a bank guarantee, this usually involves the depositing of £2,500 with the bank during the guarantee period and few are able to find such a sum. Special certificates are available to individuals only, not to partnerships or limited companies.

The 714 certificates

There are four types:-

    714I - which is issued to individuals.
    714P - which is issued to partners.
    714C - which is issued to most limited companies.
    714S - which is issued as explained above.

The I, P and S certificates include a photograph of the individual to whom it is issued in addition to his name, NIC number, signature and business name (if any). The certificate also has a serial number and an expiry date. Vouchers numbered 715 (in the case of a special certificate, 715S) are issued along with the 714I, P and S.

Individuals being issued with a certificate are asked to call at the tax office and collect them in person, when the inspector will check that the photograph and the person are in fact one and the same. Company certificates are sent by registered post. Notice of refusal to issue a certificate is given by the inspector in writing and the unsuccessful applicant may appeal against it within 30 days. The appeal will be heard by the general commissioners which is a local, independent body which hears and determines disputes between the inspector and taxpayers. The individual may appear alone and in person to put his case but it is customary for his accountant, if he has one, to accompany him and present the facts on his behalf.

Limited Companies

It is the larger, well established companies which are usually issued with a certificate 714C which relieves them of the necessity of producing a 715 voucher every time they receive a payment, and, as indicated below, they may present a "certifying document" instead of the sub-contractor's certificate to a main contractor.

A smaller company, unable to get a 714C certificate, but whose directors satisfy the requirements at (a) to (f) above may be issued with 714P certificates, each carrying the name and photograph of the director who is qualified to present it.

The Construction Industry Deduction Scheme (714's)

The 714 system in operation

(a) Holders of certificates 714I and P (including company directors holding 714P's)

Before paying a Sub-contractor in full, without deduction of tax, the Contractor must carry out detailed checks on the 714 certificate (the original, not a copy) and the Sub-contractor must produce the 714 for this purpose (see IR 14/15 paragraphs 65-70).

On being paid the Sub-contractor must complete a voucher 715 and give it to the Contractor, showing, among other things, the amount of the payment received.

(b) Holders of 714C certificates.

Individual holders of I, P and S certificates can be checked by the Contractor against the photograph on the certificate but this is not possible in the case of a limited company 714C certificate. A Sub-contractor which is a limited company may choose to produce to the Contractor either the 714C itself or a "certifying document" which it prepares especially for the purpose in accordance with Inland Revenue guidelines and which is retained by the Contractor. Whichever method is used the documents have to be checked in detail by the Contractor, if necessary by telephoning the company itself to confirm that the person presenting the document is their authorised representative

If the Contractor is satisfied he must pay the Sub-contractor in full; 715's are not used but both parties record the details of the payment in their business records.

(c) Holders of 714S certificates.

If the weekly payment to the Sub-contractor (excluding the cost to him of any materials purchased directly from another person) does not exceed £150 then the procedure outlined above for a certificate 714I and P is followed and a voucher 715S is given to the Contractor on receipt of the payment. If, however, the payment exceeds £150 for the week then the 714I and P procedure is still followed in respect of the first £150 and the procedure at (d) below is carried out for the balance of the payment.

(d) Sub-contractors with no certificate and those with S certificate payments in excess of the weekly limit.

The Contractor is obliged to deduct tax from all payments (excluding the cost of directly purchased materials) and to account to the Revenue for all amounts so withheld. To enable the Sub-contractor to prove to the inspector of taxes that he has suffered this tax deduction the Contractor must give him a certificate on form SC60 showing the amount withheld. These SC60 forms must be carefully filed for production to the Inspector after the end of his accounting year along with his

25

The Construction Industry Deduction Scheme (714's)

business profit and loss account and balance sheet. Any tax deducted in this way over and above the Sub-contractor's proper, agreed liability for the year will be repaid by the Inland Revenue. At the end of the day the Sub-contractor will pay the same amount of income tax whether or not he has a certificate, but those without one will have suffered a severe restriction in their cash flow until the repayment is made.

The main contractor periodically has to send the 715 vouchers to the Inland Revenue Computer Centre in Liverpool and makes an annual return to that Centre also.

It all amounts to a heavy burden on the trader with penalties awaiting those who are sloppy, dilatory or dishonest in its operation. Currently the Inland Revenue is consulting with interested parties to ascertain how this burden can be reduced and simplified. Any changes introduced will be included in subsequent issues of this manual.

The above is merely a summary of the very detailed instructions contained in IR 14/15 paragraphs 65-129 which must be carefully studied by anyone involved in operating the scheme either as a Contractor or Sub-contractor.

Example

A Contractor makes the following payments in respect of a "supply and fix" contract:-

```
One week's labour   £300
Materials supplied   200
                    ----
                     500
VAT at 15%            75
                    ----
                    £575
                    ----
```

(a) To a certificated Sub-contractor.

He will pay £575 to the Sub-contractor and receive from him a form 715 in respect of £300 paid without deduction of tax.

The Construction Industry Deduction Scheme (714's)

(b) To an uncertificated Sub-contractor.
   He will pay the Sub-contractor:-

```
         Labour            £300
         Less tax at 25%     75
                          ----
                           225
         Materials         200
                          ----
                           425
         VAT on £500         75
                          ----
                          £500
```
   and will pay the Inland Revenue £75.

   He will give the Sub-contractor a form SC60 showing the £75
tax deducted.

(c) To a holder of certificate 714S.
   He will pay the Sub-contractor:-

```
   Labour (no tax deducted) £150
   Labour (balance)     150
   Less tax at 25%       37    113
                      ----------
   Total labour                263
   Materials                   200
                              ----
                               463
   VAT on £500                  75
                              ----
                              £538
```
   and will pay the Inland Revenue £37.

   He will receive form 715S from the Sub-contractor for the
£150 paid in full and give the Sub-contractor form SC60 for the
£37 tax deducted.

NOTE

1. VAT is calculated on the gross amount of the payment before
   deducting income tax.

2. For the purpose of the tax deduction scheme the amounts included
   on forms 715, 715S and SC60 are the VAT exclusive figures.

Miscellaneous points

1. A payment includes anything paid out by the Contractor such as a

27

The Construction Industry Deduction Scheme (714's)

'sub' or a loan, whether by cash, cheque or credit and whether direct to the Sub-contractor or to his nominee.

2. The cost of subsistence and travelling expenses reimbursed by the contractor is included in the amount on which the tax deduction is calculated.

3. The scheme is policed by the Revenue in much the same way as they inspect PAYE documents and records for the scheme have to be made available on request.

4. A Contractor is liable to pay to the collector of taxes all amounts which he <u>should</u> have deducted from Sub-contractors, whether he made the <u>deductions</u> or not. He may, however, be excused from having to pay if he can show he took reasonable care and made the error in good faith.

    If the deductions have not been properly made the Sub-contractor himself will be asked to account for his own correct liability.

5. In a situation where tax <u>has</u> been deducted from payments made by him but the contractor has failed to account for it to the collector the Sub-contractor would be unlikely to recover any over-deductions from the Revenue.

6. Disputes between Contractors and Sub-contractors about the amount of any deduction should be referred to the inspector for a ruling.

Chapter 4: VAT and the Construction Industry

The general rule about liability to register for VAT is given in Chapter 1 and the recording of VAT in the business books is dealt with in the book-keeping chapter.

VAT is a basically simple tax made complicated by the many special arangements needed for different trades of which the construction industry is unfortunately one of the most complex. Also, the present time is one of rapid and fundamental changes in the tax which affect all traders and the building trade in particular. The wise businessman will therefore, through the medium of the national and trade press and by reading the notices sent out with his VAT forms, try to keep up with the changes and avoid falling foul of the new and extensive net of penalties which will trap not only the deliberate avoider but the ignorant and unwary trader as well. Like Income Tax, VAT has become too technical and detailed for DIY methods and professional advice should be sought in all but the simplest situations.

As a minimum the trader should have by him the VAT publications listed in Chapter 1.

Tax Periods

VAT is payable in respect of 3 monthly periods known as "tax periods" (but see the new proposals for annual accounting below) and you can apply to have the group of tax periods which fits in best with your financial year. The tax must be paid within one month of the end of each tax period. Traders who receive regular repayments of VAT can apply to have them monthly rather than quarterly.

Input and Output Tax

The amount of tax to be paid is the difference between the VAT charged out to customers (OUTPUT TAX) and that suffered on payments made to suppliers for goods and services (INPUT TAX). Unlike Income Tax there is no distinction in VAT for capital items so that the tax charged on the purchase of (for example) machinery, trucks and office furniture will normally be reclaimable as "INPUT TAX". One important exception to this is that the input tax on a car cannot be reclaimed even though it is used wholly for business purposes, however input tax suffered on the purchase of a van is deductible. Also VAT must be accounted for if a van is converted into a car (for example by fitting side windows and/or rear seats). The full rules relating to motoring expenses are at Appendix C of the booklet 700.

VAT and the Construction Industry

Examples of how VAT works are as follows:

(a) Sales invoices total   £1000
              plus VAT @ 15%   150   OUTPUT TAX £150
        The customer pays   £1150

     Purchase invoices total   £ 600
              plus VAT @ 15%   90   INPUT TAX £ 90
        You pay   £ 690

                        DUE to Customs & Excise   £ 60

If in the tax period machinery costing £2000 plus VAT £300 had also
been purchased the figures would be:

(b) Sales invoices total   £1000
              plus VAT @ 15%   150   OUTPUT TAX £150
        The customer pays   £1150

     Purchase invoices total   £2600
              plus VAT @ 15%   390   INPUT TAX £390
        You pay   £2990

                     RECLAIM from Customs & Excise   £240

Standard, Exempt and Zero-Rated Supplies

Not all types of goods and services are taxed at 15% (ie., at the
standard rate), some are exempt and others are zero-rated.

"Zero-Rated" This means that no VAT is chargeable on the goods or
services but a registered trader can reclaim any INPUT tax suffered on
his purchases. For instance a builder pays VAT on the materials he
buys, but if he is constructing a new dwelling house, this is zero-
rated and he may reclaim this VAT or set it off against any VAT due on
other, standard rated work.

"Exempt" Supplies which are exempt are less favourably treated than
those which are zero-rated. Again no VAT is chargeable on the goods
or services but the trader cannot reclaim any INPUT tax suffered on
his purchases.

"Standard Rated" All work which is not specifically stated to be
zero-rated or exempt is standard rated, ie., VAT is chargeable at the
current rate of 15% and the trader may deduct any INPUT tax suffered,
when he is making his return to the Customs and Excise.

The following paragraphs provide a broad outline of how zero-rating
and exemptions apply to the construction industry and include the
latest provisions of the Finance Act 1989 Schedule 3. However that

VAT and the Construction Industry

Schedule contains 15 pages of complex new rules about VAT on buildings and land and advice from the local VAT office and/or an accountant must be sought in any case of doubt - a mistake, for instance in "zero-rating" works which should be "standard-rated", could be costly.

"Zero-Rated" Work

From the 1st April 1989 this applies to:-

(a) New residential dwellings.

(b) New buildings intended for a "relevant residential purpose" such as a home or other institution providing communal residential accommodation.

(c) New buildings intended for a "relevant charitable purpose". This means premises for use by a charity otherwise than in the course of a business.

(d) Approved alterations to protected buildings when the buildings are of a type which would qualify for zero-rating when newly constructed.

(e) Any civil engineering work necessary for the development of a permanent park for residential caravans.

"Exempt" Work

From 1st April 1989, in general, the letting, in return for rent, of land and buildings is exempt from VAT. However, from 1st August 1989 an owner or landlord who makes such exempt supplies may elect to waive the exemption and charge VAT on the rents at the Standard Rate (15%) (subject to special transitional relief in the first year).

"Standard Rated" Work

This includes

(a) All new buildings other than those zero-rated above.

(b) Almost all new civil engineering works.

(c) Almost all demolition work.

(d) All work done to an existing building or civil engineering work, no matter how the work is described - conversion, reconstruction, alteration, extension, improvement, renovation, repairs etc.

31

VAT and the Construction Industry

Mixed Works

If only part of a building qualifies for zero-rating a reasonable apportionment must be made between the zero- and standard-rated elements.

Self-supply of Building Services

Persons who use their own labour to construct a standard-rated building for use in their business (or increase the existing floor area by 10% or more) must account for VAT on those services at market value, if the value of the self-supply is £100,000 or more.

If for any reason a trader makes a supply and fails to charge VAT when he should have done so (eg., mistakenly assuming the supply to be zero-rated) he will have to account for the VAT himself out of the proceeds. If therefore there is any doubt about the VAT position it is safer to assume the supply is standard-rated, charge the appropriate amount of VAT on the invoice and argue about it later.

Time of Supply

The time at which a supply of goods or services is treated as taking place is important and is called the "tax point". VAT must be accounted for to the Customs & Excise at the end of the accounting period in which this "tax point" occurs. For the supply of goods which are "built on site" the "basic tax point" is the date the goods are made available for the customer's use, whilst for services it is normally the date when all the work except invoicing is completed. However if you issue a tax invoice or receive a payment BEFORE this "basic tax point" then that date becomes the tax point.

In the case of contracts providing for stage and retention payments the tax point is either the date the tax invoice is issued or when payment is received, whichever is the earlier.

All the above requirements apply to sub-contractors and main contractors and it should be noted that, when a contractor deducts income tax from a payment to a sub-contractor (because he has no valid 714), VAT is payable on the full gross amount before taking off the Income Tax. (See Chapter 3)

Cash Accounting for Small Businesses

This is a recent and major change in the way VAT is accounted for.

Under the normal arrangement VAT is to be paid when the goods are delivered or the service completed (see the previous paragraph). Usually this will be before the customer has paid his bill and it can therefore produce problems of cash flow and bad debts.

Under the "cash accounting" scheme small businesses may now apply to account for VAT on the basis of cash paid to suppliers and cash received from customers. This will benefit those concerns which allow

VAT and the Construction Industry

credit to their customers or have problems with bad debts: it will be of less value to those with wholly or mainly cash customers and will probably be disadvantageous to those who receive VAT repayments (eg because of zero rating).

New starters in business with large amounts of input tax to reclaim on capital expenditure will probably be better to commence under the normal arrangements and consider changing to "cash accounting" later.

The rules governing the "cash accounting" scheme are given in Notice 731 and some of the more important ones are:-

1. The value of the taxable supplies (excluding VAT) is not expected to exceed £250,000 in the next 12 months (include standard and zero rated but not exempt supplies).

2. The business must have had a "clean" VAT record for the past 3 years and all returns and payments must be up to date.

3. The scheme must apply to the whole of a business not merely a part.

4. Once in, the business must stay in the scheme for at least 2 years.

5. All the usual VAT records set out in Notice 700 Section VIII must be kept including records of invoices issued and received together with a cash book with separate VAT columns.
   It must be possible, from the records to tie up the invoices issued and received with the entries in the cash book.

The following is a summary of the dates on which VAT is to be accounted for and reclaimed under the cash accounting scheme:-

Nature of transaction	Business Receipts	Business Payments
Cash	Date cash received	Date of receipted tax invoice
Cheque	Date cheque received or the date on the cheque whichever is later	Date cheque sent or date on the cheque whichever is later
Credit Card	Date of sales voucher (not when payment received from Card Company)	Date supplier makes out sales voucher (not date Card company is paid)
Giro, Standing Order Direct Debit	Date bank account is credited	Date bank account is debited

VAT and the Construction Industry

Although the new cash accounting scheme may appear to be complex there
is no doubt it will make the task of accounting for VAT much easier
for many concerns as well as helping the cash flow position.

In the Chapter on Book-keeping there are examples of how VAT may be
accounted for under both the traditional method and the cash
accounting scheme. Established businessmen should ask their
accountants whether they would benefit from changing over to the new
arrangements.

Notice 731, available from VAT offices gives full details of the
scheme and includes an application form at the back.

Annual Accounting Scheme

From 1 July 1988 some registered VAT businesses will be able to pay
the tax by nine monthly estimated amounts plus one final, properly
calculated payment. The main advantages of the scheme are that the
businessman knows exactly how much he has to pay during these nine
months and the monthly spread should help his cash flow; also there
is a saving of time, since only one VAT return per year will be
needed and will be made with the tenth payment.

Details of the scheme are:-

1. Who can use it

    (a) The business must have been VAT registered for at least
         one year.

    (b) The annual value of taxable supplies (both standard and
         zero rated) EXCLUDING VAT is not more than £250,000.

    (c) All VAT returns and payments must be up to date.

    (d) The business must not make regular repayment claims (this
         might apply if all or a major part of the sales are zero
         rated construction works).

2. How the Scheme Works

    (a) The Customs & Excise makes an estimate, based on the
         previous 12 months and adjusted up or down for anticipated
         business changes, of the likely VAT liability for the
         coming year. This figure is then divided by 10 to
         ascertain the monthly amount due.

    (b) The trader instructs his bank to make the 9 estimated
         monthly payments by direct debit.

    (c) When these are completed there is a two month period in
         which to calculate the exact liability for the year and

make the annual VAT return together with the tenth payment.

(d) Thereafter the process starts again for the next year.

(e) The VAT office must be told of any significant changes in the business.

(f) The business must remain in the scheme for a minimum of two years.

Full details of the scheme together with an application form are in VAT Notice 732, obtainable at all local VAT offices.

Chapter 5 Book-keeping and Cash Flow Statements

Keeping records of business transactions is regarded by many proprietors of small businesses as an unnecessary and time-consuming chore. However, in the present age with the Inland Revenue and Customs and Excise both eager to check their accuracy and with powers to levy interest charges and penalties in addition to any tax due if serious shortcomings in the records are found, the businessman neglects his books at his peril.

It is safer, easier and in the long run cheaper, to maintain accurate records from the beginning; records which can also provide essential management information for the proprietor.

There are numerous systems for recording business transactions and it is a matter of finding the one most suited to the needs of the particular business. The one described here is suitable for a small/medium sized concern which does not have enough suppliers to warrant keeping separate ledger accounts for each one. It is assumed that the general or nominal ledger will be written up by the firm's accountant when he prepares the annual accounts.

The records required by this method are:-

- An analysed (or columnar) cash book.
- A petty cash book.
- A wages book with supporting time sheets (if there are employees).
- A VAT record book (if registered for VAT).
- Costing sheets for each job or contract.
- A box file for unpaid suppliers' accounts.
- A box file for paid suppliers' accounts.
- A box file for copy sales invoices.

First open a business current account and observe the following rules:-

Receipts

Pass all receipts whether cash or cheque through the bank account. Do not use business cash directly to meet either business expenses or personal drawings. There is no quicker way to get into difficulties with the Revenue authorities than to have recurring cash deficiencies when the annual accounts are prepared and submitted.

Payments

(a) Pay suppliers and all other bills except minor ones by cheque.

(b) Pay petrol either by monthly account or by credit card but get a tax invoice for each purchase if a credit card is used.

(c) Draw cash from the bank specifically to meet wages and the proprietor's drawings.

(d) Draw small amounts of petty cash periodically to meet minor business expenses.

The main cash book

The analysed cash book should contain enough columns to itemise the business expenditure in detail.

Do not worry if all the columns are not used at first - as the business grows they will probably be needed. There are some loose-leaf ledgers on the market which are useful because at the year end it is not necessary for the whole book to go to the accountant; just carry forward the Bank balance and send him the sheets for the completed year suitably bound or tagged together.

It is appropriate here to consider the recording of VAT. The Customs and Excise Commissioners do not require VAT records to be in any particular form but they do require records to be kept of all taxable goods and services received and supplied including both standard and zero-rated items. They also require that all business records be kept for a period of 6 years (this includes orders and delivery notes, purchase invoices and copy sales invoices, credit notes, correspondence and bank statements as well as the books themselves).

This system of book-keeping is suitable whether VAT is being accounted for on the traditional basis of invoices sent and received or under the new "cash accounting" rules (see Chapter 4). The difference in recording for these systems lies only in the main cash book - all the other records are the same.

If the traditional "invoices" basis is used it is <u>not</u> necessary to have separate columns for input and output VAT in the main cash book; all VAT recording is done in the VAT Record book from which the quarterly return is prepared. All items in the main cash book are recorded gross <u>INCLUSIVE OF VAT</u>.

Under the "cash accounting" method there <u>must be</u> separate columns in the main cash book for input and <u>output</u> VAT and all items are recorded <u>EXCLUSIVE OF VAT</u>. The "imprest" system of petty cash recording should be used. It will then be possible to make up the quarterly VAT return direct from the totals in the main cash book. Despite this the Customs and Excise require that the VAT Record book should still be maintained so that their officers can, on any inspection of the books, reconcile the cash book and VAT Record book entries with the purchase and sales invoices, bank records etc.

Table 1 shows a typical page in the cash book when the traditional "invoice" method of VAT accounting is used and Table 2 shows the method of recording under the "cash accounting" rules.

Book-keeping and Cash Flow Statements

CR — RECEIPTS

DATE 89	DETAILS	√ Nb	BANK A	SALES B	EAS GRANT C	SUNDRIES D	CAP INTRO E
1/5	OPENING BAL B/FWD		8010·10			8010·10	
2/5	SMITH LTD.	26	460·00	460·00			
6/5	BROWN & Co.	27	2116·00	2116·00			
10/5	CAPITAL INTRO		5000·00				5000·00
10/5	GREEN LTD.	18	4830·00	4830·00			
19/5	CASH SALE	67	28·76	28·76			
29/5	DEPT. OF EMPLOYMENT		80·00		80·00		
			20524·85	7434·75	80·00	8010·10	5000·00

DATE 89	DETAILS	√ Nb	BANK A	SALES	EAS GRANT	SUNDRIES	CAP INTRO
1/6	OPENING BAL B/FWD		13517·06			13517·06	

DR — PAYMENTS

DATE 89	DETAILS	√ Nb	BANK F	GOODS G	MOTOR EXES H	SUB-CONTRS I	WAGES & NIC J	OWN DRAWINGS K	O'HEAD EXES L	SUNDRIES M	CAP EXPEND N
2/5	ASH & Co.	87	575·00	575·00							
4/5	COUNTY Co. RATES	88	450·00						450·00		
7/5	Br. TELECOM	89	115·00						115·00		
9/5	WAGES BK.		320·25				320·25				
12/5	STONE, J.	90	586·50			586·50					
19/5	PETTY CASH BK.		35·80							35·80	
21/5	VISA CREDIT CARD (PETROL)	91	126·50		126·50						
24/5	DIGGER LTD (NEW PLANT)	92	4398·76								4398·76
29/5	SELF DES.		400·00					400·00			
31/5	TOTALS		7007·80	575·00	126·50	586·50	320·25	400·00	565·00	35·80	4398·76
	ENDING BAL C/FWD		13517·05							1357·05	
			10524·85	575·00	126·50	586·50	320·25	400·00	565·00	7852·85	4398·75

DATE 89	DETAILS	√ Nb	BANK	GOODS	MOTOR EXES	SUB-CONTRS	WAGES & NIC	OWN DRAWINGS	O'HEAD EXES	SUNDRIES	CAP EXPEND
1/6	OPENING BAL B/FWD		13517·06							13517·06	

NOTES:
1. The spare column (used for VAT in the other method) has been allocated to capital receipts and payments.
2. The adjustment of the figures for VAT will be done by the accountant at the year-end.

Table 1

CR — RECEIPTS

DATE '89	DETAILS	Chq No	BANK A	SALES B	EAS GRANT C	SUNDRIES D	VAT E
1/5	OPENING BAL B/FWD		8010·10			8010·10	
2/5	SMITH LTD.	26	460·00	400·00			60·00
6/5	BROWN & Co.	27	2116·00	1840·00			276·00
10/5	CAPITAL INTRO		5000·00			5000·00	
10/5	GREEN LTD.	18	4830·00	4200·00			630·00
19/5	CASH SALE	67	28·75	25·00			3·75
29/5	DEPT OF EMPLOYMENT		80·00		80·00		
			20524·85	6465·00	80·00	13010·10	969·75

DATE '89	DETAILS	Vr No	BANK A	SALES B	EAS GRANT C	SUNDRIES D	VAT E
1/6	OPENING BAL B/FWD		13517·05			13517·05	

DR — PAYMENTS

DATE '89	DETAILS	Chq No	BANK F	GOODS G	MOTOR EXES H	SUB-CONTRS I	WAGES & NIC J	OWN DRAWINGS K	O'HEAD EXES L	SUNDRIES M	VAT N
2/5	ASH & Co.	87	575·00	500·00							75·00
6/5	COUNTY Co. RATES	88	450·00						450·00		
7/5	BR. TELECOM	89	115·00						100·00		15·00
8/5	WAGES BK.		320·25				320·25				
12/5	STONE. J.	90	586·50			510·00					76·50
18/5	PETTY CASH BK.	91	35·90							32·69	3·11
21/5	VISA CREDIT CARD (PETROL) DIGGER LTD (NEW PLANT)	92	4898·75		110·00					4215·00	573·75
29/5	SELF. DES.		400·00					400·00			
	TOTALS		7007·80	600·00	110·00	510·00	320·25	400·00	550·00	3957·69	759·86
1/5	ENDING BAL C/PAID		13517·05							13517·05	
			20524·85	500·00	110·00	510·00	320·25	400·00	550·00	13374·74	759·86

DATE '89	DETAILS	Vr No	BANK	GOODS	MOTOR EXES	SUB-CONTRS	WAGES & NIC	OWN DRAWINGS	O'HEAD EXES	SUNDRIES	VAT
1/6	OPENING BAL B/PAID		13517·05							13517·05	

Table 2

Book-keeping and Cash Flow Statements

Notes on cash book

To obtain a reasonably detailed analysis at least 7 columns are usually needed on the payments side. Cash books with various rulings can be obtained from office stationers.

There are many ways of laying out the columns and of balancing - this is merely one of them, however the same principles apply to all, namely:-

(a) All transactions involving cash and bank (with the exception of trivial petty cash items) must be entered in the cash book, and each must be entered <u>twice</u>: once in the bank column and once in one of the analysis columns to show the nature of the receipt or payment.

(b) The total in bank column A must equal the total of the analysis columns: B, C and D, and E. The total in bank column F must equal the total of the analysis columns G to N.

(c) Bank balances. The entries shown are those when the bank account is in credit. If it was overdrawn the opening balance would be entered as the first item on the right hand page in columns E and N and the balance at the end would appear as the last on the left hand page in columns A and D.

(d) The book should be balanced and the amount of the bank balance entered monthly. At the same time the bank account statement should be obtained and checked against the entries in the book, any corrections needed in the latter being made. From time to time the bank charges shown in the bank statement will need to be entered.

(e) As the business expands so it may also outgrow this type of cash book: the firm's accountant will say when he thinks a different system (perhaps with separate cash books for receipts and payments or a computerised system) is required. It should however serve perfectly well for most small/medium concerns.

The petty cash book

There are two methods generally in use. In Table 3 the amount of petty cash is kept to a reasonable figure but not necessarily always precisely the same amount. The expenditure is analysed into appropriate headings at the year end and added to the annual summary of cash and bank transactions.

In Table 4, known as the 'imprest' system, the balance is topped up as circumstances require and always to the same amount. This means that the cheque drawn from the bank will on each occasion correspond precisely in amount with the payments made out of petty cash and the payments can be analysed under the appropriate

PETTY CASH BOOK

CR ① RECEIPTS   DR   PAYMENTS

DATE 89	DETAILS			DATE 89	DETAILS	VCHR NO.	GROSS AMT OF PAYMENT		NET EXCLDG VAT		VAT	
MAY 1	Balance in hand B/F	30	-	MAY 2	Postage		10	-	10	-	-	-
8	Cash from bank	50	-	3	Stationery	1	5	-	4	35		65
				4	Tea & Coffee	2	3	45	3	-		45
				5	Bus fares		1	80	1	80	-	-
				6	Typewriter repair	3	7	10	6	19		91
				8	First Aid Supplies	5	8	45	7	35	1	10
				12	Bal. in hand C/FWD		44	20				
		80	-				80	-	32	69	3	11

DATE 89	DETAILS			DATE 89	DETAILS	VCHR NO.	GROSS AMT OF PAYMENT	NET EXCLDG VAT	VAT
MAY 13	Balance in hand B/F	44	20						

NOTE When VAT is paid on a purchase but is not separately shown on the invoice the VAT element = $^{15}/_{115}$ = 13·04% of the gross amount.

Table 3

DATE 89	DETAILS			DATE 89	DETAILS	VCHR NO.	GROSS AMT OF PAYMENT		NET EXCLDG VAT		VAT	
MAY 1	Balance in hand B/F	50	-	MAY 2	Postage	10	10	-	10	-	-	-
8	Cash from bank	35	80	3	Stationery	1	5	-	4	35		65
				4	Tea & Coffee	2	3	45	3	-		45
				5	Bus fares		1	80	1	80	-	-
				6	Typewriter repairs	3	7	10	6	19		91
				8	First Aid Supplies	5	8	45	7	35	1	10
				12	Bal. in hand C/FWD		50	-				
		85	80				85	80	32	69	3	11

NOTE In this system the cash from the bank always equals the gross amount paid out in purchases   35·80

DATE 89	DETAILS		
MAY 13	Balance in hand B/F	50	-

Table 4

42

heading(s) in the main cash book as each withdrawal for petty cash is made.

In this case no further end-of-year analysis is of course required.

Either method is acceptable and the businessman should use the one he feels most comfortable with except that when "cash accounting" is used for VAT the "imprest" system is more suitable.

The wages book

Many printers of business stationery produce wages books, some of which look quite complex to the new employer. It is worth shopping around to find one that is easily understood.

The VAT record book

Again there are a number of ready-printed VAT record books available at business stationers and it is recommended that one is chosen which is suitable for a business which is likely to have a mixture of standard and zero-rated supplies.

Full records of all zero-rated as well as standard rated supplies must be kept. It is recommended therefore that a standard form of invoice be used as the basis of all sales and that 'zero-rated' be noted across the VAT columns where appropriate. The invoices must carry a serial number and when accounts are paid the copy invoices should be filed in that order to facilitate checking by the accountant and the VAT authorities if they call to examine the books.

Much useful information on business records and an example of a form of VAT invoice is to be found in the Customs and Excise leaflet 'Keeping Records and Accounts'.

Tables 5 and 6 show typical rulings in a VAT Record book.

The gross amount of all items is entered in column A followed by the VAT exclusive amount in one of columns B, C and D. In the case of standard-rated items the total of columns B and E will equal that of A. In the case of zero-rated and exempt items the amount in either column C or D will be the same as in A and there will be no entry in E.

When the tax invoice has been made out and issued the details should be entered in the VAT record output section making the VAT book into a record of sales also.

Similarly all invoices received in respect of goods and services supplied to the business should be entered in the input section of the VAT book immediately on receipt and should then be placed in the 'unpaid' box file awaiting payment, after which they will be transfered to the 'paid' file.

A section of the VAT book should be reserved for credit notes received and credit notes issued. At the end of the quarter the VAT on those received should be deducted from the input tax and the VAT on those issued deducted from the output tax.

INPUT V.A.T. ACCOUNT

DATE 1989	NAME OF SUPPLIER	INVOICE No.	A GROSS PAYMENT	B STANDARD RATE ITEMS	C ZERO RATE ITEMS	D EXEMPT AND NON-DEDUCTIBLE ITEMS	E DEDUCTIBLE V.A.T.
MAY 1	Slaughter & Tyler Ltd	105	1725 –	1500 –			225 –
2	Clear Sight Ltd.	106	2000 –		2000 –		

PUT HERE THE NET
AMOUNT EXCLUDING V.A.T.

Table 5

OUTPUT V.A.T. ACCOUNT

DATE 1989	NAME OF CUSTOMER	INVOICE No.	A GROSS PAYMENT	B STANDARD RATE ITEMS	C ZERO RATE ITEMS	D EXEMPT ITEMS	E OUTPUT V.A.T.
MAY 1	S. Smith	27	575 –	500 –			75 –
2	Hi-Finance Co. Ltd	28	4000 –		4000 –		

PUT HERE THE NET
AMOUNT EXCLUDING V.A.T.

Table 6

Do not forget to include the tax on petty cash purchases and on the petrol invoices paid through a credit card in the input tax plus the tax charged on any cash sales in the output tax. The VAT Guide No. 700 should be consulted when goods or services are taken for private use.

This VAT record must be kept whether returns are being made on the traditional basis or on the new "cash accounting" basis.

When the traditional basis is in use the figures will form the basis of the VAT return.

Under the "cash accounting" system the return will be made from the totals of the cash book. Nevertheless the VAT record must still be maintained so that the Customs and Excise can check the position.

Book-keeping and Cash Flow Statements

Job costing

There are a number of ways in which job and contract costs are
recorded and it is not possible to detail them all here, but
whatever system is used it should bring together on the cost sheet
all of the following items in such a manner that none of them can
be overlooked:-

(a) Own labour and subsistence (from time and expenses sheets).

(b) The labour element of sub-contractors' payments.

(c) The materials element of sub-contractors' payments.

(d) Other materials which have been:-

    (1) purchased,

    (2) delivered directly to site by the supplier,

    (3) drawn from stores or self-built, or

    (4) transferred from other sites.

(e) Use of firm's plant and machinery, vehicles and skips (or the
cost of any of these items hired for the job).

Suppliers' accounts

When paid these should be entered in the cash book and filed in the
order in which they are paid. The unpaid invoices provide a
general check on current indebtedness though of course other
expenditures may have been incurred which have not yet been
invoiced.

Copy sales invoices

Keep in two folders, one for unpaid and one for paid accounts.
When a payment on account is made, mark it on the sales invoice but
transfer it to the paid section only when full satisfaction is
received. The unpaid section provides the basis for the monthly
'aged list' - the record of outstanding debts (see Chapter 7).
Paid copy sales invoices should be filed in order of the number
given them in the VAT book.

The cash flow statement

A number of references have been made to this, either as part of a
business start-up proposal, a bank presentation for additional loan
facilities or as part of a management information system. In all

Book-keeping and Cash Flow Statements

of these it is an essential element. It differs from a profit
forecast in that it shows only actual receipts and payments and
does not include (as the profit forecast does) creditors, debtors,
stock and depreciation, but it does include capital items, both
bought and sold, whereas the profit forecast is concerned with
revenue items only.

It is made up from a large number of estimates and assumptions
about the likely course of the business or project. In an existing
business there should be an historical record in the shape of
annual accounts and other business records to help make accurate
forecasts but with a new proposal reliance has to be placed on
sound trade and market research as a basis for the figures. In
general the better the initial research the more accurate the
forecast. Whatever the evidence for the figures they should be
under rather than over stated and in particular great care should
be taken to avoid the 'halo effect'. Almost every entrepreneur has
a rosy view of his own scheme which, in 99 out of 100 cases, is not
borne out in practice. It is helpful (some would say essential) to
have an objective, experienced mind give the figures a critical
examination. Cracks in the surface appear very quickly if the
foundations are shaky and it is better that they come to light
before the bank manager asks his questions. A Small Firms
Counsellor will give this sort of advice.

Table 7 shows a typical format for a cash flow forecast.

(a) There are vertical columns covering a 12 month period plus one
for the initial 'pre-trading' expenditure and a final total for
the year.

(b) Cash sales. These are the receipts for 'cash on completion'
transactions on which no credit terms have been offered.

(c) From debtors. These figures are built up from the credit sales
taking into account the firm's conditions of sale and its
experience (if any) of the actual credit period taken by
customers. For instance: if it is estimated that the credit
sales for the first 3 months will be £4,000, £8,000 and £12,000
respectively and that 25% of them will be paid in the first
month after the month of sale, 50% in the second and 25% in the
third, then the flow of cash will be:-

Month	1	2	3	4	5	6
Month 1 sales £4,000	-	1000	2000	1000	-	-
Month 2 sales £8,000	-	-	2000	4000	2000	-
Month 3 sales £12,000	-	-	-	3000	6000	3000
Cash Receipts	Nil	1000	4000	8000	8000	3000

12 MONTHS CASH-FLOW FORECAST

	START UP EXPENDITURE	JAN	FEB		DEC	TOTAL
RECEIPTS						
CASH SALES		350	400		200	4,800
FROM DEBTORS			2,000		15,000	145,000
CAPITAL INTRO	10,000					10,000
VAT REFUND						1,500
TOTAL CASH REC'D A	10,000	350	2,400		15,200	161,300
OPENING BANK BAL.(IF CREDIT) B	1,000	4,850			9,650	
TOTAL (A+B) C	11,000	5,200	2,400		24,850	
PAYMENTS						
MATERIALS – CASH	400	600	500		700	6,000
–do– CREDITORS		500	1,000		10,000	85,000
WAGES & SALARIES			200		400	3,400
HEAT, LIGHT, POWER						2,300
RENT	1,000				1,000	4,000
RATES						900
REPAIRS & RENEWALS		1,200	300			2,000
PHONE: STATIONERY ETC.		200	200		200	3,600
HP & LEASING PMTS	500	250	250		250	3,500
ADVERTISING	250					1,550
SUB-CONTRACTORS		200	200		550	4,150
SALES COMMNS			50		200	1,500
CAPITAL – PLANT	4,000	8,000	3,000			15,000
–do– VEHICLES		2,000				6,000
BANK INT & CHARGES					1,200	1,850
DRAWINGS/DIRECTORS SALARIES		600	600		600	7,200
VAT					1,800	6,400
TOTAL CASH PAID D	6,150	13,550	6,300		16,900	154,350
OPENING BANK BAL.(IF DEBT) E			8,350			
TOTAL (D+E) F	6,150	13,550	14,650		16,900	
DIFFERENCE BETWEEN C & F G	4,850	8,350	12,250		7,950	
	CR	DR	DR		CR	

Table 7

Book-keeping and Cash Flow Statements

(d) Materials - cash. Include purchases as and when made from suppliers with whom no credit terms are available.

(e) Materials - creditors. The businessman will be aware of his terms from suppliers and also how much credit in fact he normally takes. From this information it is possible to build up a schedule of payments similar to the one for sales. Assuming that supplier "A" offers 30 days credit and "B" 60 days and the businessman always pays on the due date to secure maximum discount, the cash flow might appear:-

Month	1	2	3	4	5
Supplier A Month 1 £2000	-	2,000	-	-	-
Supplier B Month 1 £4000	-	-	4,000	-	-
Supplier A Month 2 £4000	-	-	4,000	-	-
Supplier B Month 2 £8000	-	-	-	8,000	-
Supplier A Month 3 £8000	-	-	-	8,000	-
Supplier B Month 3 £12,000	-	-	-	-	12,000
Cash Outflow	Nil	2,000	8,000	16,000	12,000

(f) Wages and salaries. These are usually shown gross with no separate headings for PAYE and NIC.

(g) The remaining heads of expenditure should be entered for the anticipated month of payment (not averaged evenly over the twelve months).

(h) VAT These entries comprise the net amounts actually to be paid over to the C and E. If there is a refund due (perhaps because some capital item has been acquired) it appears in the 'Receipts' section and in the appropriate month.

(i) If the figures in the cash flow statement are large it is customary to show them in thousands.

(j) The headings used are for demonstration purposes only and may be varied to suit the particular circumstances.
    A brief study of the figures will show that for each month the following calculation is made:-

Book-keeping and Cash Flow Statements

```
Cash receipts                  A
Plus any money in the
  bank to begin with           B
                              ---
        TOTAL                  C
                              ---
Cash payments                  D
Plus any overdraft at
  the bank to begin with       E
                              ---
        TOTAL                  F
                              ---
```

The two totals are then compared and the difference entered at G. If C is greater than F this is the amount of money in the bank at the end of the period (marked CR) if F is greater than C this is the amount of the overdraft at the end (marked DR).

The 12 months figures can be checked for accuracy by taking the totals as follows:-

```
Opening bank balance              1,000
Receipts for the year           161,300
                                ---------
                                162,300
                                ---------
Payments for the year           154,350
Bank balance at end               7,950
                                ---------
                                162,300
                                ---------
```

The figures at G show what finance, in addition to the £11,000 already introduced, will be needed in the period to enable the project to go ahead on the scale and in the manner proposed. If the chart shows this amount to be unrealistically high or the banks decline to advance that much, the entrepreneur has to consider what economies can be made which will still leave a viable business proposition. In the example, for instance, it might be possible to delay the purchase of some of the plant or to acquire it on hire purchase terms or to lease it.

When the cash flow chart has been finally settled and trading begun, the actual cash-in and outflow should be compared with the chart forecast.

In a presentation to the bank it is usual to include a forecast profit and loss account and forecast balance sheets as well as the cash flow. It is sometimes recommended that the profit and loss forecast be done first but the discipline of first putting down all the expected cash figures for each of the 12 months can provide a sounder basis from which to work up the other two statements.

Chapter 6: Taxation

There is a saying in the accountancy profession that one should not let the taxation tail wag the commercial dog, meaning that if a certain course of action is profitable one should not hold back from it merely because of taxation considerations. This is sound advice for all businesses. Businessmen must, nevertheless, be constantly alive to the tax implications of what they do and seek the least costly legitimate way of transacting their business.

There are two types of tax-reducing measures - <u>evasion</u> and <u>avoidance</u>. The former usually involves failing to disclose one's true income and is illegal. When discovered, evasion gives rise to "back duty" enquiries and, in addition to the tax due, interest and penalties may have to be paid and in the most serious cases criminal proceedings may be instigated.

Evasion causes much anxiety and family distress and distracts the businessman from his proper objective - that of making profit - it should never be practiced.

Avoidance for the small businessman consists mainly in making the best rather than the worst of the multitude of rules which govern the taxation of businesses in a sensible and legitimate manner.

1. <u>The start-up date and the permanent accounting date (sole traders and partnerships)</u>

The income tax year ends on 5 April and assuming that profits will generally tend to increase over the years, an accounting date shortly after then (say 30 April) is more beneficial than one immediately before (say 31 March). This is because income tax is normally assessed on the profits of the 12 months to the normal accounting date in the preceding year. For example:-

A business which started several years ago has the following approximate profits:-

A			B		
1	Year ended 31/3/87	£10,000	1	Year ended 30/4/87	£10,000
2	Year ended 31/3/88	£16,000	2	Year ended 30/4/88	£16,000
3	Year ended 31/3/89	£24,000	3	Year ended 30/4/89	£24,000

Tax will be payable on these profits in two equal instalments as follows:-

	A		B	
1	Assessable 87/88 £10,000		1	Assessable 88/89 £10,000
	Tax due 1/1/88			Tax due 1/1/89
	and 1/7/88			and 1/7/89

2	Assessable 88/89 £16,000		2	Assessable 89/90 £16,000	
	Tax due 1/1/89			Tax due 1/1/90	
	and 1/7/89			and 1/7/90	
3	Assessable 89/90 £24,000		3	Assessable 90/91 £24,000	
	Tax due 1/1/90			Tax due 1/1/91	
	and 1/7/90			and 1/7/91	

The interval between earning the profits and paying the first instalment tax on them in A is 9 months and in B it is 20 months.

An existing business may change its accounting date but the rules are complex and professional accountancy advice should always be taken <u>before</u> it is done.

Those starting up may choose any date as their permanent accounting date and should bear the above in mind when making the decision. On whatever date a business commences it can have accounts prepared to the 30 April ie A business which started on 1st September 1988 could have accounts drawn up for 8 months to 30 April 1989 and thereafter for 12 months to the 30 April each year.

2. <u>The early years of trading</u>

Special rules apply on start up and profits of the first year of trading will normally form the basis of a portion of a year plus two full years of assesment. The length of the portion will vary between a few days (if the business starts on (say) 1 April) and almost a full 12 months (if the business starts shortly after 5 April).

If however the profits of the second and third years are less than the first the taxpayer has the option to elect for both those years (but not just one of them) to be assessed on the actual profits arising in them. For example:-

A starts in business on 1 May 1986 and the profits are:-

Year ended 30 April 87 £12,000

Year ended 30 April 88 £8,400

Year ended 30 April 89 £9,600

Taxation

The inspector will assess as follows:-		The trader may elect for "actual" profits to be assessed for 86/87 and 87/88 as follows:-	
	£		£
1986/87 11/12 x 12,000 =	11,000	1986/87 No change	11,000
1987/88 (1st 12 months)	12,000	1987/88 1/12 x 12,000) 11/12 x 8,400)	8,700
1988/89 (Year to 30/4/87)	12,000	1988/89 1/12 x 8,400) 11/12 x 9,600)	9,500
1989/90 (Year to 30/4/87)	8,400	1989/90 No change	8,400
TOTAL OF ASSESSMENTS	£43,400	TOTAL OF ASSESSMENTS	£37,600

A reduction in the amounts assessed for 1987/88 and 1988/89 of £5,800.

The taxpayer (or his accountant), must write and ask for this special basis to be applied - the inspector will not reduce the assessments on his own initiative.

It is important that all permissible expenses are claimed in the first 12 months of trading and that full and accurate records are kept from the beginning. Relief may be claimed for expenses such as business motoring, advertising, rent of business premises etc., incurred before trading begins and full records of this pre-trading expenditure should be kept.

Particular points to note in the first year of the business are:-

(1) In a partnership it is more tax effective to have an overdraft on the firm's account than for the partners to borrow personally and introduce it into the business as capital.

(2) Consideration might be given to leasing rather than buying plant and equipment: this could help the cash flow as well as be beneficial in relation to tax (see (d) below).

(3) Tax can be saved and it is also helpful to the business owner to employ a potential business partner for at least the first 12 months (to test his abilities and determination and check his compatibility). The proprietor must however be prepared for the added work of operating PAYE on his remuneration and paying employers Class 1 NIC in respect of the employee. When he is eventually brought in as a partner a special "continuation election" is required.

(4) If a wife works in the business, perhaps answering the phone, making appointments, writing business letters, making

up bills and keeping the books, she should be properly remunerated for it. Being a payment to a family member the inspector of taxes will be understandably cautious in allowing it in full as a business expense. The payment should be:-

(i)   Actually paid to her, preferably weekly or monthly and in addition to any house keeping monies.

(ii) Recorded in the business books.

(iii) Reasonable in amount having regard to the nature of her duties and the time spent on them.

If the wages paid to her exceed £42.99p.w. Class 1 employer and employee NIC becomes due and if they exceed £2,785 p.a. (assuming she has no other earnings) PAYE tax will also be payable.

Other matters to note are:-

(a)   Once a small business is well established and the wife's earnings are approaching the above limits, consideration may be given to bringing her in as a partner. This has a number of effects:-

(i)   Because of the "previous year" basis there is a tax advantage in the year of change.

(ii) The wife must continue to have partnership duties but there is no longer a need to relate her income (which is now a share of the profits) to the work she does.

(iii) She will pay Class 2 and Class 4 NIC instead of the more costly Class 1 contributions and PAYE will no longer apply to her earnings.

(iv) But remember - as a partner any assets she owns are vulnerable to proceedings by partnership creditors.

(b)   Many small businessmen cannot afford to rent or buy commercial premises and therefore run their enterprises from home using part of it as an office where the books and vouchers, clients records, trade manuals etc. are kept and estimates and plans are drawn up.
      In these circumstances a portion of the outgoings on the property may be claimed as a business expense. This is usually calculated as an appropriate fraction of the whole. For instance if the property comprises six main rooms and one is used as an office, one sixth of such items as rent

(if any), rates, heat and light and property insurance
should be claimed. Telephone costs would similarly be
claimed on the basis of business/private usage.

A Capital Gains Tax complication arises where the
residence is owner-occupied. A taxpayer's main residence is
exempt from charge but this does not extend to any part used
exclusively for business purposes. However, the chargeable
part of the gain is likely to be covered by the annual
exemption, currently £5,000. If in doubt consult the firm's
accountant before setting up the office.

(c) Car expenses are usually split on a fractional mileage basis
between business journeys which are allowable and private
ones which are not and a record of each should be kept. If
the business does work only on one or two sites or for only
one main contractor the inspector may argue that the true
base of operations is the work site not the residence and
seek to disallow the cost of travel between home and work.
It is therefore tax-wise and sound business practice to have
as many customers as possible and not work for just one
client.

(d) The cost of plant and machinery, vans, trucks and business
cars, etc., is capital expenditure and as such is not
deductible in arriving at the business profits. The Inland
Revenue has its own system of depreciation allowances known
as "capital allowances". For plant and machinery the
current rate is 25% p.a. calculated in the following
manner:-

	£
New van cost	6000
25% writing down allowance year 1	1500

Written down value	4500
25% writing down allowance year 2	1125

Written down value	3375
25% writing down allowance year 3	844

Written down value	£2531

In the case of cars, the allowance due each year is reduced
in respect of any private use of the vehicle i.e. if the
mileages are business 8000 and private 2000, the allowance
in year 1 would be 4/5 x 1500 = £1200

Plant bought on hire purchase is eligible for allowances on
the full cash cost even though some instalments may still be
outstanding. HP interest is revenue expenditure and is
therefore allowed as a deduction in arriving at the profits.

Where plant is leased the whole of the payments is treated as a business expense in arriving at the profits and no capital allowances are due.

There are restrictions on both capital allowances and leasing payments in respect of cars costing more than £8,000.

When contemplating the need for additional plant and machinery businessmen should always consider:-

(i)   The relative taxation and cash flow positions of outright cash purchase with and without bank loan assistance; HP, and leasing.

(ii)   Whether it is more advantageous to make the acquisition now or leave it until the next accounting period (for example: if business is moving from a period of low profits to one of high profits, it might be better to wait).

(e) As soon as the business is established and profitable the proprietor should start shopping around for the best pension provision available.

Last year the Government introduced legislation making fundamental changes in its own earnings-related pension scheme (SERPS) and encouraging individuals who are self-employed and many who are employed as well (including directors of companies) to start providing themselves with a retirement pension or to improve their current pension provision. The SERPS scheme has become so costly that the Government is offering a 2% incentive to those who contract out of it by 6 April 1993. This year too, significant changes are proposed in the existing pension framework to encourage individuals to make greater provision for their retirement.

A major incentive to making personal pension arrangements is that contributions to a scheme which has been approved by the Inland Revenue are fully tax deductible both for the individual and (in the case of an employee) for the employer too and the pension fund is free of tax on its investment income and free of Capital Gains. Pension provision is one of the most worthwhile ways of taxsaving at a time when earnings are likely to be high (and the tax rates therefore also high) with the payout at a time when income is likely to be substantially less. All proprietors of successful businesses whether operated as individuals, in partnership or through a limited company should find out which type of scheme would suit their particular circumstances best.

For those who have been in employment at some time in their working lives the start point is the DSS office which will supply form NP38. This is completed and sent to the

Taxation

Newcastle upon Tyne address given in the leaflet; they will return it with a statement showing how much SERPS pension has been earned together with an explanatory (NP 39) leaflet. The amount of any "SERPS" pension plus the basic "old-age" pension is the normal entitlement from the state and for most people the very modest total acts as a spur to top it up with some private pension provision.

In the private field the position is simplest for those trading on their own account or in partnership. Some will already have retirement annuity policies (also known as RAP's and Section 226 policies) and those can be continued. From 1 July 1988 similar policies have been available and are known as "personal pension plans" (PPP's). Self-employed persons under the age of 75 can contribute to such plans (more than one at the same time if desired).

From 1st April 1989 the position is more complicated because different limits apply to the older RAP's and the newer PPP's.

RAP's The percentage of net relevant earnings allowable remains the same and there is no limit on the amount of earnings eg., someone aged 53 fortunate enough to earn £80,000 could have £16,000 of allowable premiums.

PPP's The percentage is greater (see below) but there is a limit on earnings of £60,000. The 53 year old earning £80,000 would be allowed 30% of £60,000 = £18,000 in allowable premiums.

The table of percentages is :-

Age at beginning of tax year (6 April)	Allowable % of net relevant earnings		
	RAP's	PPP's	Max Contributions £
35 or less	17.5	17.5	10,500
36 - 45	17.5	20.0	12,000
46 - 50	17.5	25.0	15,000
51 - 55	20.0	30.0	18,000
56 - 60	22.5	35.0	21,000
61 - 74	27.5	35.0	21,000

Plans are provided by insurance companies, unit trusts, banks and building societies and come in three types: with-profit policies; value linked to unit trusts and finally deposit schemes. It is imperative that time is taken to consider the advantages and disadvantages of each type of scheme and to compare the track records of those selling the plans. Over-hasty action could result in the loss of perhaps thousands of pounds when retirement comes round.

The options available to those trading under a limited company format depend on whether or not the individual is a member of an existing pension scheme and if so whether that scheme is "contracted-in" or "contracted-out" of the SERPS scheme. Most however will not be members of any pension scheme and a number of options are available to them: they can

(i)   Make no private pension arrangements and rely on the basic state pension plus their SERPS pension to which they will continue to contribute through NI contrib-utions.

(ii)   Set up a company pension scheme.

(iii)   Take out personal pension plans with the possibility of contracting out of SERPS with the 2% incentive bonus (an existing Section 226 policy may be converted into an appropriate personal pension plan to do this).

There is only space here to outline some aspects of the scheme and to emphasise two points: first, this is a very effective and financially rewarding way to save tax: second, information and advice should be sought from a number of sources before a decision is made on which path is best for any particular person to follow and which provider of pension plans is likely to be the most profitable.

There are a number of books on this complex subject but make sure before buying one, that it includes the 1989 Finance Bill changes.

(f) Business cessation (sole trader and partnership). It is noted above that on start-up the businessman has the option of the most advantageous basis of assessment for the second and third years of trading, the corollary is that the Inland Revenue has the option (which it always exercises) for the last two full years before cessation of assessing both (but not one only) on either the normal preceding year basis or the actual profits of those years, whichever is more favourable to it. For example:-

Taxation

"B", who has been in business on his own for many years decides he would like to form a limited company and bring his two sons in as shareholders and directors. One difficult decision (among many) is what date should be chosen for the change. His profits are:-

Year ended 30 April 1985	24,000
Year ended 30 April 1986	24,000
Year ended 30 April 1987	36,000
Year ended 30 April 1988	48,000
Year ended 30 April 1989	36,000
Expected profits Year ended 30 April 1990	48,000

If the change is made at 1 May 1989 the taxation effect would be:-

	Existing assessments:	Inland Revenue would increase to:-	
1986/87 Profits: Y/E 30/4/85	£24,000	No change	24,000
1987/88 Profits: Y/E 30/4/86	£24,000	1/12 x 36,000) 11/12 x 48,000)	47,000
1988/89 Profits: Y/E 30/4/87	£36,000	1/12 x 48,000) 11/12 x 36,000)	37,000
1989/90 Profits: Y/E 30/4/88	£48,000	1/12 x 36,000) (Plus corporation tax on limited company)	3,000
TOTAL ASSESSMENTS 1987/88 1988/89	£60,000	TOTAL ASSESSMENTS 1987/88 1988/89	£84,000

The Inland Revenue would make additional assessments on £24,000 to recover the extra tax due for these two years.

If the change is made at 1 May 1990 the taxation effect would be:-

	Existing assessments:-	Inland Revenue would review as follows:-	
1987/88 Profits: Y/E 30/4/86	£24,000	No change	24,000
1988/89 Profits: Y/E 30/4/87	£36,000	1/12 x 48,000) 11/12 x 36,000)	37,000
1989/90 Profits: Y/E 30/4/88	£48,000	1/12 x 36,000) 11/12 x 48,000)	47,000

Taxation

1990/91 Profits:		1/12 x 48,000 4,000
Y/E 30/4/88	£36,000	(Plus corporation tax
		on limited company)

| TOTAL ASSESMENTS | | TOTAL ASSESSMENTS |
| 1988/89 1989/90 | £84,000 | 1988/89 1989/90 £84,000 |

The Inland Revenue test does not produce higher figures, so no additional charge will be made.

These figures illustrate how essential it is for the best date for the change to be carefully considered. Professional advice should always be sought.

(g) Appeals against assessments. To businessmen income tax assessments are an anathema; they should however resist the temptation to tear them up or put them behind the clock and forget about them. All assessments should be checked for accuracy immediately and if excessive the instructions on the notice about making an appeal should be followed and the appeal sent to the Tax District that issued the assessment. The appeal should also show how much of the tax charged should be postponed because the assessment is too high.

If this is not done within 30 days of the issue of the notice, the assessment becomes final and the inspector (and the general commissioners if they are asked to adjudicate) may well not accept a late appeal. In this event the taxpayer has no alternative but to pay the tax as charged on the assessment which may be estimated or contain additions to the profits which have not been agreed by him and his accountant. If the appeal is to be made by the accountant check with him before the 30 days are up to ensure that it has been submitted.

One final point: keep copies of all correspondence with the inspector and collector. This can be done very easily nowadays, by photocopying at a cost of a few pence per sheet. Letters can be mislaid or fail to be delivered and it is essential to have both proof of what was sent as well as a permanent record of all correspondence with official bodies.

Taxation

Some useful statistics

Income Tax   1989/90

1.   Main Personal Allowances

	£
Single person's allowance	2785
Married man's allowance	4375
Single parent with child's addition	1590
Married woman's earned income allowance (maximum)	2785

Rates of Tax

The basic rate is 25% on TAXABLE income up to £20,700 and 40% on all income thereafter. eg.

Business profits	30,000
Less personal allowance	4,375
Taxable income £	25,625

Chargeable:-

£20,700 @ 25% =	5,175
£ 4,925 @ 40% =	1,970

Total tax payable £ 7,145

Taxation of Husband and Wife: 1990/91 et seq

The present treatment of wife's income as being that of the husband is abolished from 6 April 1990. From then onwards a married woman will be treated in much the same way as a single person and will have her own personal allowance and basic rate band. Husband and wife will each make a separate return of their own income and the Inland Revenue will deal with each one in complete privacy - letters about the husband's affairs will be addressed only to him and about the wife's only to her (unless the parties indicate differently).

Wives who will be affected are those who are in employment or business or who have substantial investment income. This will include those who are regarded as employees of the husband's business or who are in partnership with him.

The allowances shown above will be replaced by new ones:-

A personal allowance
- one each for husband and   At 1989/90 rates this would
wife   be £2,785 each

61

Taxation

A married couple's allowance

This is initially due to the husband but if his income is too small to use it all he may transfer the excess to his wife by a written claim made within 6 years of the end of the Income Tax year

At 1989/90 rates this would be one amount of £1,590

Basic Rate Band

Husband and wife will each have a certain amount chargeable at the basic rate (currently 25%)

At 1989/90 rates this would be £20,700 each

There are transitional reliefs and, naturally, many detailed rules. Taxpayers will be meeting these when the next edition is due and it will contain a helpful guide and worked examples.

Date(s) tax due: Income Tax Year 1989/90

For earned income (such as trading profits) one half of the tax is due on 1 January 1990 and one half on 1 July 1990. For unearned income (such as rents) all the tax is due on 1 January 1990.

Ceiling for mortgage interest relief

This remains at £30,000.

Business Entertainment

No relief is due for expenditure on business entertainment of, or gifts to customers, whether they are from this country or overseas. However the cost of small trade gifts not exceeding £10 per person in value is still admissible. This would cover small presents for customers at Christmas.

Construction Industry

Payments to uncertified subcontractors should be made under deductions of tax at 25%.

2.   ## Capital Gains Tax (Individuals) 1989/90

Where an asset is disposed of after 5 April 1989 the first £5,000 of the gain will be exempt from tax. Any remaining gain will be chargeable as though it were the top slice of the individual's income, i.e. at either 25% or 40% or partly at one and partly at the other.

The Capital Retirement Relief of up to £125,000 has been extended so that only 50% of any gain over £125,000 up to £500,000 will be charged. Even for quite small businessmen this is a very valuable relief and anyone contemplating retirement, including early retirement, should consult his accountant before taking any steps or changing his working pattern.

Tax on gains which arose in the year ended 5 April 1989 is due in one sum on 1 December 1989 (or 30 days after the issue of the assessment if this is later). Tax on gains in the current year to 5 April 1990 will be due on 1 December 1990.

As from 14 March 1989 the general ability to postpone CGT on gifts until the recipient disposes of the asset has been withdrawn. But there are some exceptions and among them is the gift of business assets, including unquoted shares in trading companies. It will therefore still be possible to defer gains arising on the gift of such business assets if both the giver and receiver apply to the inspector in writing (professional advice should be sought before the gift is made).

3. Self employed NIC rates (from 6 April 1989)
    Class 2 Rate £4.25 per week (payable by weekly stamps or direct debit).
    If earnings are below £2,350 averaged over the year ask the DSS about "Small Income Exception", the details are in leaflet NI 27A.

    Class 4 Rate
    (a) Business profits up to £5,050 p.a.   : NIL

    (b)   "   "   between £5,050
         and £16,900 p.a.   :   6.3% of the profit

    (c) There is no charge on profits over £16,900 p.a. so the maximum amount of Class 4 contributions is £746.55

    One half of the Class 4 contribution is deducted from the profits for Income Tax purposes.
    Class 4 contributions are collected by the Inland Revenue along with the income tax due.

4. Corporation Tax
    The following notes apply to profits arising after 1 April 1989.
    Full Corporation Tax rate : 35%

    Rate for "Small Companies".
    whose profits (after deduction
    of directors remuneration) do
    not exceed £150,000   : 25%

Taxation

Where the profits are between £150,000 and £750,000 the rate is graduated so that it increases gradually from 25% to 35%. Company Capital Gains are also charged at the above rates.

Corporation Tax is due for payment 9 months after the end of the Company's accounting period.

5. Capital Allowances (Depreciation)
    On Plant and Machinery   25%
    On Industrial Buildings   4%
    On commercial and industrial
    buildings in Enterprise Zones   100%

    VAT
    Standard rate 15%
    Lower limit for registration (from 15 March 1989)
        Turnover per annum   £23,600
        Turnover per quarter   £ 8,000

Chapter 7 Keeping The Business Healthy

Many businesses are run without adequate information being available to check trends in their vital areas e.g. marketing, money and managerial efficiency. Proprietors often have the feeling that the business should be "doing better" than it is, without being able to identify what is going wrong. Sometimes there is the worrying phenomenon of a steadily increasing work programme coupled with a persistently reducing bank balance.

Some useful ways of checking the position and identifying problem areas are given below:-

Marketing

Whilst management and finance are concerned with the internal running of a business, the market is where it makes contact with the outside world in the shape of its competitors and customers. Throughout his business life the entrepreneur should study carefully the methods and approach of the former and the needs and wishes of the latter. A shortcoming frequently found in ailing concerns is that the proprietor thinks he knows better than his customers what they want.

The term "market research" sounds both difficult and expensive but a very simple form of it can be done quite effectively by the businessman and his sales staff. First, identify the type of person or business the products or service are likely to appeal to and canvass them with the double purpose of getting new business and finding out and recording what it is the customer wants in terms of price, quality, design, payment terms, follow-up service, guarantees, etc., and apply the results to the business' own range of products and services. The initial approach might be by leaflet or letter followed by a personal call. As an on-going part of management all staff with customer contact should be encouraged to enquire about and record customer preferences, complaints, etc., and feed it back to management.

Other sources of information are: friends in the trade, business journals, trade exhibitions, suppliers, representatives, etc., from whom information about trends in the trade, new techniques and products can be obtained and studied.

Valuable information can also be gained from studying competitors; questions to ask are:-

- What do they sell and at what prices.
- What inducements to buy do they offer their customers (e.g. credit facilities, guarantees, free offers, discounts, etc.)
- How do they reach their customers (local/national advertising; mail shots; salesmen; local radio and TV).
- What are the strongest aspects of their appeal to customers and have they any weaknesses.

Keeping The Business Healthy

The businessman should apply all the information gathered from customers and competitors to his own range of products with a view to making sure he is offering the right product at the right price in the most attractive way and in the most receptive market.

In a small business where the proprietor is also his own salesman he must give careful thought to how he can best present his product and himself. If he is working solely within the construction industry his main problems are likely to centre on getting a 714 and on exploiting as fully as possible trade contacts to get sub-contract work.

However, for those who serve the general public, presentation can be a vital element in getting work. The customer is looking for efficiency, reliability and honesty in a trader, and a product or service tailored to his requirements in such matters as quality, price, style, etc. To bring out these facets in discussion with a potential customer is a skilled task and for newcomers to business and those who have not had as much success to date as they hoped for, a short course on marketing techniques could pay handsome dividends. The Enterprise unit of the Manpower Service Commission will give the names and addresses of such courses locally - contact it through the job centre or make an appointment to see a Small Firms counsellor with marketing experience and talk over the problems with him.

Some indications that a market review is needed are:-

- Declining sales.
- Profit margins being squeezed.
- Fewer customers and over-reliance on a few large ones.
- Profitability not spread evenly over the product or service range - some items "not earning their keep" - perhaps through being out of date, too expensive, badly designed, poorly constructed, etc.

Finance

Unfortunately most concerns which close down do not seek help until it is too late to halt the downward trend when earlier attention to the problems may have saved some of them. There are many reasons for this and one of them is that those running the business are unable to recognise the tell-tale signs and very few accountants take the trouble to explain to their clients what to look out for. There are some tests and checks that can be done quite easily.

1. Profitability

Check the profit and loss accounts and balance sheets for the last 3 years and extract the following (known to accountants as the liquid ratio or the "acid test".)

Keeping The Business Healthy

	£		£
Cash at bank and in hand		Trade creditors	
Good trade debts		Other creditors due immediately including TAX, VAT and NIC	
Other short-period debts			
		If bank is pressing for overdraft reduction monthly contribution x 2	
TOTAL (A)	£	TOTAL (B)	£

Put A over B. If the fraction is less than 1 and the trend is worsening there is cause for concern.

A further check, the "current ratio", or the "dilute acid test," is to do the same computations as above but with the addition of the other current items - stock in hand, work in progress and the full amount of any bank overdraft.

For example	Total of current assets (in £ thousands)	Total of current liabilities (in £ thousands)
End of year 1	100	40
End of year 2	170	100
End of year 3	250	200

The fractions are year 1 100/40 = 2.5
year 2 170/100 = 1.70
year 3 250/200 = 1.25

The normal result looked for here is a figure of 2. In the example the trend is adverse and needs to be reversed before the situation becomes critical.

The liquid assets (those readily available) are becoming less in total than the bills immediately payable plus any short term borrowing facility at the bank.

2. Stock on hand

Take $\frac{\text{Stock x 52}}{\text{Sales}}$ =   ?   Weeks

This will show how many weeks' stocks are on hand.

Consider whether this is the minimum possible working amount necessary to cover the delivery time for replacements and contingencies. It is expensive in terms of money and space to carry too much stock and there is the added danger of its being spoilt, becoming out-dated or being pilfered. Make a full inventory of all stock and seek to dispose of old or surplus items for cash: institute a proper stock control.

3. Debt collection

Take $\dfrac{\text{Trade Debtors} \times 52}{\text{Sales}}$ = ?   Weeks

This shows the average number of weeks' credit being afforded to customers and in one sense each item represents an amount invested in someone else's business. Old debts are bad debts and firm control of all outstanding sums should be consistently maintained. In particular if the trend in this figure is upwards there may be cause for immediate action.

For example

Assuming business terms are cash in 30 days

The accounts show (Figures in £ thousands):-

Year 1 Sales   120 $\dfrac{10 \times 52}{120}$ =   4+ Weeks
       Debtors   10

Year 2 Sales   200 $\dfrac{40 \times 52}{200}$ = 10+ Weeks
       Debtors   40

Year 3 Sales   300 $\dfrac{70 \times 52}{300}$ = 12+ Weeks
       Debtors   70

Present time Sales running at 400 p.a. $\dfrac{120 \times 52}{400}$ = 15+ Weeks
             Debtors   120

As this business has grown, debt control has become slack or non-existent and may be threatening survival through strangling the cash flow. There is a business adage which says: he who shouts loudest, most often and first - gets paid; businessmen should ensure they are not last in the queue.

In the above situation the first task is to prepare an "aged list" for amounts outstanding at the present time and do this every month.

Keeping The Business Healthy

<u>"aged list"</u>   As at --(date)--

Name of customer	Value of this month's invoices	Amounts Outstanding			Remarks
		1 month	2 month	3 month	

Use as many columns as the business
requires: The final column should be
used for the date and nature of the
last action

The oldest and largest debtors can be seen at a glance for
immediate consideration of what further recovery action is needed -
a "good" customer is one who has paid for the goods and services
supplied to him.

The list may also show over-reliance on one or two large
customers or the need to stop supplying a particularly bad payer
until his arrears have been reduced to an acceptable level.
Consider making up bills to a date before the end of the month -
say the 24th in order to be near the head of the queue for payment,
and make sure the accounts are sent out immediately, followed by a
statement 4 weeks later. Consider giving discount for prompt
payment.

If all else fails and legal action for recovery is being
contemplated call at the County Court and ask for their booklets
EX50 (Small Claims in the County Court) and EX50C (Enforcing Money
Judgements).

4. <u>Gross percentage profit</u>

Take $\dfrac{\text{Gross Profit} \times 100}{\text{Sales}}$ =   ?   % Gross margin

The gross profit is the amount which is left after deducting from
sales the cost of the materials used in those sales and any
production costs.

The reasons for any change up or down in the gross profit
percentage should be established but most concern arises when the
trend is downwards. Possible reasons are:-

(a) The pricing of jobs is not taking full account of increases in
materials and wages and a review of pricing policy is needed.

(b) Too generous discount terms are being offered.

(c) Poor management; over manning; waste and pilferage of materials.

(d) Too much down-time on plant which is in need of replacement.

69

5. Net percentage profit

Take $$\frac{\text{Net profit (before tax)} \times 100}{\text{Sales}} = ? \quad \% \text{ Net margin}$$

The commercial net profit is arrived at by deducting from the gross
profit the business overheads, depreciation and, in the case of a
limited company, any directors' salaries, bonuses, fees and
expenses. The payments to directors should be added back to arrive
at the profit for this purpose. (In the case of sole traders and
partnerships the proprietors' earnings are not dealt with in this
way and no addition is necessary.)
    This indicates how much of each £'s worth of sales finishes up
as profit and again the trend, upward or downward, is important.
Try taking each item of expenditure in turn and consider whether
the business is getting full value from it. Ask:-

(a) Can savings be made in non-productive staff?

(b) Is sub-contracting possible in some areas and would it be
    cheaper?

(c) Have all possible energy-saving methods been fully explored?

(d) Do the company's vehicles spend too much time in the yard - can
    they be shared and their number reduced?

(e) Is the expenditure on advertising producing sales (review in
    association with "marketing" above)?

6. "Over trading"

Many inexperienced businessmen imagine that profitability equals
money in the bank. In some concerns, particularly where the
receipts are wholly in cash, this may be the case, but additional
business may mean higher stock inventories, extra wages, overheads,
increased capital expenditure on premises and plant. If the
debtors show a marked increase as the turnover rises the proprietor
may find to his surprise that each expansion of trade reduces
rather than increases his cash resources. The business, which had
enough funds for start-up, finds it does not have sufficient cash
to run at the higher level of operation and the bank manager may be
getting anxious about the increasing overdraft.
    It is essential for those who run a business which operates on
credit terms to be aware that profitability does not necessarily
mean increased cash availability. Regular monthly management
information on marketing and finance as described in this chapter
will enable "over trading" to be recognised and remedial action
taken early.
    If the situation is appreciated only when the bank and other

creditors are pressing for money, radical solutions may be
necessary such as bringing in new finance, sale and leaseback of
premises, a fundamental change in the terms of trade, or even
selling out to a buyer with more resources. Professional help from
the firm's accountant will be needed, whilst the Small Firms
Service has counsellors experienced in advising on both the
marketing and financial aspects of such situations.

7. Break-even point

The costs of a business may be divided into two types: variable and
fixed.
   Variable costs are those which increase or decrease as the
volume of work goes up or down and include materials used, direct
labour, power, machine tools, etc.
   Fixed costs are not related to turnover and are sometimes called
"fixed overheads". They include rent, rates, insurance, heat and
light, office salaries, plant depreciation, etc; these costs are
still incurred even though little or no sales are being made.
   Many small businessmen run their enterprises from home using
family labour as back-up; they sell mainly their own labour and buy
materials and hire plant only as required.
   By these means they reduce their fixed costs to a minimum and
start making profits almost immediately. However larger concerns
which have business premises, perhaps a small workshop, an office,
vehicles, etc., need to know how much they have to sell to cover
their costs and become profitable.
   In the case of a new business it is necessary to estimate the
figures but where annual accounts are available a break-even chart
based on them is readily prepared.
   Suppose the figures (real or estimated) are:-

Figures in thousands

		Percentage of sales		
Materials	150	(37.50%))	Sales	400
Labour	100	(25.00%)) 66.25%		
W'shop power etc.	15	(3.75%))		
Gross profit	135	(33.75%)		
	---			---
	400			400
	---			---
General over-heads	50	(12.50%)	Gross profit	135
Net profit	85	(21.25%) 33.75%		
	---		-----	---
	135		100%	135

71

Prepare a diagram on graph paper:-

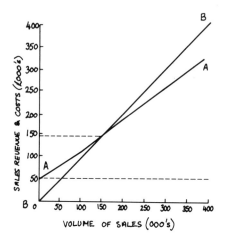

1. Mark the level of fixed costs - - - -(50).

2. Compute the fixed plus variable costs for various volumes of sales as follows:-

```
    NIL Sales : Costs: (fixed only) 50                =  50.00
    100 Sales : Costs: fixed 50 + (66.25% x 100)      = 116.25
    200 Sales : Costs: fixed 50 + (66.25% x 200)      = 182.50
    300 Sales : Costs: fixed 50 + (66.25% x 300)      = 248.75
    400 Sales : Costs: fixed 50 + (66.25% x 400)      = 315.00
```

   Mark these points on the graph and join them up (Line A).

3. Bisect the graph from 0 to 400 as shown in the diagram to indicate the volume of sales (Line B).

4. Where the lines intersect trace the horizontal line to the vertical arm of the graph - this is the break-even point and represents the sales revenue needed to cover the costs of the business - a little below £150 (thousand).

5. The graph can be checked against the formula:-

$$\text{Break-even point} = \frac{\text{Fixed Costs}}{1 - \dfrac{\text{Variable Costs}}{\text{Sales}}}$$

$$= \frac{50}{1 - \frac{265}{400}}$$

$$= \frac{50}{\frac{135}{400}}$$

$$= \frac{50 \times 400}{135}$$

$$= £148 \text{ (thousand)}$$

In practice things are never quite as clear cut as the graph and figures above show but neverthless this is a very useful tool for assessing not only the break-even point but also the approximate amount of loss or profit arising at differing levels of turnover and also for considering pricing policy.

This chapter contains only a selection of the techniques available for gauging the health of a business. Even so, interpreting the results and making decisions on them can be a puzzling and difficult job needing professional help. The firm's accountant is the person to turn to first. Many accountants however are overworked and cannot give constant attention to the problems. In this event contact the Small Firms Service which has specialists in all the fields mentioned above and can give on-the-spot and continuing advice to the businessman.

Chapter 8: Insurances

The topic of insurances is extremely specialised and expert advice
should be sought. This could be from one of the major insurance
companies or through a reputable broker. The word reputable is very
important in this context because it is of little use obtaining
cheaper insurance at the outset if the processes involved in
administering claims are long and drawn out. The advantages of using
a broker are many. The larger ones may well have one person dealing
in one type of business who will be able to recommend the right
insurance company, type of policy, and amount of cover. It is
important, however, that the broker chosen is a member of the British
Insurance Broker's Association.

There are several types of insurance available and some of these
are compulsory whilst some are not. Some form of insurance will
always be necessary where the work is being done under one of the
standard forms of building sub-contract. It is also compulsory to
have Employer's liability insurance under the Employer's Liability
(Compulsory Insurance) Act 1969. However, where a Contractor is
working in a domestic situation it is still necessary that he is
insured. It would be risky, indeed foolish, not to insure against the
possibility of things going wrong.

It should be stressed that only the main types of insurance are
discussed here. That is not to say that these are necessarily the only
insurances available and once again a reputable broker will be able to
advise. See also page 9 for FREE Advice Files from the Association of
British Insurers. The two main types of insurance are liability and
material damage and these can be sub-divided as follows.

Liability insurance	- Employer's liability insurance.
	- Public liability insurance.
Material damage insurance	- Insurance of own premises.
	- Insurance of the works.
	- Insurance of equipment.

Employer's liability insurance

This policy covers the Employer's responsibility to his employees
under the Employer's Liability (Compulsory Insurance) Act 1969. Under
this Act the Employer is liable for any injuries or disease sustained
by the Employee during the execution of his duties. It is incumbent
on the Employer to display a copy of the certificate at his premises.
There is usually no indemnity limit for Employer's liability
insurance. The type of cover provided under this policy is reasonably
standard from company to company.

Public liability insurance

This policy covers the sub-contractor's liability to the general
public for injury to body and damage to property. It is not
compulsory to have an operative policy of this nature although the
Finance (No. 2) Act 1975 indirectly enforces the need for this type of

75

cover. Under this Act, payments to Sub-contractors must be made less the relevant amount of income tax unless the Sub-contractor has an exemption certificate. However, one of the conditions set out in the Act is that in order to obtain an exemption certificate, the Sub-contractor must have a current public liability policy for the minimum amount set out in the Act. Unlike Employer's liability insurance, the type of cover provided may vary substantially from company to company so it may pay to shop around, or ask a broker to do so.

Insurance of own premises

There are two main aspects relating to this type of insurance. The first is the insurance of the building(s) itself and the second is the contents. If the building is leased then the insurance cover must comply in all respects with the stipulations in the lease.

Generally speaking the amount insured to cover the building is not related to its market value. The sum insured should be sufficient to cover the total rebuilding costs, plus the cost of demolition and removal of demolition arisings from the site (say in the case of a fire) plus the cost of professional fees (architects, surveyors, etc.). The type of cover chosen will depend upon the risk being taken and how much can be afforded for the premium. The insured risks may vary from policy to policy and a decision will have to be made whether or not the insurance is to be on the basis of cost of repair/renewal with a deduction for wear and tear or new for old. In either case the sum insured will invariably be subject to an averaging clause which means that if the sum insured does not represent the total value of the item at risk in accordance with the terms of the policy then only a corresponding proportion of any claim will be paid.

In principle the same rules regarding the type of cover and averaging also apply to contents insurance. Care should be taken to ensure that stocks are adequately covered and this applies both to those in the yard and those which may be at the current place of work. In this context it may also be necessary to insure materials which have been received but which have yet to be paid for.

Insurance of the works

There are two main aspects to this type of insurance. The first to consider is when working as a Sub-contractor to a main Contractor and the second is when working in one's own right.

When employed as a Sub-contractor the main Contractor may be responsible for the materials and goods once they are finally incorporated into the works and this will depend upon the wording of the main contract. However, it is generally advisable that the Sub-contractor carries his own policy as a safeguard to cover him when working both in new and existing buildings.

As well as insurance of the materials and goods, cover should also be extended to the client's premises, particularly if this is not covered by a separate public liability policy.

Insurances

Insurance of equipment

Tools, plant and any equipment such as ladders, scaffolding, etc., will need to be insured. It is usually necessary to specify the equipment covered and the policy will incorporate an averaging clause. Care should be exercised when hiring items of equipment to ensure that the item is either insured by the owner or that the hirer's own policy covers it. This cover should also cover consequential loss to the owner (i.e. loss of hire charges) following loss or damage to the item concerned.

All risks policy

Rather than have several individual policies for different risks, it is more common and certainly more practical to have a combined or all risks policy. This brings together several types of cover into one master policy and the principle ones are public liability, Employer's liability, insurance of the works and insurance of equipment. The wording of these policies varies from company to company so again professional advice should be sought.

Other insurance policies

As previously stated there are many types of insurance available of which the former are the main ones. However, the following may also wish to be considered:-

(1) Consequential loss insurance. This covers the losses suffered due to interruption of normal business due to loss of own premises because of an insured risk.

(2) Fidelity guarantee insurance. This covers loss due to the dishonesty of employees.

(3) Insurance of bad debts. This covers the writing off of debts which are not recoverable.

Chapter 9 : Sub-contracting

Generally

Tradesmen and small contractors can be involved in situations where they act as main contractors (working for a client direct) or as a sub-contractor (working for another contractor).

There is no contractual bond between the Sub-contractor and the Employer. In general terms this means that the Sub-contractor cannot make any claims against the Employer direct and vice-versa. It also means that the Sub-contractor should not accept any instructions from the Employer or his representative because this could be taken as establishing a privity of contract between the two parties which would not otherwise exist.

Sometimes the sub-contract carries with it the responsibility of design. In instances such as this the Sub-contractor must at tender stage ensure that he is able to meet the specified design periods and that the periods of time allowed for approval of his design are such that he is allowed sufficient time to mobilise his work force and order his materials in order to meet the programme.

A Sub-contractor must at all times monitor his own progress in order to maintain the programme. A Sub-contractor who causes a Contractor to overrun the completion date for the main contract may become liable for the full amount of liquidated damages on the main contract plus the cost of damages which the Contractor himself and his other Sub-contractors have suffered.

The well organised Sub-contractor will keep a full set of daily site records, staffing levels, plant on site, weather charts and such like. It also cannot be over emphasised that any verbal instructions which the Sub-contractor receives should be confirmed immediately to the Contractor in writing with the name of the person who has issued them. This procedure is extremely important because it may eventually save the Sub-contractor from considerable expense if someone tries to lay the blame for delays to the contract at his door. It is also of paramount importance that instructions should not be taken from anyone but the Contractor and the Contractor should be informed immediately if another party should attempt to do so.

Conditions of sub-contract

There are basically two forms of sub-contract, domestic and nominated and the essential differences between these are explained later. Regardless of the type of sub-contract, the Sub-contractor will probably be required to enter into a formal agreement with the Contractor, which will contractually bind him to a set of rules and conditions with which he must comply.

These conditions of sub-contract may vary from job to job and between different Contractors but each will normally contain certain elements which are common to all of them and these are summarised as follows.

Sub-contracting

Fixed or fluctuating prices

The prices which the Sub-contractor is asked to insert can either be fixed or fluctuating.

Fixed prices must contain all future increases in cost of labour, materials and plant. However, certain increases may be paid on fixed price contracts such as increases in VAT, income tax and other government taxes.

Fluctuating prices are based on wage rates, material prices and plant costs which are current at the time of tender. Any increases during the sub-contract period are reimbursed to the Sub-contractor normally on a net basis.

Contractor's discount

Most sub-contracts allow for a discount to the Contractor of 2½% for prompt payment. That is to say, if the Contractor pays the Sub-contractor on time, which is usually within a stated period, he is entitled to deduct 2½% from the Sub-contractor's account. This means that the Sub-contractor must build this discount into his prices and this is done by adding 1/39th to his net rates.

Payment and retention

Payment is normally made on a monthly basis. The Sub-contractor submits his account to the Contractor who then passes it on to the Architect or Employer's representative for certification of payment. When the Sub-contractor receives his payment it will be less than the amount originally invoiced. The amount deducted is known as the retention money, and although this can vary it is normally 5%. This money is held by the Employer and released in two halves. The first half or moeity is paid at the completion of work and in the Sub-contractor's case this may be either when he has finished his work or when the Contractor has completed the contract as a whole (known as practical completion). The second half is released at the end of the defects liability period (see next).

Defects liability period

This is the period of time (normally 12 months) during which the Sub-contractor is contractually bound to return to the job to rectify any mistakes or bad pieces of workmanship. This could either be 12 months from when he completes his work or 12 months from when the main contract is completed depending upon the wording of the Sub-contract.

Sub-contracting

Period for completion

More often than not the Sub-contractor will be given a period of time
in which he must complete the work and he must ensure that he has the
capability to do the work within that period because failure to meet
the agreed completion date could have dire consequences (see damages
for non-completion). Under certain circumstances, however, particularly with nominated sub-contracts, the Sub-contractor may be requested
to state the period of time he requires to do the work. If this is
the case then careful thought must be given to the time inserted. Too
short a time may put him at risk financially, but too long a time may
prejudice the opportunity of winning the job.

Damages for non-completion

A clause is usually contained within each sub-contract stating that
the Sub-contractor is liable for the financial loss which the Contractor suffers due to the Sub-contractor's non-completion of the work on
time. This will include the amount of liquidated and ascertained
damages contained within the main contract, together with the Contractor's own direct losses and the direct losses of his other Sub-contractors. As can be seen, the potential cost to the Sub-contractor can
be great and he must therefore take great care to expedite the work
with due diligence to avoid incurring these costs.

Variations

All Sub-contracts contain a clause which allow the sub-contract work
to be varied without invalidating it. The Sub-contractor will normally be paid any additional cost he incurs in carrying out the variation.

Insurances

It is normally incumbent on the Sub-contractor to insure against
injury to persons or property and against loss of plant and materials.
These insurances could be taken out for each individual job, although
it is more common nowadays to take out blanket policies based on the
turnover the firm has achieved in the previous year.

Extensions of time

The Sub-contractor will normally be entitled to a longer period of
time to complete the work if he is delayed or interrupted by reasons
beyond his control (known as an extension of time). Most sub-contracts list the reasons and in some cases the Sub-contractor may also
be entitled to additional monies as well as an extension.

Sub-contracting

Domestic sub-contracts

Of the two forms, domestic sub-contracts are the less legally complicated. Competitive quotations are obtained by the Contractor from
various Sub-contractors of his own choice and these may be based on a
bill of quantities, specification and drawings, or schedules of work.
Accompanying the enquiry should also be the form of sub-contract which
the Sub-contractor will be required to complete should he be
successful and this will normally be a standard form which the Contractor uses for all his domestic sub-contracts.

With regard to the pricing of domestic sub-contracts there are
several points which may affect costs and which the Sub-contractor
should bear in mind. These are:-

1. Whether the rates and prices are to include for any contractor's discount (normally expressed as plus 1/39th to allow
   2½%).

2. Whether the Contractor is to supply any labour or plant to
   assist the Sub-contractor either carrying out any of the work,
   or in off-loading materials.

3. What facilities (if any) the Contractor will afford the Sub-
   contractor with respect of messrooms, welfare facilities,
   office accommodation and storage facilities.

4. Whether the Contractor is to dispose of the Sub-contractor's
   rubbish.

5. Whether the rates and prices are on a fixed or fluctuating
   basis, and if on a fixed basis, whether the period during which
   the sub-contract will run includes a wage increase.

6. Who is responsible for builder's work and making good, i.e.
   cutting out holes, mortices, chases, etc., and making good
   plaster work and finishings.

As stated previously, the sub-contract itself will normally be the
Contractor's own standard form and this will need to be read carefully. Most standard forms have clauses which state that provisions of
the main contract are also binding on the Sub-contractor, although in
many instances the Sub-contractor may not automatically be allowed to
see the main contract itself. If in doubt about its contents the Sub-
contractor should always ask to see a copy of the main contract. It
is far safer to be wise before the event rather than after.

Sub-contracting

Nominated sub-contracts

In this instance the Sub-contractor is chosen by the Employer or his
representative and the Contractor is told to enter into an agreement
with the Sub-contractor creating the nominated sub-contract. Nominated sub-contracts are also generally sought on a competitive basis,
but unlike domestic sub-contracts, the procedure is much more standar-
dised throughout the building industry. The Joint Contracts Tribunal
(JCT) publish several standard forms including standard forms for
tendering and standard sub-contract conditions.

Unlike domestic subcontracts the Employer or his representative
should clearly inform the Sub-contractor in the documentation what his
rates and prices should include for and what facilities and attendances will be supplied by the Contractor. These generally include the use
of standing scaffolding and standing power operated hoisting equipment,
use of temporary roads and access ways, provision of temporary light
and water supplies, provision of space for Sub-contractor's own offices, use of Contractor's own messrooms and welfare facilities and disp-
osing of Sub-contractor's rubbish.

In addition the Sub-contractor will normally be requested to list
in his tender any further special attendances which he requires. Such
attendances may include special scaffolding, power supplies, provision
of covered storage and unloading, hoisting and distributing materials.

Chapter 10 : Contracting

Generally

As stated there are instances where a Builder will find himself
working under a private contract, either written or implied. Quite
often this takes the form of working for a domestic householder or the
small factory owner who may want some work carried out.

It is important to note that when dealing with the public one is
not working with professionals who are familiar with construction
procedures and therefore a new set of rules must be applied. The
first thing which must be said is that one of the keys to a successful
business is in supplying a sound product at reasonable cost in a
manner that does not invite criticism from the purchaser. In this way
the product is recommended to others who create a demand for it which
in turn encourages the business to flourish. The prudent Builder
will therefore avoid anything which could be construed as 'sharp
practice' at all costs, and if the following procedures are adopted
then his reputation should be enhanced.

The Estimate

The initial approach would generally come from the purchaser, i.e.
"how much will it cost to have the front drive taken up and relaid?"
At this stage he may only want an approximate cost in order to see if
he can reasonably afford to have the work done (as opposed to a
quotation - see later). Therefore a very brief description of the
work to be carried out together with an approximate price will
suffice. However, it should be made very clear that the price is an
estimate and does not constitute an offer which may be accepted by the
purchaser. The estimate may be based on a telephone conversation only,
i.e., "Yes, it will cost between £7 to £8 per square metre to relay
the drive of your house", or it could be based on a brief visit to the
house. In either case little time should be spent on an estimate and
it is generally prudent to give it as a price range.

The Quotation

A quotation, as distinct to an estimate, is generally seen as an offer
to do the work for the price quoted, and could constitute a simple
contract if accepted. It follows that some time and effort should be
spent in compiling a quotation in order to save arguments at a later
stage. One should always remember that as the tradesman, the Builder
is the expert and must use his expertise in order to guide the purchaser and should therefore discuss the work in full. He should tell the
purchaser exactly what he is getting for the price and also what he is
not. This may mean going into some detail such as whether the arisings from the old drive will be removed, how thick each coat of
tarmac will be, whether any kerbs are included etc., but the more
detail that is included at this stage the less the scope for argument
later. If possible it is also recommended that any possible extras
which it is thought may arise are also listed and priced separately

at the time of quotation, e.g. re-aligning of fencing posts next to the drive. By the same token, the Builder should ascertain from the purchaser exactly what work he will do for the Builder and what restrictions (if any) he will place upon him. For instance will the purchaser move a derelict car parked in the drive and will the Builder only be allowed entry to the premises on certain days and/or at certain times? These factors which may affect the Builder's costs should be ascertained in advance, and the costs of complying with same should be made known to the purchaser who may decide to take steps to change the restrictions.

Once the Builder has considered all the relevant factors then the formal written quotation can be produced.

It should state precisely what the purchaser is getting for his money, including when and how long the job will take and be clear, unambiguous and contain all the salient points of any discussions which have taken place.

Once a quotation has been submitted then all that needs to be done is for the purchaser to accept it. Although a verbal acceptance would constitute a binding agreement, it is always more satisfactory if the acceptance is made in writing.

Once a business has expanded it may become necessary to have some standard conditions of sale drafted, but until that time comes, the following are the main items which a good quotation should contain apart from the price itself and specification of work.

Payments

There is much debate on how and when payments should be made in domestic situations. Ideally from the Builder's point of view to be paid in advance would be the most advantageous, but this would be impracticable and unfair, and in any case the chances of the purchaser wishing to do this are remote. On the other hand, it may cause undue financial hardship on a recently self-employed Builder to have to buy all the materials himself and not get paid until all the work is completed. Whatever payment policy is adopted it must be agreed with the purchaser in advance and form part of the written quotation.

Possible alternatives are:-

1. Being paid when the work is complete. This is probably the best method from a public relations aspect and Builders who may be able to complete jobs in two to three days will have no difficulty in adopting this policy.

2. Being paid before the work is done. This is only really feasible where the Builder concerned is of unquestionable reputation or is well known to the purchaser.

3. Being paid for materials as they are bought and delivered and the balance paid when the work is complete. This could be a practical solution for smaller Builders, but the

purchaser will probably want justification of the material costs, so careful handling of invoices is necessary.

4. Some form of stage payments. Usually agreed percentages of the quotation price at set periods of time, or agreed parts of the quotation price paid after certain aspects of the work have been carried out.

There are many variations on the above and each individual Builder will no doubt arrive at the method which suits him best either as a general policy or perhaps for each individual job. No matter which policy is adopted it is essential that it is agreed beforehand and recorded in writing.

Pricing and variations

It is essential that some method of recording, pricing and being paid for variations is agreed at the outset and this is particularly relevant when dealing with the public. Unforeseen additions, more than any other single item, are the main cause of disputes between contractors and clients and are often avoidable.

The first step to avoid this is to ensure that the original quotation is as detailed as possible. It is unhelpful for a quotation to read "New concrete drive - £920". If there are no drawings involved the Builder should list the main items of work he is quoting for with a price against each item as follows:-

		£
1	Hack up existing drive and remove debris	120.00
2	Provide and lay 100mm concrete on 100mm hardcore as new drive including formwork	660.00
3	Take up 2 No. manhole covers and reset to new levels	20.00
		£ 800.00
	VAT @ 15%	£ 120.00
	TOTAL QUOTATION	£ 920.00

The detailed specification of the materials could be contained within the same descriptions or done separately. A quotation broken down in this way is detailed enough to enable the purchaser to ascertain that he is not being overcharged for any variations that may occur and yet is not so detailed that the purchaser is going to question the price of every nut and bolt.

Also, if the purchaser should wish to change anything himself then there are no arguments about on what was included in the original quotation. However, it should be stressed again that it is the Builder who is the expert in these matters and whilst it may be simple to omit certain items from the original quotation in order to win the job and then try and add them back in at a later date, this course of action will have nothing but an adverse effect on the business in the long term.

Assuming then that we have a well presented quotation, what procedure should be adopted for variations of the work. The first question to be asked is whose liability are they? These can be categorised as follows:-

1. Those instructed by the purchaser.

2. Those which should have been included in the original quotation.

3. Those which are necessary due to events which could not have been foreseen.

The liabilities for 1 and 2 are relatively straightforward. If the purchaser says he wants an oak panelled door instead of a plywood faced flush door then he must obviously bear the additional cost. Conversely, if the Builder forgets to include the cost of a scaffolding in his quotation then it is only fair that he bears the cost. Item 3 is more difficult. If it is the purchaser who is receiving the benefit of the variations and if they were not foreseeable, then it would be logical to assume that it is the purchaser who should bear the cost. One example of this would be if a Builder were replacing some roof coverings which, when removed revealed rotting timbers underneath which required replacement. Other instances may not be as clear cut as this and it may become necessary to arrive at a cost sharing arrangement if genuine doubt exists.

Variations should preferably be agreed in advance before the work is carried out. They should be recorded in writing and signed by both parties and wherever possible priced in detail and the price agreed. In the long run variations dealt with in this manner will save time and money and preserve goodwill and the good name of the company.

Call out charges

The amount charged for being called out to deal with an emergency is often a source of dispute - after the problem has been solved!

It is only fair to the client that the charge is made known to him before he incurs the cost. It is mistaken to believe that call out charges only apply to calls made outside working hours. An emergency call during the day can have a disruptive effect on the normal work pattern and this should be paid for.

Some suggested levels of charges are set out below but each

Contracting

Contractor should decide on his own rate and most importantly, let the client know the cost before the call is made. Please note that these charges are exclusive of the time spent carrying out the work which should be charged separately.

Call out charge during working hours - £15-£20
Call out charge 6pm to midnight   - £20-£30
Call out charge after midnight,
Sundays and Bank Holidays   - £30-£50

In addition a mileage charge of 25p per mile should be made plus travelling time if it exceeds half an hour total.

Chapter 11 Plant and Tool Hire

The prices contained in this chapter have been supplied by HSS Hire Shops Ltd., 25 Willow Lane, Mitcham, Surrey who have over 120 shops throughout the country and the prices include VAT.

	First 24 hrs £	Addit 24 hrs £	Per week £
ACCESS & SUPPORT			
Alloy Stairway and Span Tower			
base size 4'3" x 5'0" (1.3			
x 1.5 m) or 2'8" x 5'0"			
(0.8 x 1.5 m)			
8'3" (2.5 m)	23.00	11.50	46.00
15'0" (4.5 m)	33.35	16.68	66.70
21'6" (6.5 m)	43.70	21.85	87.40
28'0" (8.5 m)	54.05	27.02	108.10
34'6" (10.5 m)	64.00	32.20	128.80
Alloy Wide Span Tower			
Base size 4'3" x 5'0" (1.3			
x 1.5 m) or 2'8" x 8'3"			
(0.8 x 2.5 m)			
8'3" (2.5 m)	24.72	12.36	49.45
15'0" (4.5 m)	36.22	18.11	72.45
21'6" (6.5 m)	47.72	23.86	95.45
28'0" (8.5 m)	59.22	29.61	118.45
34'6" (10.5 m)	70.72	35.36	141.45
Alloy chimney scaffold unit			
half chimney surround unit	40.25	20.12	80.50
Steel domestic towers			
Base size 4'3" x 2'0" (1.3 x			
0.6m) or 4'3" x 4'3" (1.3 x 1.3m)			
4' (1.2 m)	7.47	3.73	14.95
6' (1.8 m)	9.20	4.60	18.40
8' (2.4 m)	10.92	5.46	21.85
10' (3.0 m)	12.65	6.32	25.30
12' (3.6 m)	14.37	7.18	28.75
14' (4.2 m)	16.10	8.05	32.20
16' (4.8 m)	17.82	8.91	35.65
Staircase frame	1.15	0.57	2.30

ACCESS & SUPPORT (cont'd)	First 24 hrs £	Addit 24 hrs £	Per week £

Steel industrial towers
Base Size 5' x 7' (1.7 x
2.1m) or 7' x 7'(2.1 x 2.1m)

	First 24 hrs	Addit 24 hrs	Per week
8'(2.4 m)	23.00	11.50	46.00
12'(3.6 m)	25.87	12.93	51.75
16'(4.8 m)	28.75	14.37	57.50
20'(6.0 m)	31.62	15.81	63.25
24'(7.2 m)	34.50	17.25	69.00
28'(8.5 m)	37.37	18.68	74.75
32'(9.8 m)	40.25	20.12	80.50

Alloy Ladders

Double 12' extending to 21'	6.90	3.45	13.80
16' 29'	10.35	5.17	20.70
20' 42'	17.25	8.62	34.50
Treble 12' 32'	11.50	5.75	23.00
16' 42'	23.00	11.50	46.00
20' 54'	28.75	14.37	57.50

Roof Ladders

Alloy and Wooden 14' and 16'	10.35	5.17	20.70

Ladder Stay each

	3.45	1.72	6.90

Builder's Steps

8 tread Height 5'6"	5.75	2.87	11.50
10 tread Height 7'8"	6.90	3.45	13.80
12 tread Height 9'10"	8.05	4.02	16.10

Decorator's Trestles

Height- 6'	4.60	2.30	9.20
- 8'	5.75	2.87	11.50
-10'	6.90	3.45	13.80
-12'	8.05	4.02	16.10

Steel Trestles

Nos 1 to 4 - 1'9" extending to 8'0"	-	-	2.87

Scaffold Boards
Length - 8'-10'. 11'-13'

			1.72

Plant and Tool Hire

ACCESS & SUPPORT (cont'd)	First 24 hrs £	Addit 24 hrs £	Per week £
Lightweight Staging			
Length - 8'	5.17	2.58	10.35
10'	6.32	3.16	12.65
12'	7.47	3.73	14.95
14'	8.62	4.31	17.25
16'	9.77	4.88	19.55
20'	12.07	6.03	24.15
24'	17.25	8.62	34.50
BUILDING & DECORATING			
Mini Excavator/Digger	57.50	28.75	115.00
Metal Detector	6.90	3.45	13.80
Cable Avoiding Tool	23.00	11.50	46.00
C.A.T. Signal Generator	14.37	7.18	28.75
Damp Proof Injection Unit	23.00	11.50	46.00
Woodworm/Dry Rot/Waterproofing Spray	23.00	11.50	46.00
Wallpaper Steam Strippers-Gas/E	5.75	2.87	11.50
Wallpaper Perforator	1.72	0.86	3.45
Paint Stripper, Electric	5.75	2.87	11.50
Stone Splitter	24.15	12.07	48.30
Bitumen Boiler	17.25	8.62	34.50
Tar Furnace	7.47	3.73	14.95
Tile Saw-Electric	23.00	11.50	46.00
Tile Cutter-Hand	4.60	2.30	9.20
Tile Breaker/Drill	2.30	1.15	4.60
Steel Props			
Nos 0 to 4 - 3'6" Extending to 16'0"	-	-	2.87
Jackall Prop	4.60	2.30	9.20
Building/Decorating Tools			
Blowlamp with extension hose	4.60	2.30	9.20
Bolt Croppers	4.60	2.30	9.20
Crowbar	-	-	3.45
Floorboard Cramps	2.30	1.15	4.60
G Clamps	-	-	2.30
Paperhangers Table	-	-	3.45
Paving Mallet	-	-	4.60
Pickaxe/Mattock Punner	-	-	3.45
Sash Clamps. Shovel/Spade	-	-	3.45

BUILDING & DECORATING (cont'd)	First 24 hrs £	Addit 24 hrs £	Per week £
Building/Decorating Tools			
Site Tool Box	-	-	28.75
Slate Ripper. Sledgehammer 7/14lb	-	-	3.45
Spirit Level	-	-	3.45
Tarpaulins	4.88	2.30	9.77
Tyrolean Roughcast Machine	4.60	2.30	9.20
Wheelbarrow	3.45	1.72	6.90
White Line Marker	6.90	3.45	13.80
Road Hazard Equipment			
Traffic Warning Cones	-	-	1.15
Flashing Lamp and Stand	-	-	2.30
Road Signs	-	-	3.45
Road Barrier. Cone and Cap	-	-	2.87
Road Barrier, Plank	-	-	2.87
CONCRETING & COMPACTION			
Concrete Mixers			
4ft (½bag), Petrol	5.75	2.87	11.50
4/3cu ft (½bag) Electric	5.75	2.87	11.50
5/3½cu ft Diesel	17.25	8.62	34.50
Concrete Laying and Finishing			
Poker Vibrator. Eletric	23.00	11.50	46.00
Poker Vibrator. Petrol	25.87	12.93	51.75
Poker Vibrator, Diesel	28.75	14.37	57.50
Power Finishing Trowel, Petrol	28.75	14.37	57.50
Beam Screeds, Petrol (per Unit)	28.75	14.37	57.50
Needle Gun, Scaler, Air driven	9.77	4.88	19.55
Edge Forms	-	-	-
Indent Roller	5.75	2.87	11.50
Floor Grinder, Diesel/Electric	40.25	20.12	80.50
Track/Floor Saw, Diesel	34.50	17.25	69.00
Surface Scaler/Roof Dechipper	40.25	20.12	80.50
Compactors			
Compactor, 2 Stroke Petrol	24.15	12.07	48.30
Vibrating Plate Medium, Petrol	24.15	12.07	48.30
Vibrating Plate Heavy, Petrol	28.75	14.37	57.50
Vibrating Roller, Diesel/Petrol	34.50	17.25	69.00
Site Levels			
Cowley Site Level	17.50	8.62	34.50

Plant and Tool Hire

PLUMBING. PUMPING & DRAIN CLEANING	First 24 hrs £	Addit 24 hrs £	Per week £
Plumbers Tools			
Pipe Freezing Kit CO2	17.25	8.62	34.50
Steel Pipe Bender 2" Hydraulic	23.00	11.50	46.00
Copper Pipe Bender (Machine Only)	9.20	4.60	18.40
Guides & Formers-15-28mm: 35-42mm	1.72	0.86	3.45
Steel Pipe Cutter-up to 2"	3.45	1.72	6.90
Clay Pipe Cutter-4" to 6"	9.20	4.60	18.40
Pipe Vice Stand	6.90	3.45	13.80
Pipe Wrenches-Stillson 24"/Chain 27"	3.45	1.72	6.90
Stillson 36"	4.60	2.30	9.20
Pipe Threading			
Electric Die Stock	25.87	12.93	51.75
Ratchet Die Stock	9.20	4.60	18.40
Pipe Threading Machine ½"-4" Electric	54.06	27.02	108.10
Pipe Threading Machine ½"-2" Electric	39.67	19.83	79.35
Pipe Pressure Tester	6.90	3.45	13.80
Water Pumps			
Submersible 1" Electric	12.07	6.03	24.15
Submersible 2" Electric	21.27	10.63	42.55
Centrifugal 2" Petrol	25.30	12.65	50.60
Centrifugal 3" Petrol	26.45	13.22	52.90
Spate 3" Diesel	34.50	17.25	69.00
Drain Testing/Clearing Tools			
Drain Test Kit, "U" Gauge	4.02	2.01	8.05
Air Bag Drain Stopper	4.02	2.01	8.05
Drain Plugs 4"-6" per pair	-	-	3.45
Drain Rods and Fittings 30' per set	5.75	2.87	11.50
Drain Clearing Pump	5.17	2.58	10.35
Sink Cleaner, hand operated	6.32	3.16	12.65
Drain Cleaner, hand operated	9.20	4.60	18.40
Powered Drain Cleaner, Electric	25.87	12.93	51.75

HEATING, COOLING & DRYING

Industrial Heaters-Gas

		First 24 hrs £	Addit 24 hrs £	Per week £
Plaque Heater	9,500 BTU	6.90	3.45	13.80
Forced Air	30-125,000 BTU	17.82	8.91	35.65
Forced Air	108-250,000 BTU	24.15	12.07	48.30

Industrial Heaters-Paraffin

Forced Air	60,000 BTU	16.10	8.05	32.20
Forced Air	85-100,000 BTU	17.25	8.62	34.50
Forced Air	150,000 BTU	21.27	10.63	42.55

Home/Office Heaters

Cabinet, Gas	3-16,000 BTU	6.90	3.45	13.80
Electric Fan Heater-3kw		3.45	1.72	6.90

Cooling

Industrial Blower		10.36	5.17	20.70
Air Conditioning Unit		37.37	18.68	74.75

Drying

Building Dryer-Dehumidifier-30,000ft3		23.00	11.50	46.00
Portable Building Dryer-5,000ft3		17.25	8.62	34.50

Portable Fume Extractor		31.05	15.52	62.10

LIGHTING, & WELDING & POWER

Lighting Units

	First 24 hrs	Addit 24 hrs	Per week
Gas - Large tripod mounted	5.75	2.87	11.50
Gas - Small cylinder mounted	4.60	2.30	9.20
Electric - Tripod mounted	8.05	4.02	16.10
Plasterers Light - Fluorescent	7.47	3.73	14.95
Magnetic 500W Flood	8.62	4.31	17.25
Twin 500W Flood - 5m Tower Mast	11.50	5.75	23.00
Portalite 1500W Flood-6' Mast	23.00	11.50	46.00
Festoon Lights Industrial	8.62	4.31	17.25

Welding

Arc Welder 140/180 Amp, 240 Volt	12.65	6.32	25.30
MIG Welder, 240 Volt	12.65	6.32	25.30
Spot Welder, 240 Volt (30 Amp)	12.65	6.32	25.30
Site Welder 20-170 Amp, Petrol	34.50	17.25	69.00

LIGHTING, WELDING & POWER (cont'd)	First 24 hrs £	Addit 24 hrs £	Per week £
Welding			
Welder/Generator 180 Amp, DC Diesel	34.50	17.25	69.00
Welder/Generator 250 Amp, DC Diesel	57.50	28.75	115.00
Welder/Generator 300 Amp, DC Silenced	74.75	37.37	149.50
Portapak Oxy/Acetylene Welding Kit	18.97	9.48	37.95
Generators (Continuous Rating)			
1.5 - 2.0kVA Petrol (1100 Watt)	11.50	5.75	23.00
3.0 - 3.5kVA Petrol (2200 Watt)	29.32	14.66	58.65
4.0 - 5.0kVA Diesel (3000 watt)	35.65	17.82	71.30
8.0 - 10.0kVA Diesel (6000 watt)	48.87	24.43	97.75
12.5 - 15.0kVA Diesel (9000 Watt)	63.25	31.62	126.50
Transformers (Continuous Rating)			
2.2kVA (1500 Watt)	4.31	2.01	8.62
3.0kVA (2200 watt)	6.03	2.87	12.07
4.0kVA (3000 WAtt)	8.62	4.31	17.25
5.0kVA (3500 Watt)	10.92	5.46	21.85
10 - 15kVA (7500 watt)	19.55	9.77	39.10
Extension Cable 50' Cable/drum	3.16	1.43	6.32
Fourway Junction Box	5.75	2.87	11.50
Power Breaker RCD plug	2.30	1.15	4.60

BREAKING & DRILLING

	First 24 hrs	Addit 24 hrs	Per week
Hydraulic Breaker			
Heavy Duty Petrol/Diesel	43.12	21.56	86.25
Mini, Petrol	34.50	17.25	69.00
Electric Hammers			
Heavy Breaker (inc. trolley)	28.17	14.08	56.35
Demolition Hammer	8.62	4.31	17.25
Light Hammer	8.62	4.31	17.25
Tamping Tool	-	-	4.60
Comb Holder, Bush Hammer	-	-	2.30
Rotary Hammers			
Kango 950/637	8.62	4.31	17.25
Hilti TE72/TE52	13.80	6.90	27.60
Hammer Drills			
Light Duty	11.50	5.75	23.00
Medium Duty	12.65	6.32	25.30

Plant and Tool Hire

BREAKING & DRILLING (cont'd)	First 24 hrs	Addit 24 hrs	Per week
	£	£	£
Electric Drills			
Single Speed 3/8" Chuck	4.60	2.30	9.20
Two Speed ½" Chuck	4.60	2.30	9.20
Cordless Drill	8.05	4.02	16.10
Right Angle Drill	11.50	5.75	23.00
Four Speed 3/4".1" Chuck	11.50	5.75	23.00
Magnetic Base Drills			
Magnetic Drill Stand (Drill extra)	23.00	11.50	46.00
Magnetic Drill Stand c/w Drill	34.50	17.25	69.00
Rotabench Magnetic Base Drill	34.50	17.25	69.00
FIXING, GRINDING & SANDING			
Fixing Tools			
Cartridge Hammer	12.65	6.32	25.30
Staple Tacker-Light duty	4.60	2.30	9.20
Stapling Machine-Heavy Duty	9.20	4.60	18.40
Nail Gun-Air Operated	19.55	9.77	39.10
Impact Wrench-Electric	10.35	5.17	20.70
Screwdriver-Electric	8.62	4.31	17.25
Angle Grinders			
Angle Grindette 4"/5"	5.75	2.87	11.50
Angle Grinder 9"	5.75	2.87	11.50
Angle Grinder 12"	11.50	5.75	23.00
Sanders			
Belt Sander 4"	11.50	5.75	23.00
Disc Sander 7"	11.50	5.75	23.00
Orbital Sander-Industrial	11.50	5.75	23.00
Floor Sanders			
Domestic 8"	17.25	8.62	34.50
Edging Sander 7"	14.37	7.18	28.75
Floor Sander c/w Edging Sander	23.00	11.50	46.00
Router	13.22	6.61	26.45
Laminate Trimmer	12.07	6.03	24.15
Power Plane	13.22	6.61	26.45
SAWING & CUTTING			
Metal/Masonry Saw Benches			
Clipper Bench Saw 14" Junior Electric	34.50	17.25	69.00
Clipper Bench Saw 14" Major Petrol	40.25	20.12	80.50
Table Cut Off Saw 14" Electric	23.00	11.50	46.00
Tile Saw-Electric	23.00	11.50	46.00

Plant and Tool Hire

SAWING & CUTTING (cont'd)	First 24 hrs	Addit 24 hrs	Per week
Wall Chasing Machine	£	£	£
Chasing Machine inc. Cutter	23.00	11.50	46.00
Additional Cutters	-	-	6.90
Metal Cutters			
Metal Shears	14.95	7.47	29.90
Metal Nibblers	14.95	7.47	29.90
Timber Saw Benches			
Bench Top Mitre "Chop Saw "8" Electric	23.00	11.50	46.00
Combination Saw Bench 8" Electric	25.87	12.93	51.75
Mitre/Saw Bench 10" Electric	25.87	12.93	51.75
Timber Saw Bench 12" Electric	23.00	11.50	46.00
Combination Saw Bench 12" Electric	37.37	18.68	74.75
Site Saw bench 16"-Petrol	37.37	18.68	74.75
Portable Saws			
Circular Saw 8"/9" inc. blade	12.07	6.03	24.15
Jig Saw (Blades resale only)	10.92	5.46	21.85
Reciprocating Saw (Blades resale only)	12.65	6.32	25.30
Cut Off/Power Saw 12"-2 Stroke	11.50	5.75	23.00
Cut Off/Power Saw 12"-Electric	11.50	5.75	23.00
Cut Off/Saw Trolley	4.02	2.01	8.05
Chain Saws			
18" Petrol 2 Stroke (including New Chain)	34.50	17.25	69.00
Exchange Saw Chains	17.25	-	-
Chainsaw Protective Clothing Pack	5.17	2.58	10.35
Floor Saw			
Track/Floor Saw, Diesel	34.50	17.25	69.00
SPRAY PAINTING & BLASTING			
Spray Units			
Carryspray Turbo + Gun	18.40	9.20	36.80
2.5cfm Compressor + PS3 Gun	18.40	9.20	36.80
7 cfm Compressor + PS3 Gun +	35.65	17.82	71.30
7 cfm Compressor + PS1 Gun	-	-	-
Pressure Container	43.12	21.56	86.25
7 cfm Compressor + Gravity Feed Gun	40.25	20.12	80.50
Airless Spray - Heavy Duty	64.40	32.20	128.80
Airless Spray - Medium Duty	50.60	25.30	101.20
Compressors			
Portable 2.5 cfm-Electric	13.22	6.61	26.45
Industrial 7 cfm-Electric	29.90	14.95	59.80
Industrial 15 cfm Electric/Petrol	35.65	17.82	71.30
Portable Dry Sandblast Unit	34.50	17.25	69.00

CLEANING & FLOOR MAINTENANCE	First 24 hrs £	Addit 24 hrs £	Per week £
High Pressure Washers			
1000 psi Mini Washer, Electric	13.20	6.61	26.45
1500 psi Turbo Cold Water, Electric	36.80	18.40	73.60
2000 psi Cold Water, Petrol/Diesel	51.75	25.87	103.50
900 psi Hot Water, Diesel/Electric	51.75	25.87	103.50
Wet Sand Blast Attachment (2000 psi only)	10.92	5.46	21.85
Carpet Cleaners			
Hydromist-Heavy Duty	18.40	18.40	55.20
Hydromist-Champ	16.10	16.10	48.30
Hydromist-Junior	13.80	13.80	41.40
Upholstery Cleaning Attachment	2.30	2.30	6.90
Vacuum Cleaners			
Light Industrial	10.92	5.46	21.85
Heavy Industrial	20.70	10.35	41.40
Heavy Duty-3 Motor	28.75	14.37	57.50
Wet Pick Up Vacuum	20.70	10.35	41.40
Back Pack Vacuum	16.10	8.05	32.20
Leaf and Litter Vacuum-Petrol	27.60	13.80	55.20
Industrial Floor Cleaners			
Floor Sweeper-Manual	14.37	7.18	28.75
Floor Sweeper-Petrol	34.50	17.25	69.00
Floor Scrubber/Polisher	20.70	10.35	41.40
Floor Scrubber/Vacuum	57.50	28.75	115.00
Floor Tile Stripper	28.78	14.37	57.50
Floor Scarifier-Heavy Duty (Wire Brushes ex)	23.00	11.50	46.90
Carpet Stretcher	5.75	2.87	11.50
Chimney Sweep Set	5.75	2.87	11.50
LIFTING & MATERIALS HANDLING			
Hydraulic Access Manlift	57.50	28.75	115.00
Rubbish Chute, per 1m section	2.87	1.43	5.75
Rubbish Chute Top-Hopper	5.75	2.87	11.50
Trucks and Trolleys			
Litter/Stacker-Manual	34.50	17.25	69.00
Pallet Truck	18.40	9.20	36.80
Piano Truck	6.90	3.45	13.80
Appliance Truck/Stairclimbing Trolley	5.75	2.87	11.50
Combination Trolley	6.90	3.45	13.80
Winching			
Tirfor 1600kg Lift	17.25	8.62	34.50
Tirfor 3200kg Lift	23.00	11.50	46.00

LIFTING & MATERIALS HANDLING (cont'd)	First 24 hrs £	Addit 24 hrs £	Per week £
Winching			
Gin Wheel	-	-	5.75
Panel Lifting Winch	23.00	11.50	46.00
Hoisting			
Scaffold Hoist Electric 1500kg	37.37	18.68	74.75
Chain Hoist 10cwt (500kg)	12.65	6.32	25.30
Chain Hoist 20cwt (1000kg)	14.37	7.18	28.75
Chain Hoist 30/40cwt (1500/2000kg)	17.25	8.62	34.50
Machine Moving			
Machine Moving Skates, Set of 4	19.55	9.77	39.10
Toe Jack, 5 ton-Head and Claw	13.80	6.90	27.60
Toe Jack, 25 ton-Head, 10 ton Claw	20.70	10.35	41.40
Engine Crane 10cwt (500kg)	14.95	7.47	29.90
Tape Banding Machine	8.62	4.31	17.25
Removal/Storage Crates	-	-	1.38

Chapter 12: Rates for Measured Work

Generally

The rates contained in this chapter generally apply to contracts
ranging from minor works to those up to approximately £30,000
The rates are based upon national average prices and the following
adjustments should be made for working in different regions

Scotland	- 4%
Wales	- 2%
Northern Ireland	- 9%
England	
South West	- 6%
South East	+10%
Home Counties	+10%
Inner London	+30%
Outer London	+20%
East Anglia	+10%
Midlands	+ 3%
North West	+ 1%
North East	- 2%

The rates are calculated using material and plant costs current in the
second quarter of 1988 and the wage rates by the following
organisations.

General building	-	Building and Allied Trades Joint Industry Council (BATJIC) from 26th June 1989
Plumbing	-	Joint Industry Board for Plumbing, Mechanical and Engineering Services from 27th March 1989
Roofing	-	National Federation of Roofing Contractors - from 26th June 1989
Electrical Work	-	Joint Industry Board for the Electrical Contracting Industry - 7th January 1989

The rates are exclusive of VAT which may be chargeable depending upon
the nature of the work and are divided into their component parts so
that adjustments can easily be made if necessary.

Item descriptions

Each item includes for all the work normally associated with that
particular item even if it is not expressly stated. Where the words
"**Add** to the previous prices for ...." appear in the text, the costs
which appear opposite the item represent the **additional** cost of

Rates for Measured Work

replacing the component in the main desciption with the item
described. Where the basic price of an item is expressed by the
letters BP it represents the purchase cost nett of any discounts,
which the builder could expect over the trade counter.

Labour hours

The time taken for the fixing of each of the items is expressed as a
decimal fraction of an hour, therefore 0.50 Labour hours equals thirty
minutes. The times are average and include for unloading,
distributing and fixing in position.

Nett Labour

This column gives the total labour cost of supplying and fixing the
item concerned. It is calculated by multiplying the total Labour
hours by the hourly rate.

Rates for Measured Work

General Building Work	Craftsman £		Labourer £
Annual wages 1911 hours at £3.59	6860.49	at £3.09	5904.99
Non-productive overtime 89 hours at £3.59	319.51	at £3.09	275.01
Sick pay 5 days at £10.80	54.00		54.00
Public holidays 8 days at 28.72	229.76	at £24.72	197.76
Overall allowance 49 weeks at £0.83	40.67		-
Bonus say 30% of 1911 hours at £3.59	2058.15	at £3.09	1771.50
	9562.58		8203.26
Employers NHI x 10.45%	999.29		857.24
CITB Levy	75.00		18.00
Holidays with pay 47 weeks at £13.02	611.94		611.94
Retirement benefit 52 weeks at £1.00	52.00		52.00
Death benefit 12 months at £2.60	31.20		31.20
	£ 11,332.01		£ 9773.64
Severance pay say 1½%	169.98		146.60
Employers Liability and Third Party Insurance say 2%	226.64		195.47
TOTAL COST	£ 11,728.63		£10,115.71

COST PER Hour divided by 1822
1911 less 89 = 1822 productive hours   £6.44   £5.55

Rates for Measured Work

Plumbing	Trained Plumber	Advanced Plumber	Technical Plumber
Basic rate (from 27 March 1989)	3.91	4.31	4.90
Basic rate x total hours worked (1910 hrs)	7468.10	8232.10	9359.00
Non productive overtime (50 hrs)	195.50	215.50	245.00
Public holidays (60)	234.60	258.60	294.00
Sub-total	7898.20	8706.20	9898.00
National Insurance	760.49	830.31	933.69
Annual holiday with pay and sickness benefit 47 weeks at:-			
£ 15.20	714.40		
£ 16.60		780.20	
£ 18.60			874.20
Industry pension scheme 6.5% of sub total	513.38	565.90	643.37
Tool money 45.2 weeks at £1.50	67.80	67.80	67.80
CITB levy	110.00	110.00	110.00
Sub-total	10064.27	11060.41	12527.06
Severance pay 1.5%	151.01	165.91	187.91
Employer's liability and third party insurance 2%	201.35	221.21	250.54
TOTAL ANNUAL COST	£ 10416.63	£ 11447.53	£ 12965.51
Divided by total number of productive hours 1910 hrs less 40 hrs inclement weather = 1870 hrs			
All-in rate	£ 5.57/hr	£ 6.12/hr	£6.93/hr

Rates for Measured Work

Roofing	Craftsman £			Labourer £
Annual wages 1911 hours at £3.08	5885.88	at	£2.63	5025.93
Guaranteed minimum bonus 52 x £15.015	780.78	at	£12.675	659.10
Non-productive overtime 89 hours at £3.08	274.12	at	£2.63	234.07
Sick pay 5 days at £10.13	50.65			50.65
Public holidays 8 days at £24.64	197.12	at	£21.04	168.32
Tool allowance 49 weeks at £0.72	35.28			-
Bonus say 30% of 1911 hours at £3.08	1765.76	at	£2.63	1507.78
	-------			-------
	£8989.59			£7645.85
Employers NHI at 10.45%	939.41		at 9%	688.13
CITB Levy	75.00			18.00
Holidays with pay 47 weeks at £14.80	695.60			695.60
Retirement and death benefit 52 weeks at £1.30	67.60			67.60
	-------			-------
	£10767.20			£9115.18
Severence pay say 1½%	161.51			136.73
Employers Liability and Third Party Insurance say 2%	215.34			182.30
	-------			-------
TOTAL COST	£11144.05			£9434.21
	-------			-------
COST PER HOUR divided by 1822 (1911 less 89 = 1822 productive hours)	£6.12			£5.18
	----			----

Rates for Measured Work

Electric Work	Technician	Approved Electrician	Electrician
Basic hourly rate	5.27	4.55	4.20
Annual wage x 2002 hours	10550.54	9109.10	8408.40
Non-productive overtime x 50 hours	263.50	227.50	210.00
Public holidays 8 days at x 7.5 hours	316.20	273.00	252.00
	£ 11130.24	£ 9609.60	£ 8870.40
National Insurance (10.45%)	1163.11	1004.20	926.96
JIB Combined Benefits Scheme 52 weeks @ £17.00	884.00	884.00	884.00
CITB Levy	90.00	90.00	90.00
Severance pay @ 1½%	199.01	173.82	161.57
Employers Liability and Third Party Insurance say 2%	331.68	289.70	269.28
Total Cost	£ 13798.04	£ 12051.32	£ 11202.21
COST PER Hour divided by 1962 (2002 less 40 hours inclement weather)	£ 7.03	£ 6.14	£ 5.71

Plant

Where applicable the nett cost of hiring plant is included in the plant/material column and is based upon units of full days hire.

Overheads/ profit

Overheads charges are those costs which are not directly linked to any particular contract. They are usually expressed as a percentage of the nett cost of labour and materials which is calculated by dividing the total projected annual overhead cost by the projected nett turnover. Examples of those items which normally form part of overheads are:-

1. Head office overheads - heating, lighting, rent, rates, stationery, telephones, secretarial services.

2. Sundry plant - ladders, towers, vans, etc.

3. Insurances - insurance of head office.

4. Finance charges - interest on overdrafts, bank charges, etc.

The actual percentage used for overheads varies widely. The small Builder working on his own from home who does all his own paperwork and book work in the evening will have few overhead costs and so the percentage addition will be low. However the time may come when he finds that he must expand and proper premises must be found, a secretary employed, etc., and the percentage will then increase. Eventually these new overheads should be spread over an increased turnover and the percentage will reduce. The profit, of course, is the difference between income and costs and will only be known after the accounts have been prepared.

The percentage addition for overheads and profit is taken as being 15%.

Unit

This column gives the unit in which the item is normally measured.

Total

The total column is the sum of the nett labour, nett material and overheads/profit columns.

Sundry work

It should be noted that no allowances have been made for cutting holes, mortices, chases, etc., or moving floor coverings, furniture and taking up floor boards.

Disposal of rubbish

The items for demolitions, alteration work, pulling down, breaking out and earthworks in this book do not include for the cost of removing surplus materials and the following rates should be applied:-

Rates for Measured Work

1. Loading into skips

Assuming that skips would be filled to capacity the costs should be:-

Size of skip m3	Daily Hire Rate £	Cost per m3 £
3	19.55	6.52
5	30.80	6.16
6	35.20	5.87
8	39.10	4.89

The cost of loading into barrows and wheeling say 25m is taken separately at 1.2 manhours at £5.55 = £6.66 per m3. This figure should have 15% added for profit and overheads to produce an overall charge out rate of £7.66.

The cost of final disposal is:-

Size of skip m3	Cost per m3 £	Profit/ overheads 15%	Total £
3	6.52	0.98	7.50
5	6.16	0.92	7.08
6	5.87	0.88	6.75
8	4.89	0.73	5.62

2. Loading into lorries

It is assumed that the rubbish can be barrowed into the lorries via ramps and walkboards. It is also assumed that the lorry can remove two full loads of 8m3 per day and that the hire cost of a lorry and driver in £18.80 per hour

	£ p
Lorry and driver 8 hours at £18.80	150.40
Tipping charge: 2 at £6.00	12.00

	£162.40
	------
divided by 16m3	£10.15 per m3

Removal Cost m3	Profit/ overheads	Total £
10.15	1.52	11.67

110

3. Generally

There are many variable factors affecting the decision whether to
have a skip or a lorry and each case must be carefully judged
individually depending upon the weather, the quantity to be moved,
the labour available to load and other relevant items.

DEMOLITIONS AND OPENINGS

	Labour hours	Nett labour £	Nett material £	O'heads /profit £	Unit	Total £
There are a number of factors which directly affect the cost of the demolition of buildings e.g. access, the residual value of the arisings, proximity of other buildings, etc.						

Because of this the following rates, which allow for demolition to ground level, should be treated with caution and regarded as indicative only.

Brick outbuildings;

	Labour hours	Nett labour £	Nett material £	O'heads /profit £	Unit	Total £
- single storey; detached					m3	7.00
- single storey; attached					m3	8.00
- two storey; attached					m3	8.60

FORMING OPENINGS
Labour rate £5.55 per hour

The following items are for breaking out openings up to 2m wide through existing walls but exclude the cost of propping.

Cut opening for lintel or beam
65mm deep through existing wall

	Labour hours	Nett labour £	Nett material £	O'heads /profit £	Unit	Total £
- half brick wall	0.35	1.94	-	0.29	m	2.23
- one brick wall	0.55	3.05	-	0.46	m	3.51
- one and a half brick wall	0.69	3.83	-	0.57	m	4.40
- 100mm blockwork	0.28	1.55	-	0.23	m	1.78
- 150mm blockwork	0.31	1.72	-	0.26	m	1.98
- 200mm blockwork	0.37	2.05	-	0.31	m	2.36
- 250mm blockwork	0.41	2.28	-	0.34	m	2.62

Cut opening for lintel or beam
90mm deep through existing wall

	Labour hours	Nett labour £	Nett material £	O'heads /profit £	Unit	Total £
- half brick wall	0.40	2.22	-	0.33	m	2.55
- one brick wall	0.62	3.44	-	0.52	m	3.96
- one and a half brick wall	0.75	4.16	-	0.62	m	4.78
- 100mm blockwork	0.32	1.78	-	0.27	m	2.05
- 150mm blockwork	0.35	1.94	-	0.29	m	2.23
- 200mm blockwork	0.42	2.33	-	0.35	m	2.68
- 250mm blockwork	0.45	2.50	-	0.38	m	2.88

DEMOLITIONS AND OPENINGS

FORMING OPENINGS	Labour hours	Nett labour £	Nett material £	O'heads /profit £	Unit	Total £
Cut opening for lintel or beam						
150mm deep through existing wall						
- half brick wall	0.55	3.05	-	0.46	m	3.51
- one brick wall	0.88	4.88	-	0.73	m	5.61
- one and a half brick wall	1.07	5.94	-	0.89	m	6.83
- 100mm blockwork	0.42	2.33	-	0.35	m	2.68
- 150mm blockwork	0.52	2.89	-	0.43	m	3.32
- 200mm blockwork	0.60	3.33	-	0.50	m	3.83
- 250mm blockwork	0.64	3.55	-	0.53	m	4.08
Cut opening for door or window						
through existing wall						
- half brick wall	2.10	11.66	-	1.75	m2	13.41
- one brick wall	2.95	16.37	-	2.46	m2	18.83
- one and a half brick wall	3.82	21.20	-	3.18	m2	24.38
- 100mm blockwork	1.54	8.55	-	1.28	m2	9.83
- 150mm blockwork	1.77	9.82	-	1.47	m2	11.29
- 200mm blockwork	2.35	13.04	-	1.96	m2	15.00
- 250mm blockwork	2.55	14.15	-	2.12	m2	16.27

EXCAVATION AND EARTHWORK

1. Labour Rate £5.55 per hour

2. Plant (Hired)

JCB 3C	£16.88 per hour
Dumper (1000 kg)	£113.00 per week
Compressor (175 cfm)	£125.00 per week
Vibrating Roller	£58.00 per week
Tipping charges	£6.00 per load

3. Materials

	Unit	Supply £	Waste %	Total £
Washed sand	t	7.70	10	8.47
Hardcore	m3	10.35	10	11.39

HAND EXCAVATION	Labour hours	Nett labour £	Nett material £	O'heads /profit £	Unit	Total £

The following unit rates refer to work carried out in firm ground. The following adjustments should be applied for other ground conditions.

Clay   +75%
Soft chalk +125%

HAND EXCAVATION	Labour hours	Nett labour £	Nett material £	O'heads /profit £	Unit	Total £
Cut down trees; grub up roots						
- 600 - 900mm girth	18.00	100.00	-	15.00	nr	115.00
- 900 - 1200mm girth	30.00	167.00	-	25.05	nr	192.05
Cut down hawthorn hedge, grub up roots						
- 1500mm high	2.10	11.66	-	1.75	m	13.41
- 2000mm high	2.30	12.77	-	1.92	m	14.69
Excavate topsoil, lay aside for re-use, average depth						
- 150mm	0.37	2.05	-	0.31	m2	2.36
- 200mm	0.47	2.61	-	0.39	m2	3.00

EXCAVATION AND EARTHWORK

HAND EXCAVATION Labour rate £5.55 per hour	Labour hours	Nett labour £	Nett material £	O'heads /profit £	Unit	Total £
Excavate from ground level to reduce levels, maximum depth not exceeding						
- 0.25m	2.50	13.88	-	2.08	m3	15.96
- 1.00m	2.75	15.26	-	2.29	m3	17.55
- 2.00m	3.00	16.65	-	2.50	m3	19.15
Excavate pits to receive bases, maximum depth not exceeding						
- 0.25m	3.25	18.04	-	2.71	m3	20.75
- 1.00m	4.00	22.20	-	3.33	m3	25.53
- 2.00m	4.50	24.98	-	3.75	m3	28.73
Excavate trenches to receive foundations, maximum depth not exceeding						
- 0.25m	2.70	14.99	-	2.25	m3	17.24
- 1.00m	3.00	16.65	-	2.50	m3	19.15
- 2.00m	3.25	18.04	-	2.71	m3	20.75
Excavate trenches for services not exceeding 300mm wide; back-filling with excavated material	3.75	20.81	-	3.12	m3	23.93
Extra for breaking up						
- concrete 100mm thick	0.90	5.00	-	0.75	m2	5.75
- tarmacadam 75mm thick	0.50	2.78	-	0.42	m2	3.20
- hardcore 100mm thick	0.60	3.33	-	0.50	m2	3.83
- plain concrete	7.00	38.85	-	5.83	m3	44.68
- reinforced concrete	8.00	44.40	-	6.66	m3	51.06
- soft rock	10.00	55.50	-	8.32	m3	63.82
- hard rock	11.00	61.05	-	9.16	m3	70.21

MACHINE EXCAVATION
Labour rate £5.55 per hour

The following unit rates refer to
work carried out in firm ground.
The following adjustments should
be applied for other ground
conditions

Clay   +25%
Soft chalk +50%

MACHINE EXCAVATION	Labour hours	Nett labour £	Nett plant £	O'heads /profit £	Unit	Total £
Cut down trees, grub up roots						
- 600 - 900mm girth	7.00	38.85	42.00	12.13	nr	92.98
- 900 - 1200mm girth	8.00	44.40	75.00	17.91	nr	137.31
Cut down hawthorn hedge, grub up roots						
- 1500mm high	0.50	2.78	7.00	1.47	m	11.25
- 2000mm high	0.60	3.33	7.00	1.55	m	11.88
Excavate topsoil, lay aside for re-use, average depth						
- 150mm	0.02	0.11	0.35	0.07	m2	0.53
- 200mm	0.03	0.17	0.45	0.09	m2	0.71
Excavate from ground level to reduce levels maximum depth not exceeding						
- 0.25m	0.10	0.56	1.25	0.27	m3	2.08
- 1.00m	0.10	0.56	1.10	0.25	m3	1.91
- 2.00m	0.10	0.56	1.35	0.29	m3	2.20
Excavate pits to receive bases, maximum depth not exceeding						
- 0.25m	0.30	1.67	5.00	1.00	m3	7.67
- 1.00m	0.25	1.39	5.50	1.03	m3	7.92
- 2.00m	0.28	1.55	6.00	1.13	m3	8.68
Excavate trenches to receive foundations, maximum depth not exceeding						
- 0.25m	0.35	1.94	5.00	1.04	m3	7.98
- 1.00m	0.30	1.67	5.50	1.08	m3	8.25
- 2.00m	0.34	1.89	6.00	1.18	m3	9.07
Excavate trenches for services not exceeding 300mm wide; backfilling with excavated material	0.48	2.66	4.50	1.07	m3	8.23
Extra for breaking up by compressor and tools						
- concrete 100mm thick	0.40	2.22	2.00	0.63	m2	4.85
- tarmacadam 75mm thick	0.24	1.33	1.20	0.38	m2	2.91
- hardcore 100mm thick	0.28	1.55	1.30	0.43	m2	3.28
- plain concrete	2.30	12.65	15.00	4.15	m3	31.80

MACHINE EXCAVATION	Labour hours	Nett labour £	Nett material /plant £	O'heads /profit £	Unit	Total £
Extra for breaking up by						
compressor and tools contd.,						
- reinforced concrete	3.50	19.43	20.00	5.91	m3	45.34
- soft rock	4.00	22.20	13.00	5.28	m3	40.48
- hard rock	4.40	24.42	20.00	6.66	m3	51.08

EARTHWORK SUPPORT

The rates include for using the
timber four times before renewal

Earthwork support not exceeding						
2m between opposing faces; depth						
not exceeding 1m in						
- firm ground	0.40	2.22	0.90	0.47	m2	3.59
- loose ground	1.25	6.94	1.50	1.27	m2	9.71
- sand	2.75	15.26	2.50	2.66	m2	20.42
Earthwork support not exceeding						
2m between opposing faces; depth						
not exceeding 2m in						
- firm ground	0.65	3.61	1.00	0.69	m2	5.30
- loose ground	1.35	7.49	1.70	1.38	m2	10.57
- sand	3.15	17.48	2.60	3.01	m2	23.09
Earthwork support not exceeding						
2m between opposing faces; depth						
not exceeding 4m in						
- firm ground	0.65	3.61	1.10	0.71	m2	5.42
- loose ground	1.50	8.33	2.00	1.55	m2	11.88
- sand	3.50	19.43	3.80	3.48	m2	26.71

DISPOSAL

Load surplus excavated material into barrows; wheel and deposit in temporary spoil heaps; average distance						
- 25m	2.00	11.10	-	1.66	m3	12.76
- 50m	2.65	14.71	-	2.21	m3	16.92

DISPOSAL	Labour hours	Nett labour £	Nett material /plant £	O'heads /profit £	Unit	Total £
(See page 110). Load into barrows, wheel and deposit in skip or lorry; average distance - 25m	-	-	-	-	m3	7.66
Remove from site by skip (5m3) including tipping charges	-	-	-	-	m3	7.08
Remove from site by lorry (16 tonne) including tipping charges (average 10 km to tip)	-	-	-	-	m3	11.67

FILLING

	Labour hours	Nett labour £	Nett material /plant £	O'heads /profit £	Unit	Total £
Filling material deposited on site in layers not exceeding 250mm thick, average distance 25m, compacting with vibrating roller						
- surplus excavated material	0.33	1.83	4.00	0.87	m3	6.70
- sand	0.42	2.33	11.00	2.00	m3	15.33
- hardcore	0.42	2.33	12.00	2.15	m3	16.48

SURFACE TREATMENTS

	Labour hours	Nett labour £	Nett material /plant £	O'heads /profit £	Unit	Total £
Level and compact bottom of excavation with vibrating roller	0.10	0.56	0.55	0.17	m2	1.28
Level and compact surface of filling with vibrating roller						
- surplus excavated material	0.12	0.67	0.50	0.18	m3	1.35
- sand	0.11	0.61	0.45	0.16	m3	1.22
- hardcore	˙0.12	0.67	0.50	0.18	m3	1.35

CONCRETE WORK

1. Labour Rates

Craftsman £6.44 per hour
Labourer   £5.55 per hour

2. Plant

	£ per week
Compressor (175 cfm)	125.00
Air hose (19 mm)	6.00
Vibrator (Air poker)	35.00
Scabbler	33.50
Power float	47.00
Bar bender	34.00
Mixer (5/3.5)	29.00

3. Materials

	Unit	Supply £	Waste %	Total £
Sand	t	7.70	12½	8.66
Cement	t	91.50	5	96.08
Aggregate - 20mm	t	7.02	10	7.72
- 40mm	t	7.13	10	7.84
Site mixed concrete				
(Mix A2 - 1:3:6)	m3	54.44	5	57.16
(Mix B2 - 1:2:4)	m3	56.42	5	59.24
Ready mix concrete (full loads)				
(Mix A - 1:3:6)	m3	50.96	5	54.82
(Mix B - 1:2:4)	m3	53.72	5	57.78
Bituminous emulsion waterproofer	25 l	28.12	5	29.53
Polythene sheeting 1200 gauge	100 m2	49.60	10	54.56
Plain round reinforcement bars B.S.4449				
6mm	t	619.60	10	681.56
8mm	t	614.20	10	675.62
10mm	t	619.60	10	681.56
12mm	t	609.00	10	669.90
16mm	t	609.00	10	669.90
20mm	t	609.00	10	669.90
25mm	t	624.80	10	687.28

CONCRETE WORK

	Unit	Supply £	Waste %	Total £
Steel sheet fabric reinforcement in standard sheets to B.S.4483				
Ref kg/m2				
A98 1.54	m2	1.11	10	1.22
A142 2.22	m2	1.40	10	1.54
A193 3.02	m2	1.89	10	2.08
A252 3.95	m2	2.46	10	2.71
A393 6.16	m2	3.91	10	4.30
B196 3.05	m2	2.09	10	2.30
B283 3.73	m2	2.47	10	2.72
B385 4.53	m2	2.97	10	3.27
B503 5.93	m2	3.79	10	4.17
B785 8.14	m2	5.21	10	5.73
B1131 10.90	m2	7.04	10	7.74
C283 2.61	m2	1.79	10	1.97
C385 3.41	m2	2.28	10	2.51
C503 4.34	m2	2.81	10	3.09
C636 5.55	m2	3.60	10	3.96
C785 6.72	m2	4.35	10	4.79
Sawn softwood	m3	174.25	10	191.68
19mm plywood	m2	6.80	10	7.48
Precast prestressed concrete lintels				
75 x 65mm	m	3.85	-	3.85
100 x 65mm	m	4.21	-	4.21
150 x 65mm	m	5.79	-	5.79
250 x 65mm	m	10.62	-	10.62
100 x 150mm	m	8.22	-	8.22
225 x 100mm	m	9.70	-	9.70
225 x 150mm	m	13.10	-	13.10
Precast concrete copings once weathered and throated				
150 x 75mm	m	10.65	-	10.65
300 x 75mm	m	13.80	-	13.80
Precast concrete saddleback copings twice weathered and throated				
150 x 75mm	m	11.00	-	11.00
300 x 75mm	m	14.15	-	14.15
Sulphate resisting				
cement	t	101.50	5	105.68

CONCRETE WORK

	Unit	Supply £	Waste %	Total £
Flexcell joint filler 12.5mm thick; width				
over 300mm	m2	7.14	5	7.50
100mm	m	1.47	5	1.54
200mm	m	1.84	5	1.93
Flexcell joint filler 20mm thick; width				
over 300mm	m2	8.66	5	9.09
100mm	m	1.76	5	1.85
200mm	m	2.52	5	2.65
Flexcell joint filler 25mm thick; width				
over 300mm	m2	10.66	5	11.19
100mm	m	2.00	5	2.10
200mm	m	2.84	5	2.98
Plastic bituminous sealing compound	5 1	9.98	10	10.48

ALTERATIONS Labour rate £5.55 per hour	Labour hours	Nett labour £	Nett plant £	O'heads /profit £	Unit	Total £
Rates include wheeling and depositing in skip						
Pull down concrete walls						
- 100mm thick	1.35	7.49	5.61	1.97	m2	15.07
- 150mm thick	1.90	10.55	8.03	2.79	m2	21.37
- 200mm thick	2.85	15.82	9.46	3.79	m2	29.07
Pull down reinforced concrete walls						
- 100mm thick	1.60	8.88	7.70	2.49	m2	19.07
- 150mm thick	2.24	12.43	11.17	3.54	m2	27.14
- 200mm thick	3.15	17.48	14.30	4.77	m2	36.55
Break up concrete ground floor slabs						
- 100mm thick	0.64	3.55	4.46	1.20	m2	9.21
- 150mm thick	0.95	5.27	6.05	1.70	m2	13.02
Break up reinforced concrete ground floor slab						
- 100mm thick	0.98	5.44	6.11	1.73	m2	13.28
- 150mm thick	1.15	6.38	8.38	2.21	m2	16.97

CONCRETE WORK

ALTERATIONS	Labour hours	Nett labour £	Nett material £	O'heads /profit £	Unit	Total £
Break up suspended concrete floor slabs						
- 150mm thick	2.26	12.54	4.52	2.56	m2	19.62
- 200mm thick	3.42	18.98	6.13	3.77	m2	28.88
Break up suspended reinforced concrete floor slab						
- 150mm thick	3.20	17.76	6.18	3.59	m2	27.53
- 200mm thick	3.90	21.65	8.17	4.47	m2	34.29
Form opening through reinforced concrete wall or suspended slab						
- 150mm thick	2.80	15.54	5.64	3.18	m2	24.36
- 200mm thick	3.65	20.26	7.53	4.17	m2	31.96
Cut hole in 100mm thick reinforced concrete and make good for						
- small pipe	0.75	4.16	1.56	0.86	nr	6.58
- large pipe	1.12	6.22	2.15	1.26	nr	9.63
Cut hole in 150mm thick reinforced concrete and make good for						
- small pipe	0.85	4.72	2.37	1.06	nr	8.15
- large pipe	1.30	7.22	3.08	1.54	nr	11.84
Cut out and enlarge crack in concrete, fill with mortar	0.65	3.61	1.29	0.73	m	5.63
Make good exposed face of existing concrete after cutting back						
- up to 200mm wide	0.35	1.94	3.00	0.74	m	5.68
- 200 - 500mm wide	0.60	3.33	4.30	1.14	m	8.77
- 500 - 1000mm wide	1.20	6.66	10.75	2.61	m	20.02
- over 1000mm wide	1.20	6.66	12.90	2.93	m2	22.49
Prepare, clean face of existing concrete to receive new finish	0.90	5.00	1.00	0.90	m2	6.90
Make good opening in existing concrete slab 100mm thick						
- up to 0.25m2	0.30	1.67	4.52	0.93	nr	7.12
- 0.25 - 0.5m2	0.45	2.50	5.97	1.27	nr	9.74
- 0.5 - 1m2	0.80	4.44	11.13	2.34	nr	17.91

CONCRETE WORK

ALTERATIONS	Labour hours	Nett labour £	Nett material £	O'heads /profit £	Unit	Total £
Make good opening in existing concrete slab 150mm thick						
- up to 0.25m2	0.40	2.22	6.56	1.32	m2	10.10
- 0.25 - 0.5m2	0.74	4.11	8.49	1.89	m2	14.49
- 0.5 - 1m2	1.05	5.83	13.17	2.85	m2	21.85
Make good opening in existing concrete wall 100mm thick; formwork both sides						
- up to 0.25m2	0.32	1.78	7.26	1.36	m2	10.40
- 0.25 - 0.5m2	0.65	3.61	10.21	2.07	m2	15.89
- 0.5 - 1m2	1.00	5.55	19.35	3.73	m2	28.63
Make good opening in existing concrete wall 150mm thick; formwork both sides						
- up to 0.25m2	0.60	3.33	8.61	1.79	m2	13.73
- 0.25 - 0.5m2	0.75	4.16	13.98	2.72	m2	20.86
- 0.5 - 1m2	1.30	7.22	21.50	4.31	m2	33.03

NEW WORK

SITE MIXED CONCRETE

	Labour hours	Nett labour £	Nett material £	O'heads /profit £	Unit	Total £
Mix A plain concrete, foundations in trenches						
- over 300mm thick	1.35	7.49	57.16	9.70	m3	74.35
- 150 - 300mm thick	1.70	9.44	57.16	10.00	m3	75.59
- 100 - 150mm thick	2.00	11.10	57.16	10.24	m3	78.50
Isolated bases	1.90	10.55	57.16	10.16	m3	77.87
Filling to hollow walls						
- not exceeding 100mm thick	4.60	25.53	57.16	12.40	m3	95.09
- 100 - 150mm thick	4.20	23.31	57.16	12.07	m3	92.54

SITE MIXED CONCRETE	Labour hours	Nett labour £	Nett material £	O'heads /profit £	Unit	Total £
Extra for placing concrete around reinforcement	0.55	3.05	-	0.46	m3	3.51
Mix B plain concrete, foundations in trenches						
- over 300mm thick	1.35	7.49	59.24	10.01	m3	76.74
- 150 - 300mm thick	1.70	9.44	59.24	10.30	m3	78.98
- 100 - 150mm thick	2.00	11.10	59.24	10.55	m3	80.89
Isolated bases	1.90	10.55	59.24	10.47	m3	80.26
Beds						
- over 300mm thick	1.35	7.49	59.24	10.01	m3	76.74
- 150 - 300mm thick	1.70	9.44	59.24	10.30	m3	78.98
- 100 - 150mm thick	2.00	11.10	59.24	10.55	m3	80.89
- not exceeding 100mm thick	3.20	17.76	59.24	11.55	m3	88.55
Suspended slabs						
- over 300mm thick	1.35	7.49	59.24	10.01	m3	76.74
- 150 - 300mm thick	1.70	9.44	59.24	10.30	m3	78.98
- 100 - 150mm thick	2.00	11.10	59.24	10.55	m3	80.89
- not exceeding 100mm thick	3.20	17.76	59.24	11.55	m3	88.55
Walls						
- over 300mm thick	2.60	14.43	59.24	11.05	m3	84.72
- 150 - 300mm thick	3.60	19.98	59.24	11.88	m3	91.10
- 100 - 150mm thick	4.10	22.76	59.24	12.30	m3	94.30
- not exceeding 100mm thick	5.10	28.31	59.24	13.13	m3	100.68
Casings to beams, cross sectional area						
- over 0.25m2	4.50	24.98	59.24	12.63	m3	96.85
- 0.1 - 0.25m2	4.90	27.20	59.24	12.97	m3	99.40
- 0.03 - 0.1m2	5.70	31.64	59.24	13.63	m3	104.51
- not exceeding 0.03m2	7.00	38.85	59.24	14.71	m3	112.80
Isolated columns, cross sectional area						
- over 0.25m2	4.50	24.98	59.24	12.63	m3	96.85
- 0.1 - 0.25m2	4.90	27.20	59.24	12.97	m3	99.40
- 0.03 - 0.1m2	5.70	31.64	59.24	13.63	m3	104.51
- not exceeding 0.03m2	7.00	38.85	59.24	14.71	m3	112.80
Machine bases	1.90	10.55	59.24	10.47	m3	80.26

CONCRETE WORK

SITE MIXED CONCRETE Labour rate £5.55 per hour	Labour hours	Nett labour £	Nett material £	O'heads /profit £	Unit	Total £
Upstands and kerbs, sectional area						
- over 0.25m2	4.65	25.81	59.24	12.76	m3	97.81
- 0.1 - 0.25m2	5.40	29.97	59.24	13.38	m3	102.59
- 0.03 - 0.1m2	6.20	34.41	59.24	14.05	m3	107.70
- not exceeding 0.03m2	8.45	46.90	59.24	15.92	m3	122.06

NEW WORK

Mix A - 11.5 N/mm2, 40mm
      aggregate (1:3:6)

Mix B - 21 N/mm2, 20mm aggregate
     (1:2:4)

READY MIXED CONCRETE
Labour rate £5.55 per hour

	Labour hours	Nett labour	Nett material	O'heads /profit	Unit	Total
Mix A plain concrete, foundations in trenches						
- over 300mm thick	1.35	7.49	54.82	9.35	m3	71.66
- 150 - 300mm thick	1.70	9.44	54.82	9.64	m3	73.90
- 100 - 150mm thick	2.00	11.10	54.82	9.89	m3	75.81
Isolated bases	1.90	10.55	54.82	9.81	m3	75.18
Filling to hollow walls						
- not exceeding 100mm thick	4.60	25.53	54.82	12.05	m3	92.40
- 100 - 150mm thick	4.20	23.31	54.82	11.72	m3	89.85
Extra for placing concrete around reinforcement	0.55	3.05	-	0.46	m3	3.51
Mix B plain concrete, foundations in trenches						
- over 300mm thick	1.35	7.49	57.78	9.79	m3	75.06
- 150 - 300mm thick	1.70	9.44	57.78	10.08	m3	77.30
- 100 - 150mm thick	2.00	11.10	57.78	10.33	m3	79.21
Isolated bases	1.90	10.55	57.78	10.25	m3	78.58
Beds						
- over 300mm thick	1.35	7.49	57.78	9.79	m3	75.06
- 150 - 300mm thick	1.70	9.44	57.78	10.08	m3	77.30

SITE MIXED CONCRETE Labour rate £5.55 per hour	Labour hours	Nett labour £	Nett material £	O'heads /profit £	Unit	Total £
Beds contd.,						
- 100 - 150mm thick	2.00	11.10	57.78	10.33	m3	79.21
- not exceeding 100mm thick	3.20	17.76	57.78	11.33	m3	86.87
Suspended slabs						
- over 300mm thick	1.35	7.49	57.78	9.79	m3	75.06
- 150 - 300mm thick	1.70	9.44	57.78	10.08	m3	77.30
- 100 - 150mm thick	2.00	11.10	57.78	10.33	m3	79.21
- not exceeding 100mm thick	3.20	17.76	57.78	11.33	m3	86.87
Walls						
- over 300mm thick	2.60	14.43	57.78	10.83	m3	83.04
- 150 - 300mm thick	3.60	19.98	57.78	11.66	m3	89.42
- 100 - 150mm thick	4.10	22.76	57.78	12.08	m3	92.62
- not exceeding 100mm thick	5.10	28.31	57.78	12.91	m3	99.00
Casings to beams, cross sectional area						
- over 0.25m2	4.50	24.98	57.78	12.41	m3	95.17
- 0.1 - 0.25m2	4.90	27.20	57.78	12.75	m3	97.73
- 0.03 - 0.1m2	5.70	31.64	57.78	13.41	m3	102.83
- not exceeding 0.03m2	7.00	38.85	57.78	14.49	m3	111.12
Isolated columns, cross sectional area						
- over 0.25m2	4.50	24.98	57.78	12.41	m3	95.17
- 0.1 - 0.25m2	4.90	27.20	57.78	12.75	m3	97.73
- 0.03 - 0.1m2	5.70	31.64	57.78	13.41	m3	102.83
- not exceeding 0.03m2	7.00	38.85	57.78	14.49	m3	111.12
Machine bases	1.90	10.55	57.78	10.25	m3	78.58
Upstands and kerbs, sectional area						
- over 0.25m2	4.65	25.81	57.78	12.54	m3	96.13
- 0.1 - 0.25m2	5.40	29.97	57.78	13.16	m3	100.91
- 0.03 - 0.1m2	6.20	34.41	57.78	13.83	m3	106.02
- not exceeding 0.03m2	8.45	46.90	57.78	15.70	m3	120.38
Extra for						
- placing around reinforcement	0.50	2.78	-	0.42	m3	3.20
- laying to slopes not exceeding 15°	0.50	2.78	-	0.42	m2	3.20
- laying to slopes over 15°	0.70	3.89	-	0.58	m2	4.47
- sulphate resisting cement	-	-	2.10	0.31	m3	2.41

CONCRETE SUNDRIES	Labour hours	Nett labour £	Nett material £	O'heads /profit £	Unit	Total £
Prepare level surfaces of unset concrete						
- tamping	0.06	0.33	-	0.05	m2	0.38
- spade finish	0.15	0.83	-	0.12	m2	0.95
- trowelling	0.23	1.28	-	0.19	m2	1.47
- power floating	0.15	0.83	0.60	0.21	m2	1.64
Expansion joint, 12.5mm thick 'Flexcell' filler including formwork; width						
- over 300mm	1.90	10.55	7.50	2.71	m2	20.76
- 100mm	0.38	2.11	1.54	0.55	m	4.20
- 200mm	0.57	3.16	1.93	0.76	m	5.85
Expansion joint 20mm thick 'Flexcell' filler, including formwork; width						
- over 300mm	2.10	11.66	9.09	3.11	m2	23.86
- 100mm	0.45	2.50	1.85	0.65	m	5.00
- 200mm	0.65	3.61	2.65	0.94	m	7.20
Expansion joint, 25mm thick 'Flexcell' filler, including formwork, width						
- over 300mm	2.20	12.21	11.19	3.51	m2	26.91
- 100mm	0.54	3.00	2.10	0.76	m	5.86
- 200mm	0.73	4.05	2.98	1.05	m	8.08
Seal joint with 'Pliastic' bituminous compound, 25mm deep, width						
- 12.5mm	0.30	1.67	0.55	0.33	m	2.55
- 20mm	0.34	1.89	0.70	0.39	m	2.98
- 25mm	0.38	2.11	0.90	0.45	m	3.46

MEMBRANES

	Labour hours	Nett labour £	Nett material £	O'heads /profit £	Unit	Total £
Two coats bituminous emulsion on concrete horizontal surfaces blinded with sand; width						
- over 300mm	0.35	1.94	2.08	0.60	m2	4.62

CONCRETE WORK

MEMBRANES	Labour hours	Nett labour £	Nett material £	O'heads /profit £	Unit	Total £
Three coats bituminous emulsion on concrete vertical surfaces blinded with sand; width						
- over 300mm	0.40	2.22	2.65	0.73	m2	5.60
One layer polythene sheeting laid on concrete floor; 1200 gauge	0.05	0.28	0.55	0.12	m2	0.95

REINFORCEMENT
Labour rate £6.44 per hour

Reinforcement bars, plain round steel to B.S.4449, straight or bent						
- 6mm	0.12	0.77	0.68	0.72	kg	1.67
- 8mm	0.10	0.64	0.68	0.20	kg	1.52
- 10mm	0.09	0.58	0.68	0.19	kg	1.45
- 12mm	0.08	0.52	0.70	0.18	kg	1.40
- 16mm	0.07	0.45	0.70	0.17	kg	1.32
- 20mm	0.06	0.39	0.70	0.16	kg	1.25
- 25mm	0.05	0.32	0.69	0.15	kg	1.16

Steel fabric reinforcement, B.S.4483, lapped, laid in concrete beds

Ref	kg/m2	Labour hours	Nett labour	Nett material	O'heads/profit	Unit	Total
- A98	1.54	0.11	0.71	1.22	0.29	m2	2.22
- A142	2.22	0.12	0.77	1.54	0.35	m2	2.66
- A193	3.02	0.15	0.97	2.08	0.46	m2	3.51
- A252	3.95	0.17	1.09	2.71	0.57	m2	4.37
- A393	6.16	0.20	1.29	4.30	0.84	m2	6.43
- B196	3.05	0.15	0.97	2.30	0.49	m2	3.76
- B283	3.73	0.16	1.03	2.72	0.56	m2	4.31
- B385	4.53	0.17	1.09	3.72	0.65	m2	5.01
- B503	5.93	0.19	1.22	4.17	0.81	m2	6.20
- B785	8.14	0.22	1.42	5.73	1.07	m2	8.22
- B1131	10.90	0.24	1.55	7.74	1.39	m2	10.68
- C283	2.61	0.13	0.84	1.97	0.42	m2	3.23
- C385	3.41	0.16	1.03	2.51	0.53	m2	4.07
- C503	4.34	0.18	1.16	3.09	0.64	m2	4.89
- C636	5.55	0.19	1.22	3.96	0.78	m2	5.96
- C785	6.72	0.21	1.35	4.79	0.92	m2	7.06

CONCRETE WORK

REINFORCEMENT	Labour hours	Nett labour £	Nett material £	O'heads /profit £	Unit	Total £
Cutting on mesh reinforcement						
- raking	0.15	0.97	-	0.15	m	2.23
- curved	0.20	1.29	-	0.19	m	3.71

FORMWORK
Labour rate £6.44 per hour

All the following rates are based on five uses.

	Labour hours	Nett labour £	Nett material £	O'heads /profit £	Unit	Total £
To edges or faces of foundations, bases, beams or beds; height						
- over 1m	2.30	14.81	5.93	3.11	m2	23.85
- not exceeding 250mm	0.75	4.83	1.68	0.98	m	7.49
- 250 - 500mm	1.28	8.24	2.94	1.68	m	12.86
- 500mm - 1m	1.68	10.82	5.93	2.51	m	19.26
Left in to edges or faces of foundations, bases, beams or beds; height						
- over 1m	5.50	35.42	16.28	7.75	m2	59.45
- not exceeding 250mm	2.38	15.33	4.73	3.10	m	23.07
- 250 - 500mm	3.40	21.90	7.56	4.42	m	33.88
- 500mm - 1m	4.74	30.52	16.28	7.02	m	53.82
To horizontal soffits of slabs not exceeding 3.5m high; thickness						
- not exceeding 200mm	2.40	15.46	5.67	3.17	m2	24.30
- 200 - 300mm	2.60	16.74	5.67	3.36	m2	25.77
- 300 - 400mm	2.80	18.03	5.67	3.55	m2	27.25
Left in to horizontal soffits of slabs not exceeding 3.5m high; thickness						
- not exceeding 200mm	5.70	36.71	15.91	7.89	m2	60.51
- 200 - 300mm	5.90	38.00	15.91	8.09	m2	62.00
- 300 - 400mm	6.20	39.93	15.91	8.38	m2	64.22
To sides and soffits of attached beams	3.20	20.61	5.67	3.94	m2	30.22

CONCRETE WORK

FORMWORK	Labour hours	Nett labour £	Nett material £	O'heads /profit £	Unit	Total £
To sides of kerbs and upstands						
- not exceeding 200mm high	0.70	4.51	1.47	0.90	m	6.88
- 200 - 400mm high	1.60	10.30	2.52	1.92	m	14.74
To staircase risers not exceeding 200mm high	1.10	7.08	1.47	1.28	m	9.83
To vertical face of walls	2.44	15.71	6.88	3.39	m2	25.98
To ends of walls; width						
- 150mm	0.60	3.86	1.21	0.76	m	5.83
- 200mm	1.05	6.76	1.42	1.23	m	9.41
Cutting on formwork						
- raking	0.12	0.77	-	0.12	m	0.89
- curved	0.18	1.16	-	0.17	m	1.33
Mortice in concrete for rag bolt, grout in cement mortar (1:1); depth						
- 50mm	0.25	1.61	0.42	0.30	m	2.33
- 100mm	0.30	1.93	0.58	0.38	m	2.89
- 150mm	0.35	2.25	0.84	0.46	m	3.55
Mortice in concrete for holding down bolt and plates, grout in cement mortar (1:3); depth						
- 200mm	0.60	3.86	1.89	0.86	m	6.61
- 400mm	0.84	5.41	2.47	1.18	m	9.06

PRECAST CONCRETE

	Labour hours	Nett labour £	Nett material £	O'heads /profit £	Unit	Total £
Lintels (21 N/mm2) prestressed, bedded and pointed in cement mortar (1:3); size						
- 75 x 65mm	0.30	1.93	3.85	0.87	m	6.65
- 100 x 65mm	0.30	1.93	4.21	0.92	m	7.06
- 150 x 65mm	0.35	2.25	5.79	1.21	m	9.25
- 250 x 65mm	0.40	2.58	10.62	1.98	m	15.18
- 100 x 150mm	0.35	2.25	8.22	1.57	m	12.04
- 225 x 100mm	0.40	2.58	9.70	1.84	m	14.12
- 225 x 150mm	0.50	3.22	13.10	2.45	m	18.77

CONCRETE WORK

PRECAST CONCRETE	Labour hours	Nett labour £	Nett material £	O'heads /profit £	Unit	Total £
Copings (30 N/mm2) weathered and throated bedded in cement mortar (1:3)						
- 150 x 75mm	0.62	3.99	10.65	2.20	m	16.84
- 300 x 75mm	0.80	5.15	13.80	2.84	m	21.79
Copings (30 N/mm2) twice weathered and twice throated, bedded in cement mortar (1:3)						
- 150 x 75mm	0.62	3.99	11.00	2.25	m	17.24
- 300 x 75mm	0.80	5.15	14.15	2.89	m	22.19

BRICKWORK AND BLOCKWORK

1. Labour

Small works

Craftsman   £6.44 per hour
Labourer   £5.55 per hour

Gang work

2 Craftsmen at £6.44	12.88
1 Labourer at £5.55	5.55
	£18.43
divided by 2	£9.22

2. Materials

	Unit	Basic Price	Waste %	Total £
Common bricks	1000	130.00	5	136.50
	100	16.00	5	16.80
Facing bricks	1000	340.00	5	357.00
	100	40.00	5	42.00
Class 'B' Engineering bricks	1000	235.00	5	246.75
	100	29.70	5	31.19
Portland cement (bagged)	t	91.50	5	96.08
Building sand	t	9.60	10	10.56
Hydrated lime	25 kg	4.35	5	4.57

Cement mortar (1:3)

Cement	0.36t at £96.08	34.59
Sand	1.45t at £10.56	15.31
Labour	1.5 hours at £5.55	8.33
Mixer	1.5 hours at £1.00	1.50
		59.73
Waste 10%		5.97
Cost per m3		£65.70

Gauged Mortar (1:1:6)

Cement	0.22t at £96.08	21.14
Hydrated lime	0.11t at £182.80	20.11
Sand	1.45t at £10.56	15.31
Labour	1.5 hours at £5.55	8.33
Mixer	1.5 hours at £1.00	1.50
		66.49
Waste 10%		6.65
Cost per m3		£73.14

BRICKWORK AND BLOCKWORK

Cost of mortar in brickwork

	Cement Mortar (1:3) £	Gauged Mortar (1:1:6) £
Half brick	1.97	2.19
One brick	3.94	4.39
One and a half brick	5.91	6.58
Two brick	7.88	8.78

Cost of mortar in blockwork

	£
Solid - 75mm	0.37
- 100mm	0.51
- 140mm	0.66
Hollow - 140mm	0.76
- 190mm	0.95
- 215mm	1.02

	Unit	Supply £	Waste %	Total £
Precast concrete dense aggregate blocks (to B.S.6073)				
Solid - 75mm	m2	5.11	12½	5.75
- 100mm	m2	6.06	12½	6.82
- 140mm	m2	8.97	12½	10.09
Hollow - 140mm	m2	8.34	12½	9.38
- 190mm	m2	10.04	7½	10.79
- 215mm	m2	10.87	7½	11.69
Precast concrete lightweight aggregate blocks (to B.S.6073)				
Solid - 75mm	m2	5.83	12½	6.56
- 100mm	m2	7.26	12½	8.17
- 140mm	m2	10.40	12½	11.70
Hollow - 140mm	m2	10.20	12½	11.48
- 190mm	m2	13.16	7½	14.15
- 215mm	m2	13.81	7½	14.85
Damp proof courses				
Hessian base	m2	4.29	5	4.50
- 75mm	m	0.38	5	0.40
- 100mm	m	0.43	5	0.45
- 112mm	m	0.48	5	0.50
- 150mm	m	0.64	5	0.67
- 225mm	m	0.96	5	1.00

BRICKWORK AND BLOCKWORK

	Unit	Supply £	Waste %	Total £
Asbestos based	m2	4.24	5	4.45
- 75mm	m	0.40	5	0.42
- 100mm	m	0.48	5	0.50
- 112mm	m	0.53	5	0.56
- 150mm	m	0.71	5	0.75
- 225mm	m	1.06	5	1.11
Asbestos based with				
lead core	m2	11.44	5	12.01
- 75mm	m	0.96	5	1.01
- 100mm	m	1.14	5	1.20
- 112mm	m	1.29	5	1.35
- 150mm	m	1.72	5	1.81
- 225mm	m	2.57	5	2.70
Pitch Polymer	m2	4.56	5	4.79
- 75mm	m	0.42	5	0.44
- 100mm	m	0.50	5	0.53
- 112mm	m	0.57	5	0.60
- 150mm	m	0.75	5	0.79
- 225mm	m	1.14	5	1.20
Expanded polystyrene insulation				
25mm	m2	1.77	20	2.12
50mm	m2	3.53	20	4.24
Exmet brick reinforcement width				
65mm	m	0.24	5	0.25
115mm	m	0.41	5	0.43
175mm	m	0.62	5	0.65
225mm	m	0.83	5	0.87
Terracotta air bricks, square hole				
220 x 70mm	nr	1.04	5	1.09
220 x 145mm	nr	1.73	5	1.82
220 x 220mm	nr	3.74	5	3.93
Terracotta air bricks louvres				
220 x 70mm	nr	1.82	5	1.91
220 x 145mm	nr	1.96	5	2.06
220 x 220mm	nr	5.36	5	5.63
Galvanised cast iron air bricks louvre pattern				
225 x 75mm	nr	2.68	5	2.81
225 x 150mm	nr	4.77	5	5.01
225 x 225mm	nr	8.01	5	8.41

BRICKWORK AND BLOCKWORK

	Unit	Supply £	Waste %	Total £
Gas flue lining system, Typex 115 range				
- recess panel (PXY 218)	nr	3.37	5	3.54
- lintel unit (1Y)	nr	4.81	5	5.05
- entry and exit unit (2Y)	nr	6.28	5	6.59
- straight block (3YA)	nr	3.04	5	3.19
- straight block (3YB)	nr	3.15	5	3.31
- offset unit (4Y)	nr	3.79	5	3.98
- reverse rebate unit (5Y)	nr	3.10	5	3.26
- conversion corbel unit (6Y)	nr	5.92	5	6.22
- vertical conversion unit (7Y)	nr	6.25	5	6.56
- back offset unit (8Y)	nr	9.33	5	9.80
- back offset unit (9Y)	nr	8.69	5	9.12
Gas flue lining system Typex 150 range				
- recess panel (RPX 305)	nr	4.74	5	4.98
- offset lintel (1X1)	nr	5.31	5	5.58
- twin channel flue block (2X1)	nr	4.84	5	5.08
- twin channel flue block (3X)	nr	3.90	5	4.10
- single flue block (3X1)	nr	3.40	5	3.57
- side offset block (4X1)	nr	3.80	5	3.99
- back offset block (4X4)	nr	3.55	5	3.73
- single flue block (5X)	nr	2.53	5	2.66
- single flue block (5X1)	nr	3.06	5	3.21
- single flue block (5X2)	nr	3.10	5	3.26
- single flue block (5X3)	nr	3.09	5	3.24
- single flue block (5X5)	nr	3.09	5	3.24
- separating withe (8X)	nr	1.89	5	1.98
- separating withe (8X4)	nr	2.80	5	2.94

BRICKWORK AND BLOCKWORK

	Unit	Supply £	Waste %	Total £
Gas flue lining system Typex 150 range contd.;				
- end terminal cap unit (9X)	nr	5.98	5	6.28
- inter terminal cap unit (9X1)	nr	4.18	5	4.39
- end terminal cap unit (9X6)	nr	6.22	5	6.53
- inter terminal cap unit (9X7)	nr	5.05	5	5.30
- single flue cap unit (9X9)	nr	11.09	5	11.64
- conversion unit (10X1)	nr	3.51	5	3.69
- angled conversion unit (10X2)	nr	5.25	5	5.51
- aluminium louvre (MLX)	nr	6.32	5	6.64
Terracotta chimney pot tapered or canon head 185mm diameter, height				
- 300mm	nr	11.17	5	11.73
- 375mm	nr	12.95	5	13.60
- 450mm	nr	13.35	5	14.02
- 600mm	nr	19.36	5	20.33
- 750mm	nr	25.83	5	27.12
- 900mm	nr	34.65	5	36.38

ALTERATION AND REPAIRS	Labour hours	Nett labour £	Nett material £	O'heads /profit £	Unit	Total £
The items listed here are for work where there is no requirement for supports during the pulling down. Breaking out openings where supports are required is dealt with separately.						

If the materials being demolished are required for re-use 40% should be added to total rate to allow for the extra cost in carefully taking down and laying aside for re-use.

BRICKWORK
Labour rate £5.55 per hour

	Labour hours	Nett labour	Nett material	O'heads /profit	Unit	Total
Pull down brick walls in gauged mortar; thickness						
- half brick	0.80	4.44	-	0.67	m2	5.11
- one brick	1.35	7.49	-	1.12	m2	8.61
- one and a half brick	1.95	10.82	-	1.62	m2	12.44
- two brick	2.48	13.76	-	2.06	m2	15.82
Pull down brick walls in cement mortar; thickness						
- half brick	1.32	7.33	-	1.10	m2	8.43
- one brick	1.80	9.99	-	1.50	m2	11.49
- one and a half brick	2.50	13.88	-	2.08	m2	15.96
- two brick	3.31	18.37	-	2.76	m2	21.13
Take out timber or tiled fireplace surround; size						
- 1000 x 900mm	0.60	3.33	-	0.50	nr	3.83
- 1200 x 900mm	0.70	3.89	-	0.58	nr	4.47
Take out tiled concrete hearth; size						
- 1000 x 450mm	0.75	4.16	-	0.62	nr	4.78
- 1200 x 600mm	0.92	5.11	-	0.77	nr	5.88

BRICKWORK Labour rate £6.44 per hour	Labour hours	Nett labour £	Nett material £	O'heads /profit £	Unit	Total £
Take down brick chimney to below roof level; cap with slates in cement mortar (1:3); size						
- 450 x 450mm x 900mm high	9.40	60.54	15.05	11.34	nr	86.93
- 450 x 900mm x 1200mm high	13.60	87.58	22.77	16.55	nr	126.90
Cut back brick chimney breast projections; size						
- half brick thick	2.18	14.04	3.89	2.69	m2	20.62
- one brick thick	2.78	17.90	5.74	3.55	m2	27.19
- one and a half brick thick	4.10	26.40	9.47	5.38	m2	41.25
Make good newly exposed end of wall in common brickwork to form new jambs to receive plaster; thickness						
- half brick wall	0.42	2.70	2.53	0.78	m	6.01
- one brick wall	0.69	4.44	4.09	1.28	m	9.81
- one and a half brick wall	0.95	6.12	5.45	1.74	m	13.31
Make good newly exposed end of wall in common brickwork to form new jambs; fair faced and flush pointed						
- half brick wall	0.50	3.22	3.06	0.94	m	7.22
- one brick wall	0.82	5.28	5.23	1.58	m	12.09
- one and a half brick wall	1.21	7.79	6.79	2.19	m	16.77
Prepare face of existing brickwork; rake out joints to receive cement render or plaster	0.36	2.32	-	0.35	m2	2.67
Rake out joints of existing brickwork; point in cement mortar (1:3)						
- flush pointing	1.11	7.15	0.19	1.10	m2	8.44
- weather pointing	1.16	7.47	0.19	1.15	m2	8.81
Cut out single brick in half brick walls; replace in gauged mortar (1:1:6)						
- commons	0.26	1.67	0.32	0.30	nr	2.29
- facings	0.30	1.93	0.52	0.37	nr	2.82

BRICKWORK AND BLOCKWORK

BRICKWORK Labour rate £6.44 per hour	Labour hours	Nett labour £	Nett material £	O'heads /profit £	Unit	Total £
Cut out single brick in one brick wall; replace in gauged mortar (1:1:6)						
- commons	0.38	2.45	0.42	0.43	nr	3.30
- facings	0.44	2.83	0.64	0.52	nr	3.99
Cut out single brick in half brick wall; replace in cement mortar (1:3)						
- commons	0.32	2.06	0.34	0.36	nr	2.76
- facings	0.38	2.45	0.55	0.45	nr	3.45
Cut out single brick in one brick wall; replace in cement mortar (1:3)						
- commons	0.45	2.90	0.45	0.50	nr	3.85
- facings	0.51	3.28	0.67	0.59	nr	4.54
Cut out decayed brickwork in half brick wall; areas 0.5 to 1m2; replace in gauged mortar (1:1:6)						
- commons	5.20	33.49	12.67	6.92	nr	53.08
- facings	6.00	38.64	25.82	9.67	nr	74.13
Cut out decayed brickwork in one brick wall; areas 0.5 to 1m2; replace in gauged mortar (1:1:6)						
- commons	7.60	48.94	21.12	10.51	nr	80.57
- facings	8.80	56.67	31.68	13.25	nr	101.60
Cut out decayed brickwork in half brick wall; areas 0.5 to 1m2 replace in cement mortar (1:3)						
- commons	6.28	40.44	13.92	8.15	nr	62.51
- facings	7.24	46.63	31.37	11.70	nr	89.70
Cut out decayed brickwork in one brick wall; areas 0.5 to 1m2; replace in cement mortar (1:3)						
- commons	9.38	60.41	25.40	12.87	nr	98.68
- facings	10.64	68.52	38.50	16.05	nr	123.07

BRICKWORK AND BLOCKWORK

BRICKWORK Labour rate £6.44 per hour	Labour hours	Nett labour £	Nett material £	O'heads /profit £	Unit	Total £
Cut out vertical, horizontal or stepped cracks in half brick wall; replace average 350mm width in gauged mortar (1:1:6)						
- commons	2.76	17.77	6.86	3.69	m	28.32
- facings	3.12	20.09	15.99	5.41	m	41.49
Cut out vertical, horizontal or stepped cracks in one brick wall; replace average 350mm width in gauged mortar (1:1:6)						
- commons	5.18	33.36	15.07	7.26	m	55.69
- facings	6.10	39.28	28.93	10.23	m	78.44
Cut out vertical, horizontal or stepped cracks in one and a half brick wall; replace average 350mm width in gauged mortar (1:1:6)						
- commons	8.12	52.29	23.06	11.30	m	86.65
- facings	9.25	59.57	41.10	15.10	m	115.77
Cut out vertical, horizontal or stepped cracks in half brick wall; replace average 350mm width in cement mortar (1:3)						
- commons	3.38	21.77	7.37	4.37	m	33.51
- facings	3.80	24.47	17.71	6.33	m	48.51
Cut out vertical, horizontal or stepped cracks in one brick wall; replace average 350mm width in cement mortar (1:3)						
- commons	6.20	39.93	16.61	8.48	m	65.02
- facings	7.22	46.50	31.83	11.75	m	90.08
Cut out vertical, horizontal or stepped cracks in one and a half brick wall; replace average 350mm width in cement mortar (1:3)						
- commons	9.72	62.60	25.23	13.17	m	101.00
- facings	11.10	71.48	45.10	17.49	m	134.07

BRICKWORK Labour rate £6.44 per hour	Labour hours	Nett labour £	Nett material £	O'heads /profit £	Unit	Total £
Cut out defective brick on end soldier arch to half brick thick; replace in gauged mortar (1:1:6)						
- commons	0.81	5.22	2.87	1.21	m	9.30
- facings	0.94	6.05	9.39	2.32	m	17.76
Cut out defective brick on end soldier arch to half brick thick; replace in cement mortar (1:3)						
- commons	0.98	6.31	3.22	1.43	m	10.96
- facings	1.14	7.34	10.43	2.67	m	20.44
Cut out defective segmental arch half brick thick; replace in gauged mortar (1:1:6)						
- commons	1.24	7.99	3.85	1.78	m	13.62
- facings	1.38	8.89	10.43	2.90	m	22.22
Cut out defective segmental arch one brick thick; replace in gauged mortar (1:1:6)						
- commons	1.41	9.08	5.92	2.25	m	17.25
- facings	1.65	10.63	13.39	3.60	m	27.62
Cut out defective brick on edge arch one brick thick; replace in gauged mortar (1:1:6)						
- commons	0.84	5.41	3.06	1.27	m	9.74
- facings	1.05	6.76	5.50	1.84	m	14.10
Cut out defective segmental arch half brick thick; replace in cement mortar (1:3)						
- commons	1.50	9.66	4.24	2.09	m	15.99
- facings	1.57	10.11	11.48	3.24	m	24.83
Cut out defective segmental arch one brick thick; replace in cement mortar (1:3)						
- commons	1.69	10.88	6.55	2.61	m	20.04
- facings	1.98	12.75	14.77	4.13	m	31.65

BRICKWORK Labour rate £6.44 per hour	Labour hours	Nett labour £	Nett material £	O'heads /profit £	Unit	Total £
Cut out defective brick on edge arch one brick thick; replace in cement mortar (1:3)						
- commons	1.02	6.57	3.39	1.49	m	11.45
- facings	1.23	7.92	6.14	2.11	m	16.17
Cut out defective terracotta air brick; replace						
- 220 x 70mm	0.35	2.25	1.87	0.62	nr	4.74
- 220 x 145mm	0.50	3.22	2.90	0.92	nr	7.04
Rake out joint in cement mortar (1:3); re-fix existing flashing; point up						
- horizontal	0.38	2.45	0.44	0.44	m	3.32
- stepped	0.54	3.48	0.44	0.59	m	4.51
Rake out joints in existing brickwork and point up in cement mortar (1:3)	0.90	5.80	0.90	1.00	m2	7.70
Cut out one course of half brick wall; insert hessian based damp proof course 112mm wide, replace with new bricks in gauged mortar (1:1:6)						
- commons	1.92	12.36	2.51	2.23	m	17.10
- facings	1.92	12.36	2.79	2.27	m	17.42
Cut out one course of one brick wall, insert hessian based damp proof course 225mm wide, replace with new bricks in gauged mortar (1:1:6)						
- commons	4.20	27.05	3.56	4.59	m	35.20
- facings	4.20	27.05	3.88	4.64	m	35.57
Cut out one course of half brick wall; insert hessian based damp proof course 112mm wide, replace with new bricks in cement mortar (1:3)						
- commons	2.28	14.68	2.75	2.61	m	20.04
- facings	2.28	14.68	3.06	2.66	m	20.40

BRICKWORK AND BLOCKWORK

BRICKWORK	Labour	Nett	Nett	O'heads	Unit	Total
Labour rate £6.44 per hour	hours	labour	material	/profit		£
		£	£	£		
Cut out one course of one brick wall, insert hessian based damp proof course 225mm wide, replace with new bricks in cement mortar (1:3)						
- commons	4.86	31.30	3.91	5.28	m	40.49
- facings	4.86	31.30	4.41	5.36	m	41.07
Cut out one course of half brick wall; insert pitch polymer damp proof course 112mm wide, replace with new bricks in gauged mortar (1:1:6)						
- commons	1.92	12.36	2.71	2.26	m	17.33
- facings	1.92	12.36	2.90	2.29	m	17.55
Cut out one course of one brick wall, insert pitch polymer damp proof course 225mm wide, replace with new bricks in gauged mortar (1:1:6)						
- commons	4.20	27.05	3.89	4.64	m	35.58
- facings	4.20	27.05	4.16	4.68	m	35.89
Cut out one course of half brick wall; insert pitch polymer damp proof course 112mm wide, replace with new bricks in cement mortar (1:3)						
- commons	2.28	14.68	2.93	2.64	m	20.25
- facings	2.28	14.68	3.25	2.69	m	20.62
Cut out one course of one brick wall, insert pitch polymer damp proof course 225mm wide, replace with new bricks in cement mortar (1:3)						
- commons	4.86	31.30	4.20	5.33	m	40.83
- facings	4.86	31.30	4.49	5.37	m	41.16

BRICKWORK AND BLOCKWORK

BRICKWORK Labour rate £6.44 per hour	Labour hours	Nett labour £	Nett material £	O'heads /profit £	Unit	Total £
Cut out one course of half brick wall; insert bitumen based lead cored damp proof course 112mm wide, replace with new bricks in gauged mortar (1:1:6)						
- commons	1.92	12.36	3.72	2.41	m	18.49
- facings	1.92	12.36	4.09	2.47	m	18.92
Cut out one course of one brick wall, insert bitumen based lead cored damp proof course 225mm wide, replace with new bricks in gauged mortar (1:1:6)						
- commons	4.20	27.05	4.47	4.73	m	36.25
- facings	4.20	27.05	4.68	4.76	m	36.49
Cut out one course of half brick wall; insert bitumen based lead cored damp proof course 112mm wide, replace with new bricks in cement mortar (1:3)						
- commons	2.28	14.68	3.92	2.79	m	21.39
- facings	2.28	14.68	4.37	2.86	m	21.91
Cut out one course of one brick wall, insert bitumen based lead cored damp proof course 225mm wide, replace with new bricks in cement mortar (1:3)						
- commons	4.86	31.30	4.74	5.41	m	41.45
- facings	4.86	31.30	4.95	5.44	m	41.69

BLOCKWORK
Labour rate £6.44 per hour

Pull down block walls in gauged mortar (1:1:6), thickness						
- 100mm	0.87	5.60	-	0.84	m2	6.44
- 150mm	1.10	7.08	-	1.06	m2	8.14
- 200mm	1.32	8.50	-	1.28	m2	9.78
- 250mm	1.63	10.50	-	1.58	m2	12.08

BLOCKWORK Labour rate £6.44 per hour	Labour hours	Nett labour £	Nett material £	O'heads /profit £	Unit	Total £
Cut out single block, replace in gauged mortar (1:1:6) thickness						
- 100mm	0.22	1.42	1.45	0.43	nr	3.30
- 150mm	0.34	2.19	1.93	0.62	nr	4.74
- 200mm	0.38	2.45	2.53	0.75	nr	5.73
- 250mm	0.44	2.83	3.63	0.97	nr	7.43
Pull down block walls in cement mortar (1:3), thickness						
- 100mm	1.08	6.96	-	1.04	m2	8.00
- 150mm	1.32	8.50	-	1.28	m2	9.78
- 200mm	1.60	10.30	-	1.55	m2	11.85
- 250mm	2.42	15.58	-	2.34	m2	17.92
Cut out single block, replace in cement mortar (1:3) thickness						
- 100mm	0.28	1.80	1.52	0.50	nr	3.82
- 150mm	0.42	2.70	1.98	0.70	nr	5.38
- 200mm	0.50	3.22	2.71	0.89	nr	6.82
- 250mm	0.56	3.61	3.83	1.12	nr	8.56
Hack off plaster from existing blockwork	0.13	0.84	-	0.13	m2	0.97
Hack face of existing blockwork and form key for plaster	0.17	1.09	-	0.16	m2	1.25
Rake out joints of existing blockwork and point up in cement mortar (1:3)	0.70	4.51	0.64	0.77	m2	5.92

NEW WORK

The basic price of common and
facing bricks has been taken as
£130.00 and £340.00 per thousand
respectively.

For each variation of £5 to these
rates, the following adjustments
should be made to the Total.

Half brick wall	£0.30 per m2
One brick wall	£0.60 per m2

BRICKWORK AND BLOCKWORK

NEW WORK	Labour hours	Nett labour £	Nett material £	O'heads /profit £	Unit	Total £
One and a half brick wall £0.90 per m2						
Two brick wall £1.20 per m2						

BRICKWORK
Labour rate £9.22 per hour

Common bricks (BP £130.00 per 1000)
in gauged mortar (1:1:6)

	Labour hours	Nett labour £	Nett material £	O'heads /profit £	Unit	Total £
Walls						
- half brick thick	1.54	14.20	10.16	3.65	m2	28.01
- one brick thick	2.70	24.89	20.05	6.74	m2	51.68
- one and a half brick thick	3.24	29.87	30.21	9.01	m2	69.09
- two brick thick	4.00	36.88	40.09	11.55	m2	88.52
Skins of hollow walls						
- half brick thick	1.54	14.20	10.16	3.65	m2	28.01
- one brick thick	2.70	24.89	20.05	6.74	m2	51.68
Honeycombe walls						
- half brick thick	1.02	9.40	8.19	2.64	m2	20.23
Dwarf solid walls						
- half brick thick	1.21	11.16	10.16	3.20	m2	24.52
Isolated piers						
- one brick thick	3.38	31.16	20.05	7.68	m2	58.89
- one and a half brick thick	4.05	37.34	30.21	10.13	m2	77.68
- two brick thick	4.98	45.92	40.09	12.90	m2	98.91
Chimney stacks						
- one brick thick	3.71	34.21	20.05	8.14	m2	62.40
- one and a half brick thick	4.47	41.21	30.21	10.71	m2	82.13
- two brick thick	5.48	50.53	40.09	13.59	m2	104.21
Backing to masonry, cutting and building						
- one brick thick	4.10	37.80	20.05	8.68	m2	66.53
- one and a half brick thick	4.93	45.45	30.21	11.35	m2	87.01
Projections of chimney breasts						
- half brick thick	1.92	17.70	10.16	4.18	m2	32.04
- one brick thick	3.08	28.40	20.05	7.27	m2	55.72
- one and a half brick thick	3.67	33.84	30.21	9.61	m2	73.66

BRICKWORK AND BLOCKWORK

BRICKWORK Labour rate £9.22 per hour	Labour hours	Nett labour £	Nett material £	O'heads /profit £	Unit	Total £
Projections of chimney breasts contd.,						
- two brick thick	4.50	41.49	40.09	12.24	m2	93.82
Projections of attached piers, plinths, bands and the like						
- 225 x 112mm	0.55	5.07	3.05	1.22	m	9.34
- 225 x 225mm	1.47	13.55	6.02	2.94	m	22.51
- 337 x 225mm	2.10	19.36	9.06	4.26	m	32.68
Common bricks (BP £130.00 per 1000) in cement mortar (1:3)						
Walls						
- half brick thick	1.60	14.75	11.38	3.92	m2	30.05
- one brick thick	2.76	25.45	20.50	6.89	m2	52.84
- one and a half brick thick	3.31	30.52	30.88	9.21	m2	70.61
- two brick thick	4.08	37.62	41.00	11.79	m2	90.41
Skins of hollow walls						
- half brick thick	1.60	14.75	11.38	3.92	m2	30.05
- one brick thick	2.76	25.45	20.50	6.89	m2	52.84
Honeycombe walls						
- half brick thick	1.08	9.96	9.00	2.84	m2	21.80
Dwarf solid walls						
- half brick thick	1.27	11.71	11.38	3.46	m2	26.55
Isolated piers						
- one brick thick	3.47	31.99	20.50	7.87	m2	60.36
- one and a half brick thick	4.12	37.99	30.88	10.33	m2	79.20
- two brick thick	5.08	46.84	41.00	13.18	m2	101.02
Chimney stacks						
- one brick thick	3.77	34.76	20.50	8.29	m2	63.55
- one and a half brick thick	4.53	41.77	30.88	10.90	m2	83.55
- two brick thick	5.58	51.45	41.00	13.87	m2	106.32
Backing to masonry, cutting and building						
- one brick thick	4.20	38.72	20.50	8.88	m2	68.10
- one and a half brick thick	5.04	46.47	30.88	11.60	m2	88.95

BRICKWORK AND BLOCKWORK

BRICKWORK Labour rate £9.22 per hour	Labour hours	Nett labour £	Nett material £	O'heads /profit £	Unit	Total £
Projections of chimney breasts						
- half brick thick	2.00	18.44	11.38	4.47	m2	34.29
- one brick thick	3.17	29.23	20.50	7.46	m2	57.19
- one and a half brick thick	3.78	34.85	30.88	9.86	m2	75.59
- two brick thick	4.60	42.41	41.00	12.51	m2	95.92
Projections of attached piers, **plinths, bands and the like**						
- 225 x 112mm	0.62	5.72	3.41	1.37	m	10.50
- 225 x 225mm	1.55	14.29	6.15	3.07	m	23.51
- 337 x 225mm	2.18	20.10	9.26	4.40	m	33.76
Class 'B' engineering bricks **(BP £235.00 per 1000) in** **cement mortar (1:3)**						
Walls						
- half brick thick	1.70	15.67	16.78	4.87	m2	37.32
- one brick thick	2.92	26.92	33.05	9.00	m2	68.97
- one and a half brick thick	3.50	32.27	49.83	12.32	m2	94.42
- two brick thick	4.38	40.38	66.11	15.97	m2	122.46
Skins of hollow walls						
- half brick thick	1.70	15.67	16.78	4.87	m2	37.32
- one brick thick	2.92	26.92	33.05	9.00	m2	68.97
Isolated piers						
- one brick thick	3.62	33.38	33.05	9.96	m2	76.39
- one and a half brick thick	4.36	40.20	49.83	13.50	m2	103.53
- two brick thick	5.38	49.60	66.11	17.36	m2	133.07
Chimney stacks						
- one brick thick	4.00	36.88	33.05	10.49	m2	80.42
- one and a half brick thick	4.75	43.80	49.83	14.04	m2	107.67
- two brick thick	5.88	54.21	66.11	18.05	m2	138.37
Backing to masonry, cutting and **building**						
- one brick thick	4.45	41.03	33.05	11.11	m2	85.19
- one and a half brick thick	5.45	50.25	49.83	15.01	m2	115.09

148

BRICKWORK	Labour	Nett	Nett	O'heads	Unit	Total
Labour rate £9.22 per hour	hours	labour	material	/profit		£
		£	£	£		
Projections of chimney breasts						
- half brick thick	2.10	19.36	16.78	5.42	m2	41.56
- one brick thick	3.34	30.79	33.05	9.58	m2	73.42
- one and a half brick thick	4.18	38.54	49.83	13.26	m2	101.63
- two brick thick	4.96	45.73	66.11	16.78	m2	128.62
Projections of attached piers,						
plinths, bands and the like						
- 225 x 112mm	0.71	6.55	5.03	1.74	m	13.32
- 225 x 225mm	1.70	15.67	9.92	3.84	m	29.43
- 337 x 225mm	2.32	21.39	14.95	5.45	m	41.79

FACINGS (Basic Price £340.00 per
1000) in gauged mortar (1:1:6)
Labour rate £9.22 per hour

Walls, flush pointing one side						
- half brick thick	2.04	18.81	23.29	6.32	m2	48.42
- half brick skin of hollow wall	2.14	19.73	23.29	6.45	m2	49.47
- one brick thick	3.20	29.50	46.07	11.34	m2	86.91
Walls, flush pointing both sides						
- half brick thick	2.31	21.30	23.29	6.69	m2	51.28
- one brick thick	3.47	31.99	46.07	11.71	m2	89.77
Walls, weather pointed one side						
- half brick thick	2.04	18.81	23.29	6.32	m2	48.42
- half brick skin of hollow wall	2.14	19.73	23.29	6.45	m2	49.47
- one brick thick	3.20	29.50	46.07	11.34	m2	86.91

FACED BRICKWORK
Labour rate £9.22 per hour

Extra over common brickwork for						
fair face to walls						
- flush pointing	0.27	2.49	-	0.37	m2	2.86
- weather pointing	0.34	3.13	-	0.47	m2	3.60
Extra over common brickwork for						
fair face to margins						
- flush pointing	0.07	0.65	-	0.10	m2	0.75
- weather pointing	0.07	0.65	-	0.10	m2	0.75

FACED BRICKWORK Labour rate £9.22 per hour	Labour hours	Nett labour £	Nett material £	O'heads /profit £	Unit	Total £
Extra over Class 'B' engineering brickwork for fair face to walls						
- flush pointing	0.56	5.16	-	0.77	m2	5.93
- weather pointing	0.65	5.99	-	0.90	m2	6.89
Extra over Class 'B' engineering brickwork for fair face to margins						
- flush pointing	0.15	1.38	-	0.21	m2	1.59
- weather pointing	0.15	1.38	-	0.21	m2	1.59
Walls in common bricks in gauged mortar (1:1:6) fair face and flush pointing both sides						
- half brick thick	2.08	19.18	10.73	4.49	m2	34.40
- one brick thick	3.24	29.87	20.59	7.57	m2	58.03
- one and a half brick thick	3.78	34.85	30.75	9.84	m2	75.44
Walls in common bricks in gauged mortar (1:1:6) fair face and weather pointing both sides						
- half brick thick	2.22	20.47	10.84	4.70	m2	36.01
- one brick thick	3.38	31.16	20.73	7.78	m2	59.67
- one and a half brick thick	3.92	36.14	30.85	10.05	m2	77.04
Walls in common bricks in cement mortar (1:3); fair face and flush pointing both sides						
- half brick thick	2.08	19.18	11.92	4.67	m2	35.77
- one brick thick	3.24	29.87	21.04	7.64	m2	58.55
- one and a half brick thick	3.78	34.85	41.54	11.46	m2	87.85
Walls in common bricks in cement mortar (1:3) fair face and weather pointing both sides						
- half brick thick	2.22	20.47	12.06	4.88	m2	37.41
- one brick thick	3.38	31.16	21.14	7.85	m2	60.15
- one and a half brick thick	3.92	36.14	31.52	10.15	m2	77.81
Walls in Class 'B' engineering bricks in cement mortar (1:3) fair face and flush pointing both sides						
- half brick thick	2.82	26.00	17.32	6.50	m2	49.82
- one brick thick	4.04	37.25	33.59	10.63	m2	81.47
- one and a half brick thick	4.62	42.60	50.37	13.95	m2	106.92

FACED BRICKWORK	Labour	Nett	Nett	O'heads	Unit	Total
Labour rate £9.22 per hour	hours	labour	material	/profit		£
		£	£	£		

Walls in Class 'B' engineering
bricks in cement mortar (1:3) fair
face and weather pointing both sides

- half brick thick	3.00	27.66	17.42	6.76	m2	51.84
- one brick thick	4.22	38.91	33.69	10.89	m2	83.49
- one and a half brick thick	4.80	44.26	50.47	14.21	m2	108.94

Isolated piers

- one brick thick	3.88	35.77	33.05	10.32	m2	79.14
- one and a half brick thick	4.64	42.78	49.83	13.89	m2	106.50

Chimney stacks

- one brick thick	4.32	39.83	33.05	10.93	m2	83.81
- one and a half brick thick	4.82	44.44	49.83	14.14	m2	108.41
- two brick thick	6.00	55.32	66.11	18.21	m2	139.64

Extra over facing bricks in
gauged mortar for

- sunk band 25mm deep	0.18	1.66	-	0.25	m	1.91
- projecting band 25mm deep	0.22	2.03	-	0.30	m	2.33
- sunk brick-on-end bands 25mm deep	0.27	2.49	-	0.37	m	2.86
- projecting brick-on-end bands 25mm deep	0.33	3.04	-	0.46	m	3.50
- flat arch, brick-on-edge 215mm side soffit, 102mm wide face	1.21	11.16	-	1.67	m	12.83
- flat arch, brick-on-end 102mm wide soffit 215mm high	1.48	13.65	-	2.05	m	15.70

Brick-on-edge sills, weather pointing all round, set sloping	0.95	8.76	6.00	2.21	m	16.97

Brick-on-edge copings, weather pointing all round	0.90	8.30	5.90	2.13	m	16.33

BLOCKWORK
Labour rate £9.22 per hour

Precast concrete dense aggregate
block (to B.S.6073) in gauged
mortar (1:1:6)

BRICKWORK AND BLOCKWORK

BLOCKWORK Labour rate £9.22 per hour	Labour hours	Nett labour £	Nett material £	O'heads /profit £	Unit	Total £
Solid blocks in walls and partitions thickness						
- 75mm	0.98	9.04	6.12	2.27	m2	17.43
- 100mm	1.14	10.51	7.33	2.68	m2	20.52
- 140mm	1.32	12.17	10.75	3.44	m2	26.36
Hollow blocks in walls and partitions thickness						
- 140mm	1.43	13.18	10.14	3.50	m2	26.82
- 190mm	1.76	16.23	11.74	4.20	m2	32.17
- 215mm	2.02	18.62	12.71	4.70	m2	36.03
Solid blocks in skins of hollow walls thickness						
- 75mm	1.12	10.33	6.12	2.47	m2	18.92
- 100mm	1.24	11.43	7.33	2.81	m2	21.57
- 140mm	1.47	13.55	10.75	3.65	m2	27.95
Hollow blocks in skins of hollow walls thickness						
- 140mm	1.56	14.38	10.14	3.68	m2	28.20
- 190mm	1.90	17.52	11.74	4.39	m2	33.65
- 215mm	2.15	19.82	12.71	4.88	m2	37.41
Solid blocks in piers and chimney stacks thickness						
- 75mm	1.28	11.80	6.12	2.69	m2	20.61
- 100mm	1.40	12.91	7.33	3.04	m2	23.28
- 140mm	1.68	15.49	10.75	3.94	m2	30.18
Hollow blocks in piers and chimney stacks thickness						
- 140mm	1.68	15.49	10.14	3.84	m2	29.47
- 190mm	2.04	18.81	11.74	4.58	m2	35.13
- 215mm	2.37	21.85	12.71	5.18	m2	39.74
Solid blocks in isolated casings thickness						
- 75mm	1.28	11.80	6.12	2.69	m2	20.61
- 100mm	1.90	17.52	7.33	3.73	m2	28.58
- 140mm	2.15	19.82	10.75	4.59	m2	35.16

BLOCKWORK Labour rate £9.22 per hour	Labour hours	Nett labour £	Nett material £	O'heads /profit £	Unit	Total £
Hollow blocks in isolated casings **thickness**						
- 140mm	1.68	15.49	10.14	3.84	m2	29.47
- 190mm	2.04	18.81	11.74	4.58	m2	35.13
- 215mm	2.37	21.85	12.71	5.18	m2	39.74
Extra for fair face and flush **pointing**						
- one side	0.16	1.48	-	0.22	m2	1.70
- both sides	0.33	3.04	-	0.46	m2	3.50
Fair returns, width						
- 75mm	0.05	0.46	-	0.07	m	0.53
- 100mm	0.08	0.74	-	0.11	m	0.85
- 140mm	0.12	1.11	-	0.17	m	1.28
- 190mm	0.16	1.48	-	0.22	m	1.70
- 215mm	0.21	1.94	-	0.29	m	2.23
Rough cutting to form chamfered **angles, width**						
- 50mm	0.32	2.95	-	0.44	m	3.39
- 100mm	0.38	3.50	-	0.53	m	4.03
Rough cutting to form rounded **angles, width**						
- 50mm	0.44	4.06	-	0.61	m	4.67
- 100mm	0.55	5.07	-	0.76	m	5.83
Fair cutting soffits width						
- 75mm	0.14	1.29	-	0.19	m	1.48
- 100mm	0.17	1.57	-	0.24	m	1.81
- 140mm	0.22	2.03	-	0.30	m	2.33
- 190mm	0.25	2.31	-	0.35	m	2.66
- 215mm	0.27	2.49	-	0.37	m	2.86
Bonding ends of blockwork to **brickwork in alternate course** **width**						
- 75mm	0.30	2.77	0.77	0.53	m	4.07
- 100mm	0.38	3.50	0.88	0.66	m	5.04
- 140mm	0.44	4.06	1.23	0.79	m	6.08
- 190mm	0.55	5.07	1.34	0.96	m	7.37
- 215mm	0.62	5.72	1.46	1.08	m	8.26

BLOCKWORK	Labour	Nett	Nett	O'heads	Unit	Total
Labour rate £9.22 per hour	hours	labour	material	/profit		£
		£	£	£		

Precast concrete lightweight
aggregate block (to B.S.6073) in
gauged mortar (1:1:6)

Solid blocks in walls and
partitions thickness

- 75mm	0.87	8.02	6.96	2.25	m2	17.23
- 100mm	1.03	9.50	8.68	2.73	m2	20.91
- 140mm	1.18	10.88	12.36	3.49	m2	26.73

Hollow blocks in walls and
partitions thickness

- 140mm	1.32	12.17	12.24	3.66	m2	28.07
- 190mm	1.65	15.21	15.10	4.55	m2	34.86
- 215mm	1.88	17.33	15.87	4.98	m2	38.18

Solid blocks in skins of hollow
walls thickness

- 75mm	1.00	9.22	6.96	2.43	m2	18.61
- 100mm	1.10	10.14	8.68	2.82	m2	21.64
- 140mm	1.31	12.08	12.36	3.67	m2	28.11

Hollow blocks in skins of hollow
walls thickness

- 140mm	1.41	13.00	12.24	3.79	m2	29.03
- 190mm	1.72	15.86	15.10	4.64	m2	35.60
- 215mm	1.98	18.26	15.87	5.12	m2	39.25

Solid blocks in piers and chimney
stacks thickness

- 75mm	1.18	10.88	6.96	2.68	m2	20.52
- 100mm	1.28	11.80	8.68	3.07	m2	23.55
- 140mm	1.52	14.01	12.36	3.96	m2	30.33

Hollow blocks in piers and
chimney stacks thickness

- 140mm	1.54	14.20	12.24	3.97	m2	30.41
- 190mm	1.88	17.33	15.10	4.86	m2	37.29
- 215mm	2.15	19.82	15.87	5.35	m2	41.04

Solid blocks in isolated casings
thickness

- 75mm	1.18	10.88	6.96	2.68	m2	20.52
- 100mm	1.74	16.04	8.68	3.71	m2	28.43
- 140mm	1.97	18.16	12.36	4.58	m2	35.10

BLOCKWORK	Labour	Nett	Nett	O'heads	Unit	Total
Labour rate £9.22 per hour	hours	labour	material	/profit		£
		£	£	£		
Hollow blocks in isolated casings thickness						
- 140mm	1.52	14.01	12.24	3.94	m2	30.19
- 190mm	1.87	17.24	15.10	4.85	m2	37.19
- 215mm	2.02	18.62	15.87	5.17	m2	39.66
Extra for fair face and flush pointing						
- one side	0.14	1.29	-	0.19	m2	1.48
- both sides	0.27	2.49	-	0.37	m2	2.86
Fair returns, width						
- 75mm	0.04	0.37	-	0.06	m	0.43
- 100mm	0.07	0.65	-	0.10	m	0.75
- 140mm	0.10	0.92	-	0.14	m	1.06
- 190mm	0.14	1.29	-	0.19	m	1.48
- 215mm	0.18	1.66	-	0.25	m	1.91
Rough cutting to form chamfered angles, width						
- 50mm	0.27	2.49	-	0.37	m	2.86
- 100mm	0.32	2.95	-	0.44	m	3.39
Rough cutting to form rounded angles, width						
- 50mm	0.36	3.32	-	0.50	m	3.82
- 100mm	0.47	4.33	-	0.65	m	4.98
Fair cutting to soffits width						
- 75mm	0.12	1.11	-	0.17	m	1.28
- 100mm	0.15	1.38	-	0.21	m	1.59
- 140mm	0.20	1.84	-	0.28	m	2.12
- 190mm	0.22	2.03	-	0.30	m	2.33
- 215mm	0.24	2.21	-	0.33	m	2.54
Bonding ends of blockwork to brickwork in alternate course width						
- 75mm	0.28	2.58	0.92	0.53	m	4.03
- 100mm	0.33	3.04	1.06	0.61	m	4.71
- 140mm	0.38	3.50	1.19	0.70	m	5.39
- 190mm	0.46	4.24	1.29	0.83	m	6.36
- 215mm	0.54	4.98	1.36	0.95	m	7.29

BRICKWORK AND BLOCKWORK

DAMP PROOF COURSES Labour rate £9.22 per hour	Labour hours	Nett labour £	Nett material £	O'heads /profit £	Unit	Total £
Hessian based bitumen damp proof course in gauged mortar (1:1:6)						
Horizontal width						
- over 225mm	0.35	3.23	4.50	1.16	m2	8.89
- 75mm	0.07	0.65	0.40	0.16	m	1.21
- 100mm	0.07	0.65	0.45	0.17	m	1.27
- 112mm	0.07	0.65	0.51	0.17	m	1.33
- 150mm	0.08	0.74	0.67	0.21	m	1.62
- 225mm	0.10	0.92	1.00	0.29	m	2.21
Vertical width						
- 75mm	0.10	0.92	0.40	0.20	m	1.52
- 100mm	0.10	0.92	0.45	0.21	m	1.58
- 112mm	0.10	0.92	0.51	0.21	m	1.64
- 150mm	0.13	1.20	0.67	0.28	m	2.15
- 225mm	0.15	1.38	1.00	0.36	m	2.74
Asbestos based bitumen damp proof course in gauged mortar (1:1:6)						
Horizontal width						
- over 225mm	0.35	3.23	4.65	1.18	m2	9.06
- 75mm	0.07	0.65	0.47	0.17	m	1.29
- 100mm	0.07	0.65	0.52	0.18	m	1.35
- 112mm	0.07	0.65	0.59	0.19	m	1.43
- 150mm	0.08	0.74	0.80	0.23	m	1.77
- 225mm	0.10	0.92	1.16	0.31	m	2.39
Vertical width						
- 75mm	0.10	0.92	0.47	0.21	m	1.60
- 100mm	0.10	0.92	0.52	0.22	m	1.66
- 112mm	0.10	0.92	0.59	0.23	m	1.74
- 150mm	0.13	1.20	0.80	0.30	m	2.30
- 225mm	0.15	1.38	1.16	0.38	m	2.92
Pitch polymer damp proof course in gauged mortar (1:1:6)						
Horizontal width						
- over 225mm	0.35	3.23	5.00	1.23	m2	9.46
- 75mm	0.07	0.65	0.46	0.17	m	1.28
- 100mm	0.07	0.65	0.55	0.18	m	1.38
- 112mm	0.07	0.65	0.63	0.19	m	1.47
- 150mm	0.08	0.74	0.84	0.24	m	1.82

BRICKWORK AND BLOCKWORK

DAMP PROOF COURSES Labour rate £9.22 per hour	Labour hours	Nett labour £	Nett material £	O'heads /profit £	Unit	Total £
Pitch polymer damp proof course in gauged mortar (1:1:6)						
- 225mm	0.10	0.92	1.25	0.33	m	2.50
Vertical width						
- 75mm	0.10	0.92	0.46	0.21	m	1.59
- 100mm	0.10	0.92	0.55	0.22	m	1.69
- 112mm	0.10	0.92	0.63	0.23	m	1.78
- 150mm	0.13	1.20	0.84	0.31	m	2.35
- 225mm	0.15	1.38	1.25	0.39	m	3.02
Asbestos based with lead core damp proof course in gauged mortar (1:1:6)						
Horizontal width						
- over 225mm	0.35	3.23	12.25	2.32	m2	17.80
- 75mm	0.07	0.65	1.04	0.25	m	1.94
- 100mm	0.07	0.65	1.23	0.28	m	2.16
- 112mm	0.07	0.65	1.40	0.31	m	2.36
- 150mm	0.08	0.74	1.86	0.39	m	2.99
- 225mm	0.10	0.92	2.75	0.55	m	4.22
Vertical width						
- 75mm	0.10	0.92	1.04	0.29	m	2.25
- 100mm	0.10	0.92	1.23	0.32	m	2.47
- 112mm	0.10	0.92	1.40	0.35	m	2.67
- 150mm	0.13	1.20	1.86	0.46	m	3.52
- 225mm	0.15	1.38	2.75	0.62	m	4.75
Slate damp proof course bedded and pointed in cement mortar (1:3) 112mm wide						
- single course	0.23	2.12	5.29	1.11	m	8.52
- double course	0.48	4.43	9.44	2.08	m	15.95
Slate damp proof course bedded and pointed in cement mortar (1:3) 225mm wide						
- single course	0.39	3.60	11.07	2.20	m	16.87
- double course	0.82	7.56	19.12	4.00	m	30.68

DAMP PROOF COURSES Labour rate £9.22 per hour	Labour hours	Nett labour £	Nett material £	O'heads /profit £	Unit	Total £
Three coats 'synthaprufe' waterproofing liquid brushed on surfaces						
- vertically	0.42	3.87	3.36	1.08	m2	8.31
- horizontally	0.33	3.04	3.36	0.96	m2	7.36

SUNDRIES
Labour rate £9.22 per hour

	Labour hours	Nett labour	Nett material	O'heads /profit	Unit	Total
Form 50mm cavity between skin of hollow walls, 3 ties per m2						
- galvanised steel butterfly ties	0.10	0.92	0.33	0.19	m2	1.44
- galvanised steel twisted ties	0.10	0.92	0.50	0.21	m2	1.63
- stainless steel twisted ties	0.10	0.92	0.43	0.20	m2	1.55
Form 75mm cavity between skin of hollow walls, 3 ties per m2						
- galvanised steel butterfly ties	0.10	0.92	0.33	0.19	m2	1.44
- galvanised steel twisted ties	0.10	0.92	0.50	0.21	m2	1.63
- stainless steel ties	0.10	0.92	0.43	0.20	m2	1.55
Cavity wall insulation expanded polystyrene sheets						
- 25mm	0.16	1.48	2.59	0.61	m2	4.68
- 50mm	0.16	1.48	3.86	0.80	m2	6.14
Galvanised brick reinforcement, 'Exmet' width						
- 65mm	0.07	0.65	0.21	0.13	m	0.99
- 115mm	0.09	0.83	0.33	0.17	m	1.33
- 175mm	0.12	1.11	0.50	0.24	m	1.85
- 225mm	0.15	1.38	0.68	0.31	m	2.37
Bedding in cement mortar (1:3)						
- wood plates and frames	0.13	1.20	0.18	0.21	m	1.59
- metal frames and cills	0.17	1.57	0.15	0.26	m	1.98
Point frames with mastic						
- one side	0.12	1.11	0.70	0.27	m	2.08
- two sides	0.20	1.84	1.30	0.47	m	3.61

BRICKWORK AND BLOCKWORK

SUNDRIES Labour rate £9.22 per hour	Labour hours	Nett labour £	Nett material £	O'heads /profit £	Unit	Total £
Form hole in new brickwork for large pipe						
- half brick thick	1.10	10.14	-	1.52	nr	11.66
- one brick thick	1.41	13.00	-	1.95	nr	14.95
- one and a half brick thick	1.65	15.21	-	2.28	nr	17.49
Form hole in existing brickwork for small pipe						
- half brick thick	1.18	10.88	-	1.63	nr	12.51
- one brick thick	1.40	12.91	-	1.94	nr	14.85
- one and a half brick thick	1.70	15.67	-	2.35	nr	18.02
Form hole in existing brickwork for large pipe						
- half brick thick	1.32	12.17	-	1.83	nr	14.00
- one brick thick	1.52	14.01	-	2.10	nr	16.11
- on and a half brick thick	1.82	16.78	-	2.52	nr	19.30
Point frames with polysulphide sealant						
- one side	0.12	1.11	1.30	0.36	m	2.77
- two sides	0.20	1.84	2.20	0.61	m	4.65
Rake out joints of brickwork for flashing and point up on completion						
- horizontal	0.09	0.83	0.10	0.14	m	1.07
- stepped	0.17	1.57	0.10	0.25	m	1.92
Form groove in brickwork and grout in cement mortar (1:3)	0.38	3.50	0.12	0.54	m	4.16
Form hole in new brickwork for small pipe						
- half brick thick	0.95	8.76	-	1.31	nr	10.07
- one brick thick	1.32	12.17	-	1.83	nr	14.00
- one and a half brick thick	1.61	14.84	-	2.23	nr	17.07
Make good fair face or facings around						
- small pipe	0.21	1.94	-	0.29	nr	2.23
- large pipe	0.33	3.04	-	0.46	nr	3.50

BRICKWORK AND BLOCKWORK

SUNDRIES Labour rate £9.22 per hour	Labour hours	Nett labour £	Nett material £	O'heads /profit £	Unit	Total £
Mortice in brickwork, grout up in cement mortar (1:3)						
- 50 x 50 x 100mm	0.32	2.95	0.23	0.48	nr	3.66
- 75 x 75 x 150mm	0.40	3.69	0.38	0.61	nr	4.68
- 75 x 75 x 200mm	0.48	4.43	0.55	0.75	nr	5.73
Form opening in cavity wall for air brick, seal cavity with slates in cement mortar (1:3) size						
- 225 x 75mm	0.30	2.77	1.80	0.69	nr	5.26
- 225 x 150mm	0.42	3.87	2.45	0.95	nr	7.27
- 225 x 225mm	0.54	4.98	3.40	1.26	nr	9.64
Terracotta louvre pattern air bricks, size						
- 220 x 70mm	0.10	0.92	1.91	0.42	nr	3.25
- 220 x 145mm	0.10	0.92	2.06	0.45	nr	3.43
- 220 x 220mm	0.10	0.92	5.63	0.98	nr	7.53
Terracotta square hole pattern air bricks, size						
- 220 x 70mm	0.10	0.92	1.09	0.30	nr	2.31
- 220 x 145mm	0.10	0.92	1.82	0.41	nr	3.15
- 220 x 220mm	0.10	0.92	3.93	0.73	nr	5.58
Galvanised cast iron louvre pattern air bricks, size						
- 225 x 75mm	0.12	1.11	2.81	0.59	nr	4.51
- 225 x 150mm	0.12	1.11	5.01	0.92	nr	7.04
- 225 x 225mm	0.12	1.11	8.41	1.43	nr	10.95
Gas flue lining system, Typex 115 range bedded in refractory mortar (1:2:5) building in to blockwork or brickwork walls						
- recess panel (PXY 218)	0.18	1.66	3.54	0.78	nr	5.98
- lintel unit (1Y)	0.18	1.66	5.05	1.01	nr	7.72
- entry and exit unit (2Y)	0.18	1.66	6.59	1.24	nr	9.49
- straight block (3YA)	0.18	1.66	3.19	0.73	nr	5.58
- straight block (3YB)	0.18	1.66	3.31	0.75	nr	5.72
- offset unit (4Y)	0.18	1.66	3.98	0.85	nr	6.49
- reverse rebate unit (5Y)	0.18	1.66	3.26	0.74	nr	5.66
- conversion corbel unit (6Y)	0.18	1.66	6.22	1.18	nr	9.06
- vertical conversion unit (7Y)	0.18	1.66	6.56	1.23	nr	9.45

SUNDRIES Labour rate £9.22 per hour	Labour hours	Nett labour £	Nett material £	O'heads /profit £	Unit	Total £
Gas flue lining system, Typex 115 **range bedded in refractory mortar** **(1:2:5) building in to blockwork** **or brickwork walls contd.;**						
- back offset unit (8Y)	0.18	1.66	9.80	1.72	nr	13.18
- back offset unit (9Y)	0.18	1.66	9.12	1.62	nr	12.40
Gas flue lining system Typex 150 **range bedded in refractory mortar** **(1:2:5) building in to blockwork** **or brickwork walls**						
- recess panel (RPX 305)	0.18	1.66	4.98	1.00	nr	7.64
- offset lintel (1X1)	0.18	1.66	5.58	1.09	nr	8.33
- twin channel flue block (2X1)	0.18	1.66	5.08	1.01	nr	7.75
- twin channel flue block (3X)	0.18	1.66	4.10	0.86	nr	6.62
- single flue block (3X1)	0.18	1.66	3.57	0.78	nr	6.01
- side offset block (4X1)	0.18	1.66	3.99	0.85	nr	6.50
- back offset block (4X4)	0.18	1.66	3.73	0.81	nr	6.20
- single flue block (5X)	0.18	1.66	2.66	0.65	nr	4.97
- single flue block (5X1)	0.18	1.66	3.21	0.73	nr	5.60
- single flue block (5X2)	0.18	1.66	3.26	0.74	nr	5.66
- single flue block (5X3)	0.18	1.66	3.24	0.74	nr	5.64
- single flue block (5X5)	0.18	1.66	3.24	0.74	nr	5.64
- separating withe (8X)	0.18	1.66	1.98	0.55	nr	4.19
- separating withe (8X4)	0.18	1.66	2.94	0.69	nr	5.29
- end terminal cap unit (9X)	0.40	3.69	6.28	1.50	nr	11.47
- inter terminal cap unit (9X1)	0.40	3.69	4.39	1.21	nr	9.29
- end terminal cap unit (9X6)	0.40	3.69	6.53	1.53	nr	11.75
- inter terminal cap unit (9X7)	0.40	3.69	5.30	1.35	nr	10.34
- single flue cap unit (9X9)	0.40	3.69	11.64	2.30	nr	17.63
- conversion unit (10X1)	0.18	1.66	3.69	0.80	nr	6.15
- angled conversion unit (10X2)	0.18	1.66	5.51	1.08	nr	8.25
- aluminium louvre (MLX)	0.18	1.66	6.64	1.25	nr	9.55
Terracotta chimney pot, tapered **or canon head setting and** **flaunching in cement mortar,** **185mm diameter, height**						
- 300mm	2.30	21.21	11.73	4.94	nr	37.88
- 375mm	2.30	21.21	13.60	5.22	nr	40.03
- 450mm	2.75	25.36	14.02	5.91	nr	45.29
- 600mm	3.25	29.97	20.33	7.55	nr	57.85
- 750mm	3.75	34.58	27.12	9.26	nr	70.96
- 900mm	4.75	43.80	36.38	12.03	nr	92.21

RUBBLE WALLING

1. Labour

1 Craftsman	6.44
1 Labourer	5.55

Hourly gang rate £11.99	
	-----

2. Materials

	Unit	Basic Price £	Waste %	Total £
Cement mortar	m3	-	-	65.70
Gauged mortar	m3	-	-	73.14
Rough rubble	t	52.20	15	63.48
Irregular squared rubble	t	69.00	10	75.90
Coursed rubble	t	86.25	5	90.56

ALTERATION WORK Labour rate £5.55 per hour	Labour hours	Nett labour £	Nett material £	O'heads /profit £	Unit	Total £
Pull down rubble walling in gauged mortar, thickness						
- 200mm	0.55	3.05	-	0.46	m2	3.51
- 300mm	0.65	3.61	-	0.54	m2	4.15
- 450mm	0.80	4.44	-	0.67	m2	5.11
Labour rate £11.99 per hour						
Cut out areas not exceeding 1m2 in uncoursed rubble walling; clean off and reset in gauged mortar (1:1:6), thickness						
- 200mm	4.30	51.56	27.41	11.85	m2	90.82
- 300mm	5.20	62.35	41.09	15.52	m2	118.96
- 450mm	6.85	82.13	61.63	21.56	m2	165.32
Cut out areas not exceeding 1m2 in coursed rubble walling, clean off and re-set in gauged mortar (1:1:6), thickness						
- 200mm	4.50	53.96	32.38	12.95	m2	99.29
- 300mm	5.40	64.75	48.54	16.99	m2	130.28
- 450mm	7.05	84.53	72.81	23.60	m2	180.94

ALTERATION WORK	Labour	Nett	Nett	O'heads	Unit	Total
Labour rate £11.99 per hour	hours	labour	material	/profit		£
		£	£	£		

Rake out joints of rubble
walling; point in gauged mortar
(1:1:6)

Uncoursed

- flush pointing	0.48	5.76	1.00	1.01	m2	7.77
- weather pointing	0.48	5.76	1.10	1.03	m2	7.89

Coursed

- flush pointing	0.48	5.76	1.00	1.01	m2	7.77
- weather pointing	0.48	5.76	1.10	1.03	m2	7.89

NEW WORK
Labour rate £11.99 per hour

Random rubble walling, laid dry,
thickness

- 300mm	3.00	35.97	38.09	11.11	m2	85.17
- 450mm	3.25	38.97	57.13	14.42	m2	110.52

Random rubble walling, laid dry
battered both faces, average

thickness 450mm	3.75	44.96	57.13	15.31	m2	117.40

Random rubble walling in gauged
mortar (1:1:6), thickness

- 300mm	1.50	17.99	41.09	8.86	m2	67.94
- 450mm	2.25	26.98	61.63	13.29	m2	101.90
- 550mm	2.75	32.97	75.33	16.25	m2	124.55

Random rubble walling in cement
mortar (1:3), thickness

- 300mm	1.50	17.99	40.30	8.74	m2	67.03
- 450mm	2.25	26.98	61.00	13.20	m2	101.18
- 550mm	2.75	32.97	74.50	16.12	m2	123.59

Irregular coursed rubble walling
in gauged mortar (1:1:6),
thickness

- 300mm	1.95	23.38	48.54	10.79	m2	82.71
- 450mm	2.92	35.01	72.81	16.17	m2	123.99
- 550mm	3.58	42.92	88.99	19.79	m2	151.70

RUBBLE WALLING

NEW WORK Labour rate £11.99 per hour	Labour hours	Nett labour £	Nett material £	O'heads /profit £	Unit	Total £
Irregular coursed rubble walling in cement mortar (1:3), thickness						
- 300mm	1.95	23.38	47.50	10.63	m2	81.51
- 450mm	2.92	35.01	72.00	16.05	m2	123.06
- 550mm	3.58	42.92	88.00	19.64	m2	150.56
Coursed rubble walling in gauged mortar (1:1:6), thickness						
- 300mm	1.60	19.18	57.34	11.48	m2	88.00
- 450mm	2.40	28.78	86.00	17.22	m2	132.00
- 550mm	2.93	35.13	105.12	21.04	m2	161.29
Coursed rubble walling in cement mortar (1:3), thickness						
- 300mm	1.60	19.18	56.70	11.38	m2	87.26
- 450mm	2.40	28.78	85.00	17.07	m2	130.85
- 550mm	2.93	35.13	104.20	20.90	m2	160.23

MASONRY

The type of work normally
included in this work section
covers highly specialised
products and skills which are
unlikely to be required within
the scope of work this book is
intended to cover.

Reference should be made to a
specialist stonework firm for
quotations if the need arose.

	Unit	Specialist Prices £
The rates shown against item descriptions in this section are gross rates supplied by a specialist firm. They are intended to be used as a guide only and relate to work in areas not exceeding 75 m2.		

ALTERATION WORK

All rates include for placing
debris in skips

**Hack up vertical or horizontal
asphalt work**

	Unit	£
- two coats	m2	3.50
- three coats	m2	4.10

**Hack off skirtings and flashings
100 - 200mm wide**

- two coats	m	1.25
- three coats	m	1.40

**Cut out crack in vertical or
horizontal asphalt, make good to
match existing**

- two coats	m	10.00
- three coats	m	11.30

**Cut out isolated defective
asphalt horizontal areas not
exceeding 1m2, make good to match
existing**

- two coats	nr	20.00
- three coats	nr	22.00

**Cut out isolated defective
asphalt, vertical areas not
exceeding 1m2, make good to match
existing**

- two coats	nr	22.00
- three coats	nr	24.00

NEW WORK	Unit	Specialist Prices £

Damp proofing and tanking

20mm two coat mastic asphalt to
B.S.1097 over 300mm wide

- flat	m2	15.80
- sloping 10 - 45°	m2	18.00
- sloping 46 - 90°	m2	21.00
- vertical	m2	21.00

20mm two coat mastic ashpalt to
B.S.1097 not exceeding 150mm wide

- flat	m	5.00
- sloping 10 - 45°	m	5.00
- sloping 46 - 90°	m	6.50
- vertical	m	6.50

20mm two coat mastic asphalt to
B.S.1097 150 - 300mm wide

- flat	m	5.80
- sloping 10 - 45°	m	5.80
- sloping 46 - 90°	m	8.00
- vertical	m	8.00

30mm three coat mastic asphalt to
B.S.1097 over 300mm

- flat	m2	20.00
- sloping 10 - 45°	m2	21.50
- sloping 46 - 90°	m2	23.00
- vertical	m2	23.00

30mm three coat mastic asphalt to
B.S.1097 not exceeding 150mm wide

- flat	m	5.80
- sloping 10 - 45°	m	5.80
- sloping 46 - 90°	m	8.50
- vertical	m	8.50

30mm three coat mastic asphalt to
B.S.1097 150 - 300mm wide

- flat	m	8.00
- sloping 10 - 45°	m	8.00
- sloping 46 - 90°	m	10.00
- vertical	m	10.00

ASPHALT WORK

NEW WORK	Unit	Specialist Prices £
20mm two coat mastic asphalt to B.S.6577 over 300mm wide		
- flat	m2	20.00
- sloping 10 - 45°	m2	22.00
- sloping 46 - 90°	m2	25.00
- vertical	m2	25.00
20mm two coat mastic ashpalt to B.S.6577 not exceeding 150mm wide		
- flat	m	6.00
- sloping 10 - 45°	m	6.00
- sloping 46 - 90°	m	8.00
- vertical	m	8.00
20mm two coat mastic asphalt to B.S.6577 150 - 300mm wide		
- flat	m	7.00
- sloping 10 - 45°	m	7.00
- sloping 46 - 90°	m	9.30
- vertical	m	9.30
30mm three coat mastic asphalt to B.S.6577 over 300mm		
- flat	m2	26.50
- sloping 10 - 45°	m2	28.00
- sloping 46 - 90°	m2	31.00
- vertical	m2	31.00
30mm three coat mastic asphalt to B.S.6577 not exceeding 150mm wide		
- flat	m	7.00
- sloping 10 - 45°	m	7.00
- sloping 46 - 90°	m	8.50
- vertical	m	8.50
30mm three coat mastic asphalt to B.S.6577 150 - 300mm wide		
- flat	m	8.30
- sloping 10 - 45°	m	8.30
- sloping 46 - 90°	m	9.80
- vertical	m	9.80

NEW WORK	Unit	Specialist Prices £

Pavings

20mm two coat mastic asphalt to
B.S.1076 over 300mm wide

- flat	m2	18.00
- sloping 10 - 45°	m2	21.00
- sloping 46 - 90°	m2	24.00
- vertical	m2	24.00

20mm two coat mastic asphalt to
B.S.1076 not exceeding 150mm wide

- flat	m	5.80
- sloping 10 - 45°	m	5.80
- sloping 46 - 90°	m	7.40
- vertical	m	7.40

20mm two coat mastic asphalt to
B.S.1076 150 - 300mm wide

- flat	m	6.80
- sloping 10 - 45°	m	6.80
- sloping 46 - 90°	m	8.50
- vertical	m	8.50

Roofing

20mm two coat mastic asphalt to
B.S.988 over 300mm wide

- flat	m2	19.00
- sloping 10 - 45°	m2	22.00
- sloping 46 - 90°	m2	24.50
- vertical	m2	24.50

20mm two coat mastic asphalt to
B.S.988 not exceeding 150mm wide

- flat	m	5.20
- sloping 10 - 45°	m	5.20
- sloping 46 - 90°	m	8.00
- vertical	m	8.00

20mm two coat mastic asphalt to
B.S.988 150 - 300mm wide

- flat	m	7.00
- sloping 10 - 45°	m	7.00
- sloping 46 - 90°	m	9.50
- vertical	m	9.50

REPAIR AND ALTERATIONS	Labour hours	Nett labour £	Nett material £	O'heads /profit £	Unit	Total £
Take up roof coverings from pitched roof						
- tiles	0.80	6.97	-	1.05	m2	8.02
- slates	0.80	6.97	-	1.05	m2	8.02
- timber boarding	1.00	8.71	-	1.31	m2	10.02
- metal sheeting	0.10	0.87	-	0.13	m2	1.00
- flat sheeting	0.30	2.61	-	0.39	m2	3.00
- corrugated sheeting	0.30	2.61	-	0.39	m2	3.00
- underfelt	0.08	0.70	-	0.11	m2	0.81
Take up roof coverings from flat roof						
- bituminous felt	0.25	2.18	-	0.33	m2	2.51
- metal sheeting	0.50	4.35	-	0.65	m2	5.00
- wood wool slabs	0.50	4.35	-	0.65	m2	5.00
- fillings	0.10	0.87	-	0.13	m2	1.00
Take up roof coverings from pitched roof; carefully lay aside for re-use						
- tiles	1.10	9.58	-	1.44	m2	11.02
- slates	1.10	9.58	-	1.44	m2	11.02
- metal sheeting	0.80	6.97	-	1.05	m2	8.20
- flat sheeting	0.50	4.35	-	0.65	m2	5.00
- corrugated sheeting	0.50	4.35	-	0.65	m2	5.00
Take up roof coverings from flat roof; carefully lay aside for re-use						
- metal sheeting	0.70	6.10	-	0.92	m2	7.02
- wood wool slabs	0.70	6.10	-	0.92	m2	7.02
Inspect roof battens, refix loose and replace 25% with new size 38 x 19mm; centres						
- 250mm	0.16	1.39	0.54	0.29	m2	2.22
- 450mm	0.12	1.05	0.38	0.22	m2	1.65
- 600mm	0.10	0.87	0.30	0.18	m2	1.35

REPAIR AND ALTERATIONS (cont'd)	Labour hours	Nett labour £	Nett material £	O'heads /profit £	Unit	Total £
Inspect roof battens, replace 100% with new size						
38 x 19mm; centres						
- 250mm	0.48	4.18	2.14	0.95	m2	7.27
- 450mm	0.40	3.48	1.51	0.75	m2	5.74
- 600mm	0.32	2.79	1.22	0.60	m2	4.61
Inspect roof battens, refix loose and replace 25% with new size						
50 x 25mm; centres						
- 250mm	0.18	1.57	0.83	0.36	m2	2.76
- 450mm	0.14	1.22	0.60	0.27	m2	2.09
- 600mm	0.12	1.05	0.47	0.23	m2	1.75
Inspect roof battens, replace 100% with new size						
50 x 25mm; centres						
- 250mm	0.50	4.36	3.31	1.15	m2	8.82
- 450mm	0.41	3.57	2.36	0.89	m2	6.82
- 600mm	0.34	2.96	1.89	0.73	m2	5.58

Repairs to slate roofing

	Labour hours	Nett labour £	Nett material £	O'heads /profit £	Unit	Total £
Remove single broken slate; replace with slate previously laid aside	1.00	8.71	-	1.31	nr	10.02
Remove single broken slate; replace with new Welsh slates						
- 405 x 205mm	1.20	10.45	0.90	1.70	nr	13.05
- 405 x 255mm	1.20	10.45	1.15	1.74	nr	13.34
Remove slates in areas not exceeding 1m2; replace with slates previously laid aside	3.00	26.13	-	3.92	nr	30.05
Remove slates in areas not exceeding 1m2; replace with new Welsh slates						
- 405 x 205mm	4.50	39.20	26.81	9.90	nr	75.91
- 405 x 255mm	4.50	39.20	27.31	9.98	nr	76.49

REPAIR AND ALTERATIONS (cont'd)	Labour hours	Nett labour £	Nett material £	O'heads /profit £	Unit	Total £
Repairs to tile roofing						
Remove single broken tile; replace with tile previously laid aside	0.30	2.61	-	0.39	nr	3.00
Remove single broken tile; replace with new						
- 265 x 165mm Marley Plain tile	0.30	2.61	0.22	0.43	nr	3.26
- 380 x 230mm Marley Anglia Plus tile	0.30	2.61	0.43	0.46	nr	3.50
- 413 x 330mm Marley Mendip tile	0.30	2.61	0.62	0.49	nr	3.72
- 419 x 330mm Marley Bold Roll Premium tile	0.30	2.61	0.72	0.50	nr	3.83
- 418 x 330mm Redland Renown tile	0.30	2.61	0.51	0.47	nr	3.59
- 418 x 332mm Redland Grovebury tile	0.30	2.61	0.58	0.48	nr	3.67
- 430 x 380mm Redland Delta tile	0.30	2.61	0.83	0.52	nr	3.96
Remove tiles in areas not exceeding $1m^2$; replace with tiles previously laid aside	2.00	17.42	-	2.61	nr	20.03
Remove tiles in areas not exceeding $1m^2$; replace with new						
- 265 x 165mm Marley Plain tile	2.00	17.42	12.90	4.55	nr	34.87
- 380 x 230mm Marley Anglia Plus tile	1.28	11.15	6.60	2.66	nr	20.41
- 413 x 330mm Marley Mendip tile	1.12	9.76	5.92	2.35	nr	18.03
- 419 x 330mm Marley Bold Roll tile	1.12	9.76	5.92	2.35	nr	18.03
- 418 x 330mm Redland Renown tile	0.90	7.84	4.94	1.92	nr	14.70
- 418 x 332mm Redland Grovebury tile	0.90	7.84	5.61	2.02	nr	15.47
- 430 x 380mm Redland Delta tile	0.90	7.84	6.78	2.19	nr	16.81

REPAIR AND ALTERATIONS (cont'd)	Labour hours	Nett labour £	Nett material £	O'heads /profit £	Unit	Total £
Take off defective ridge cappings and refix including pointing in coloured cement mortar (1:3)						
- segmental capping	0.84	7.32	1.50	1.32	m	10.14
- Modern ridge	1.14	9.93	1.50	1.72	m	13.15
- Redland ridge	1.10	9.58	1.50	1.66	m	12.74
Take off defective ridge cappings and replace with new including pointing in coloured cement mortar (1:3)						
- segmental capping	0.84	7.32	5.38	1.91	m	14.61
- Modern ridge	1.14	9.93	5.66	2.34	m	17.93
- Redland ridge	1.10	9.58	4.57	2.12	m	16.27

Repairs to bituminous felt roofing

Cut out defective layer of roofing felt in areas not exceeding 1m2; prepare and rebond new layer in hot bitumen						
- fibre based bitumen felt type 1B	0.18	1.57	2.90	0.67	nr	5.14
- fibre based bitumen felt type 2B	0.18	1.57	4.05	0.84	nr	6.46
- fibre based mineral surfaced bitumen felt type 1E.	0.18	1.57	4.60	0.93	nr	7.10

NATURAL SLATING

Blue/grey slates size 405 x 255mm, 75mm lap, 50 x 25mm softwood battens, type 1F reinforcing underlay						
- sloping	1.35	11.76	29.57	6.20	m2	47.53
- vertical	1.45	12.63	29.57	6.33	m2	48.53
- mansard	1.45	12.63	29.57	6.33	m2	48.53
Extra for						
- double eaves course	0.50	4.36	4.51	1.33	m	10.20
- single verge undercloak course	0.72	6.27	3.16	1.42	m	10.85
- angled ridge or hip tiles	0.70	6.10	10.30	2.46	m	18.86

NATURAL SLATING (cont'd)	Labour hours	Nett labour £	Nett material £	O'heads /profit £	Unit	Total £
- mitred hips	0.70	6.10	-	0.92	m	7.02
- cutting	0.60	5.23	-	0.79	m	6.02
- hole for small pipes	0.40	3.48	-	0.52	nr	4.00
- fix only lead soakers	0.45	3.92	-	0.59	nr	4.51
Blue/grey slates size 510 x 255mm, 75mm lap, 50 x 25mm softwood battens, type 1F reinforced underlay						
- sloping	1.27	11.06	35.48	6.98	m2	53.52
- vertical	1.37	11.93	35.48	7.11	m2	54.52
- mansard	1.37	11.93	35.48	7.11	m2	54.52
Extra for						
- double eaves course	0.50	4.36	7.28	1.75	m	13.39
- single verge undercloak course	0.72	6.27	5.10	1.71	m	13.08
- angled ridge or hip tiles	0.70	6.10	10.30	2.46	m	18.86
- mitred hips	0.70	6.10	-	0.92	m	7.02
- cutting	0.60	5.23	-	0.79	m	6.02
- hole for small pipes	0.40	3.48	-	0.52	nr	4.00
- fix only lead soakers	0.45	3.92	-	0.59	nr	4.51
RECONSTRUCTED STONE SLATING						
Marley Monarch interlocking slate size 325 x 330mm, battens size 38 x 25mm, type 1F reinforcing underlay						
- 75mm lap; pitch 25-90 degrees	1.24	10.80	15.07	3.88	m2	29.75
- 100mm lap, pitch 25-90 degrees	1.26	10.98	16.32	4.10	m2	31.40
Extra for						
- nailing every tile with aluminium nails	0.09	0.78	0.10	0.13	m2	1.01
- verge, 150 mm wide natural slate undercloak	0.20	1.74	1.10	0.43	m	3.27
- dry verge system with white PVC interlocking units	0.20	1.74	5.20	1.04	m	7.98
- Modern ridge tiles	0.62	5.40	5.66	1.66	m	12.72
- Modern monoridge	0.62	5.40	8.43	2.08	m	15.91
- dry ridge system	0.50	4.36	3.49	1.18	m	9.03

RECONSTRUCTED STONE SLATING (cont'd)	Labour hours	Nett labour £	Nett material £	O'heads /profit £	Unit	Total £
- Modern hip tiles	0.62	5.40	5.66	1.66	m	12.72
- ventilated ridge terminal	0.60	5.23	24.67	4.49	nr	34.39
- gas vent terminal	0.60	5.23	36.75	6.30	nr	48.28
- soil vent terminal	0.60	5.23	23.10	4.25	nr	32.58
- cutting	0.20	1.74	-	0.26	m	2.00
- holes for pipes	0.35	3.05	-	0.46	nr	3.51

Asbestos-free slates

Asbestos-free cement slates size
600 x 600mm, lap 100mm, 38 x 35mm
treated softwood battens

- sloping	0.40	3.48	10.44	2.09	m2	16.01

Extra for

- double eaves course	0.40	3.48	3.52	1.05	m	8.05
- single verge undercloak course	0.30	2.61	1.82	0.67	m	5.10
- half round ridge or hip coverings	0.30	2.61	5.28	1.18	m	9.07
- cutting	0.60	5.23	-	0.79	m	6.02
- mitred hips	0.70	6.10	-	0.92	m	7.02
- hole for small pipes	0.40	3.48	-	0.52	nr	4.00
- fix only lead soakers	0.45	3.92	-	0.59	nr	4.51

CONCRETE ROOF TILING

Marley Plain granuled or smooth
finish tiles size 267 x 165mm,
65mm lap, 35 degrees pitch, type
1F reinforced underlay

- battens size 38 x 19mm

- gauge 100mm	1.73	15.07	15.18	4.54	m2	34.79
- gauge 95mm	1.75	15.24	16.04	4.69	m2	35.97
- gauge 90mm	1.78	15.50	16.90	4.86	m2	37.26

- battens size 38 x 25mm

- gauge 100mm	1.83	15.94	15.37	4.70	m2	36.01
- gauge 95mm	1.85	16.11	16.23	4.85	m2	37.19
- gauge 90mm	1.88	16.38	17.09	5.02	m2	38.49

CONCRETE ROOF TILING (cont'd)	Labour hours	Nett labour £	Nett material £	O'heads /profit £	Unit	Total £
Extra for						
- nailing every tile with aluminium nails	0.05	0.44	0.10	0.08	m2	0.62
- verge, tile and a half alternate courses	0.30	2.61	1.30	0.59	m	4.50
- verge, 150mm wide asbestos strip undercloak	0.20	1.74	0.86	0.39	m	2.99
- double course at eaves	0.35	3.05	1.50	0.68	m	5.23
- segmental ridge tile	0.42	3.66	5.38	1.36	m	10.40
- segmental monoridge tiles	0.62	5.40	8.43	2.08	m	15.91
- valley trough tiles	0.62	5.40	5.56	1.64	m	12.60
- segmental hip tiles	0.62	5.40	5.38	1.62	m	12.40
- bonnet hip tiles	0.80	6.97	5.56	1.88	m	14.41
- ventilated ridge terminal	0.60	5.23	24.67	4.49	nr	34.39
- gas vent terminal	0.60	5.23	36.75	6.30	nr	48.28
- soil vent terminal	0.60	5.23	23.10	4.25	nr	32.58
- cutting	0.20	1.74	-	0.26	m	2.00
- holes for pipes	0.35	3.05	-	0.46	nr	3.51
Marley Modern smooth finish tiles size 420 x 330mm, battens size 38 x 25mm, type 1F reinforcing underlay						
- 75mm lap, pitch 22½-44 degrees	0.86	7.49	7.60	2.26	m2	17.35
Extra for						
- nailing every tile with aluminium nails	0.09	0.78	0.10	0.13	m2	1.01
- verge, 150mm wide asbestos strip undercloak	0.20	1.74	0.86	0.39	m	2.99
- dry verge system with white PVC interlocking units	0.20	1.74	5.34	1.06	m	8.14
- Modern ridge tiles	0.62	5.40	5.66	6.66	m	12.72
- Modern monoridge	0.62	5.40	8.43	2.08	m	15.91
- dry ridge system	0.50	4.36	3.49	1.18	m	9.03
- Modern hip tiles	0.62	5.40	5.66	1.66	m	12.72
- ventilated ridge terminal	0.60	5.23	24.67	4.49	nr	34.39
- gas vent terminal	0.60	5.23	36.75	6.30	nr	48.28
- soil vent terminal	0.60	5.23	23.10	4.25	nr	35.58
- cutting	0.20	1.74	-	0.26	m	2.00
- holes for pipes	0.35	3.05	-	0.46	nr	3.51

CONCRETE ROOF TILING (cont'd)	Labour hours	Nett labour £	Nett material £	O'heads /profit £	Unit	Total £
Redland Renown granular faced or through coloured tiles size 418 x 330mm, 75mm lap, 343mm gauge, pitch 30-44 degrees, type 1F reinforcing underlay						
- battens size 38 x 22mm	0.75	6.53	6.43	1.94	m2	14.90
- battens size 38 x 25mm	0.78	6.79	6.48	1.99	m2	15.26
Extra for						
- nailing every tile with two aluminium nails	0.09	0.78	0.19	0.15	m2	1.12
- Redvent eaves ventilator	0.15	1.31	6.26	1.14	m	8.71
- cloaked verge tile	0.20	1.74	6.00	1.16	m	8.90
- half round ridge or hip tile	0.55	4.79	4.57	1.40	m	10.76
- third round ridge tile	0.55	4.79	4.57	1.40	m	10.76
- Redvent ridge terminal	0.70	6.10	28.19	5.14	nr	39.43
- gas flue ridge terminal	0.70	6.10	33.82	5.99	nr	45.91
- Dryvent ridge	0.75	6.53	8.40	2.24	m	17.17
- third round hip	0.55	4.79	4.57	1.40	m	10.76
- Universal valley trough	0.30	2.61	8.87	1.72	m	13.20
- cutting	0.20	1.74	-	0.26	m	2.00
- holes for pipes	0.35	3.05	-	0.46	nr	3.51
Redland Regent through coloured tiles size 418 x 332mm, 75mm lap, 343mm gauge pitch 22½-40 degrees, type 1F reinforcing underlay						
- battens size 38 x 22mm	0.72	6.27	7.10	2.01	m2	15.38
- battens size 38 x 25mm	0.74	6.45	7.15	2.04	m2	15.64
Extra for						
- nailing every tile with two aluminium nails	0.09	0.78	0.19	0.15	m2	1.12
- Redvent eaves ventilator	0.15	1.31	6.26	1.14	m	8.71
- cloaked verge tile	0.20	1.74	6.00	1.16	m	8.90
- half round ridge or hip tile	0.55	4.79	4.57	1.40	m	10.76
- Dryvent ridge	0.75	6.53	8.40	2.24	m	17.17
- Redvent ridge terminal	0.70	6.10	28.19	5.14	nr	39.43
- gas flue ridge terminal	0.70	6.10	33.82	5.99	nr	45.91

CONCRETE ROOF TILING (cont'd)	Labour hours	Nett labour £	Nett material £	O'heads /profit £	Unit	Total £
- third round hip tile	0.55	4.79	4.57	1.40	m	10.76
- third round hip and dentil						
slips 41mm wide	0.60	5.23	2.01	1.09	m	8.33
- Universal valley trough	0.30	2.61	8.87	1.72	m	13.20
- cutting	0.20	1.74	-	0.26	m	2.00
- holes for pipes	0.35	3.05	-	0.46	nr	3.51

WOODWOOL SLAB DECKING

'Woodcemair' unreinforced
wood wool slabs (type 5B)
in standard lengths, fixed
to timber joists, thickness
50mm, (type 500)

- 1800mm lengths	0.68	5.92	5.42	1.70	m2	13.04
- 2000mm lengths	0.68	5.92	5.42	1.70	m2	13.04
- 2400mm lengths	0.68	5.92	5.42	1.70	m2	13.04
- 2700mm lengths	0.68	5.92	5.54	1.72	m2	13.18
- 3000mm lengths	0.68	5.92	5.54	1.72	m2	13.18

'Woodcemair' unreinforced
wood wool slabs (type 5B)
in standard lengths, fixed
to timber joists, thickness
100mm, (type 1000)

- 3000mm lengths	0.86	7.49	10.04	2.63	m2	20.16
- 3300mm lengths	0.86	7.49	10.04	2.63	m2	20.16
- 3800mm lengths	0.86	7.49	10.04	2.63	m2	20.16

'Woodcelip' reinforced
wood wool slabs, in standard
lengths, fixed to timber joists,
thickness 75mm, (type 751)

- 1800mm lengths	0.98	8.54	17.97	3.98	m2	30.49
- 2000mm lengths	0.98	8.54	17.97	3.98	m2	30.49
- 2400mm lengths	0.98	8.54	17.97	3.98	m2	30.49
- 2700mm lengths	0.98	8.54	18.05	3.99	m2	30.58
- 3000mm lengths	0.98	8.54	18.05	3.99	m2	30.58

WOODWOOL SLAB DECKING (cont'd)	Labour hours	Nett labour £	Nett material £	O'heads /profit £	Unit	Total £
'Woodcelip' reinforced wood wool slabs, in standard lengths, fixed to timber joists, thickness 75mm, (type 753)						
- 2400mm lengths	0.98	8.54	18.21	4.01	m2	30.76
- 2700mm lengths	0.98	8.54	18.98	4.13	m2	31.65
- 3000mm lengths	0.98	8.54	18.98	4.13	m2	31.65
- 3300mm lengths	0.98	8.54	22.47	4.65	m2	35.66
- 3600mm lengths	0.98	8.54	22.47	4.65	m2	35.66
- 3900mm lengths	0.98	8.54	22.47	4.65	m2	35.66

Underfelt and battens

Treated softwood counter battens
nailed with galvanised nails to
softwood joists size

	Labour hours	Nett labour £	Nett material £	O'heads /profit £	Unit	Total £
- 38 x 19 mm						
450 mm centres	0.07	0.61	0.40	0.15	m2	1.16
600 mm centres	0.05	0.44	0.23	0.10	m2	0.77
750 mm centres	0.03	0.26	0.22	0.07	m2	0.55
- 38 x 25 mm						
450 mm centres	0.08	0.70	0.51	0.18	m2	1.39
600 mm centres	0.06	0.52	0.30	0.12	m2	0.94
750 mm centres	0.04	0.35	0.28	0.10	m2	0.73
Slaters type 1F reinforced underlay with 150mm laps secured with battens	0.03	0.26	1.17	0.22	m2	1.65

LEAD SHEET COVERINGS/ FLASHINGS	Labour hours	Nett labour £	Nett material £	O'heads /profit £	Unit	Total £
Code 5 lead 2.24mm thick, 25.4 kg/m2, colour coded red fixed with brass screws and copper nails						
Flat roof with falls not exceeding 10°	4.20	36.58	34.54	10.67	m2	81.79
Roof sloping over 10° but not exceeding 50°	4.40	38.32	34.54	10.93	m2	83.79
Roof sloping over 50°	4.60	40.07	34.54	11.19	m2	85.80
Dormers and the like	5.00	43.55	34.54	11.71	m2	89.80
Flashing						
- 150mm girth	0.45	3.92	5.18	1.37	m	10.47
- 200mm girth	0.60	5.23	6.90	1.82	m	13.95
- 300mm girth	0.85	7.40	10.36	2.66	m	20.42
Stepped flashing						
- 150mm girth	0.55	4.79	5.18	1.50	m	11.47
- 200mm girth	0.90	7.84	6.90	2.21	m	16.95
- 300mm girth	1.10	9.58	10.36	2.99	m	22.93
Apron						
- 200mm girth	0.60	5.23	6.90	1.82	m	13.95
- 300mm girth	0.90	7.84	10.36	2.73	m	20.93
- 400mm girth	1.20	10.45	13.82	3.64	m	27.91
Capping to ridge or hip						
- 200mm girth	0.60	5.23	6.90	1.82	m	13.95
- 300mm girth	0.90	7.84	10.36	2.73	m	20.93
- 400mm girth	1.20	10.45	13.82	3.64	m	27.91
Lining to valley or gutter						
- 400mm girth	1.20	10.45	13.82	3.64	m	27.91
- 600mm girth	1.40	12.19	20.72	4.94	m	37.85
- 800mm girth	1.60	13.94	27.63	6.24	m	47.81

LEAD SHEET COVERINGS/ FLASHINGS (cont'd)	Labour hours	Nett labour £	Nett material £	O'heads /profit £	Unit	Total £
Slate 400 x 400mm with collar						
200mm high around pipe						
- 100mm diameter	1.60	13.94	11.00	3.74	nr	28.68
- 150mm diameter	1.80	15.68	14.00	4.45	nr	34.13
Raking cutting	0.30	2.61	-	0.39	m	3.00
Curved cutting	0.40	3.48	-	0.52	m	4.00
Welted edge	0.35	3.05	-	0.46	m	3.51
Beaded edge	0.35	3.05	-	0.46	m	3.51
Welted seam	0.50	4.36	-	0.65	m	5.01
Wedging into groove with lead						
wedges	0.30	2.61	0.25	0.43	m	3.29
Leadburned angle	0.50	4.36	-	0.65	m	5.01
Leadburned seam	0.50	4.36	-	0.65	m	5.01
Dressing over						
- glass and glazing bars	0.35	3.05	-	0.46	m	3.51
- along corrugation of corrugated						
roofing	1.05	9.15	-	1.37	m	10.52
- across corrugations of						
corrugated roofing	0.95	8.28	-	1.24	m	9.52
- fillers 200mm girth	0.35	3.05	-	0.46	m	3.51
- hollows 200mm girth	0.35	3.05	-	0.46	m	3.51
- channels 200mm girth	0.35	3.05	-	0.46	m	3.51

CORRUGATED SHEET ROOFING

Standard sheeting

Corrugated reinforced cement
sheeting, lapped one corrugation
at sides and 150 mm at ends, fixed
with hook bolts and washers to steel
purlins

Profile 3 grey sheets	0.85	7.40	5.61	1.95	m2	14.96
Profile 3 coloured sheets	0.85	7.40	6.16	2.03	m2	15.59
Profile 6 grey sheets	0.80	6.97	5.63	1.89	m2	14.49
Profile 6 coloured sheets	0.80	6.97	6.20	1.98	m2	15.15

CORRUGATED SHEET ROOFING (cont'd)	Labour hours	Nett labour £	Nett material £	O'heads /profit £	Unit	Total £
Fittings to Profile 3 sheets						
- ridge fitting	0.35	3.05	6.51	1.43	nr	10.99
- eaves filler	0.20	1.74	3.99	0.86	m	6.59
- eaves closure 75 mm	0.20	1.74	3.99	0.86	m	6.59
- apron flashing	0.25	2.18	4.49	1.00	m	7.67
Fittings to Profile 6 sheets						
- ridge fitting	0.35	3.05	9.77	1.92	nr	14.74
- eaves filler	0.20	1.74	5.34	1.06	m	8.14
- eaves closure 100mm	0.20	1.74	5.34	1.06	m	8.14
- eaves bend sheet 1525 mm (300 mm radius)	0.35	3.05	18.71	3.26	nr	25.02
- apron flashing	0.25	2.18	5.50	1.15	m	8.83

BUILT UP ROOFING

Built up bituminous felt
roof coverings to areas over
300mm wide laid to falls and
crossfalls not exceeding 10
degrees from horizontal

	Labour hours	Nett labour £	Nett material £	O'heads /profit £	Unit	Total £
Fibre based granule surfaced felt type 1B weighing 14 kg/10m2						
- one layer	0.22	1.92	0.65	0.39	m2	2.96
Fibre based granule surfaced felt type 1B weighing 18 kg/10m2						
- one layer	0.23	2.00	0.83	0.42	m2	3.25
- two layers	0.30	2.61	1.66	0.64	m2	4.91
- three layers	0.45	3.92	2.49	0.96	m2	7.37
Fibre based granule surfaced felt type 1B weighing 25kg/10m2						
- one layer	0.24	2.09	1.17	0.49	m2	3.75
- two layers	0.32	2.79	2.34	0.77	m2	5.90
- three layers	0.47	4.09	3.51	1.14	m2	8.74
Fibre based granule surfaced felt type 1E weighing 38kg/10m2						
- one layer	0.26	2.26	1.50	0.56	m2	4.32

BUILT UP ROOFING (cont'd)	Labour hours	Nett labour £	Nett material £	O'heads /profit £	Unit	Total £
Fibre based reinforced felt type 1F weighing 15kg/10m2						
- one layer	0.25	2.18	1.53	0.56	m2	4.27
Asbestos based granule surfaced felt type 2B weighing 18kg/10m2						
- one layer	0.29	2.53	3.46	0.90	m2	6.89
- two layers	0.39	3.40	6.92	1.55	m2	11.87
- three layers	0.56	4.88	10.38	2.29	m2	17.55
Glass fibre based granule surfaced felt type 3B weighing 18kg/10m2						
- one layer	0.23	2.00	1.95	0.59	m2	4.54
- two layers	0.30	2.61	3.90	0.98	m2	7.49
- three layers	0.45	3.92	5.85	1.47	m2	11.24
Glass fibre based mineral surfaced felt type 3E weighing 28kg/10m2						
- one layer	0.26	2.27	1.41	0.55	m2	4.23
Glass fibre based venting layer felt type 3G weighing 26kg/10m2						
- one layer	0.28	2.44	1.64	0.61	m2	4.69
Built up bituminous felt roof coverings over 150 mm but not exceeding 300mm wide laid to falls and crossfalls not exceeding 10 degrees from horizontal						
Fibre based granule surfaced felt type 1B weighing 14kg/10m2						
- one layer	0.08	0.70	0.65	0.20	m	1.55
Fibre based granule surfaced felt type 1B weighing 18kg/10m2						
- one layer	0.08	0.70	0.83	0.23	m	1.76
- two layers	0.10	0.87	1.66	0.38	m	2.91
- three layers	0.16	1.39	2.49	0.58	m	4.46

BUILT UP ROOFING (cont'd)	Labour hours	Nett labour £	Nett material £	O'heads /profit £	Unit	Total £
Fibre based granule surfaced felt type 1B weighing 25kg/10m2						
- one layer	0.08	0.70	1.17	0.28	m	2.15
- two layers	0.11	0.96	2.34	0.50	m	3.80
- three layers	0.16	1.39	3.51	0.74	m	5.64
Fibre based mineral surfaced felt type 1E weighing 38kg/10m2						
- one layer	0.09	0.78	1.50	0.34	m	2.62
Fibre based reinforced felt type 1F weighing 15kg/10m2						
- one layer	0.09	0.78	1.53	0.35	m	2.66
Asbestos based granule surfaced felt type 2B weighing 18kg/10m2						
- one layer	0.10	0.87	3.46	0.65	m	4.98
- two layers	0.13	1.13	6.92	1.21	m	9.26
- three layers	0.19	1.66	10.38	1.81	m	13.85
Glass fibre based granule surfaced felt type 3B weighing 18kg/10m2						
- one layer	0.08	0.70	1.95	0.40	m	3.05
- two layers	0.10	0.87	3.90	0.72	m	5.49
- three layers	0.16	1.39	5.85	1.09	m	8.33
Glass fibre based mineral surfaced felt type 3E weighing 28kg/10m2						
- one layer	0.09	0.78	1.41	0.33	m	2.52
Glass fibre based venting layer felt type 3G weighing 26kg/10m2						
- one layer	0.10	0.87	1.64	0.38	m	2.89
Collars around pipes and the like; three layers; two layers granule surfaced; top layer mineral surfaced; 150mm high						
- small diameter	0.16	1.39	1.30	0.40	nr	3.09
- large diameter	0.23	2.00	1.75	0.56	nr	4.31
- extra large diameter	0.35	3.05	2.10	0.77	nr	5.92

BUILT UP ROOFING (cont'd)	Labour hours	Nett labour £	Nett material £	O'heads /profit £	Unit	Total £
Working covering into outlets, gulleys or the like						
- three layer felt	0.23	2.00	-	0.30	nr	2.30
Labours						
Raking cutting						
- one layer	0.09	0.78	-	0.12	m	0.90
- two layers	0.12	1.05	-	0.16	m	1.21
- three layer	0.17	1.48	-	0.22	m	1.70
Curved cutting						
- one layer	0.11	0.96	-	0.14	m	1.10
- two layers	0.14	1.22	-	0.18	m	1.40
- three layers	0.20	1.74	-	0.26	m	2.00
Sundries						
6mm thick layer of limestone or granite chippings	0.25	2.18	1.20	0.51	m2	3.89
13mm thick layer of pea gravel	0.32	2.79	1.40	0.63	m2	4.82

WOODWORK

1. Labour

Craftsman   £6.44 per hour
Labourer   £5.55 per hour

2. Materials

	Unit	Basic Price	Waste %	Total £
Sawn softwood untreated				
25 x 50mm	100m	29.25	5	30.71
25 x 75mm	100m	40.30	5	42.32
25 x 100mm	100m	52.65	5	55.28
25 x 150mm	100m	77.35	5	81.22
38 x 50mm	100m	40.00	5	42.00
38 x 75mm	100m	62.40	5	65.52
38 x 100mm	100m	77.35	5	81.22
38 x 150mm	100m	116.35	5	122.17
50 x 50mm	100m	49.40	5	51.87
50 x 75mm	100m	78.50	5	82.43
50 x 100mm	100m	91.00	5	95.55
50 x 125mm	100m	123.01	5	129.16
50 x 150mm	100m	137.15	5	144.01
50 x 175mm	100m	163.00	5	171.15
50 x 200mm	100m	185.25	5	194.51
75 x 75mm	100m	117.00	5	122.85
75 x 100mm	100m	138.00	5	144.90
75 x 125mm	100m	180.00	5	189.00
75 x 150mm	100m	219.05	5	230.00
Skirting				
19 x 75mm	100m	77.00	5	80.85
19 x 100mm	100m	97.00	5	101.85
25 x 150mm	100m	140.00	5	147.00
Butt jointed boarding, thickness				
19 x 75mm	100m	63.00	5	66.15
25 x 100mm	100m	69.00	5	72.45
Tongued and grooved boarding, thickness				
19 x 125mm	100m	78.00	5	81.90
25 x 150mm	100m	105.30	5	110.57
Chipboard, thickness				
12mm	m2	2.22	5	2.33
18mm	m2	2.89	5	3.04
25mm	m2	4.90	5	5.15

WOODWORK

	Unit	Basic Price	Waste %	Total £
Plywood exterior (WBP) thickness				
6mm	m2	4.40	5	4.62
9mm	m2	6.43	5	6.75
12mm	m2	8.07	5	8.47
15mm	m2	10.00	5	10.50
18mm	m2	11.92	5	12.52
25mm	m2	17.00	5	17.85
Plywood interior quality thickness				
15mm	m2	9.20	5	9.66
18mm	m2	11.00	5	11.55
Plywood marine grade thickness				
12mm	m2	7.26	5	7.62
15mm	m2	9.00	5	9.45
18mm	m2	10.72	5	11.26
25mm	m2	15.30	5	16.07

Wrought softwood

	Unit	Basic Price	Waste %	Total £
Architraves, skirtings, chamfered				
19 x 50mm	m	0.67	5	0.70
19 x 63mm	m	0.75	5	0.79
25 x 50mm	m	0.80	5	0.84
25 x 63mm	m	0.90	5	0.95
25 x 75mm	m	1.13	5	1.19
25 x 100mm	m	1.30	5	1.37
25 x 125mm	m	1.40	5	1.47
25 x 150mm	m	1.75	5	1.84
Rails, moulded				
19 x 50mm	m	0.67	5	0.70
19 x 75mm	m	0.70	5	0.74
19 x 100mm	m	0.75	5	0.79
25 x 50mm	m	0.80	5	0.84
25 x 75mm	m	1.13	5	1.19
25 x 100mm	m	1.30	5	1.37
Handrail, mopstick				
50 x 50mm	m	2.29	5	2.41
Glazing beads				
13 x 25mm	m	0.70	5	0.74
19 x 36mm	m	0.88	5	0.92
19 x 50mm	m	0.98	5	1.03

WOODWORK

	Unit	Basic Price	Waste %	Total £
Shelving worktops 19mm thick, width				
150mm	m	2.35	5	2.47
225mm	m	2.95	5	3.10
300mm	m	6.20	5	6.51
Shelving bearers				
19 x 50mm	m	0.55	5	0.58
25 x 50mm	m	0.60	5	0.63

Wrought hardwood

	Unit	Basic Price	Waste %	Total £
Architraves, skirtings, chamfered				
19 x 50mm	m	1.45	5	1.52
19 x 63mm	m	1.65	5	1.73
25 x 50mm	m	1.75	5	1.84
25 x 63mm	m	1.90	5	2.00
25 x 75mm	m	2.40	5	2.52
25 x 100mm	m	2.70	5	2.84
25 x 125mm	m	3.00	5	3.15
25 x 150mm	m	3.70	5	3.89
Rails, moulded				
19 x 50mm	m	1.45	5	1.52
19 x 75mm	m	1.55	5	1.63
19 x 100mm	m	1.65	5	1.73
25 x 50mm	m	1.90	5	2.00
25 x 75mm	m	2.40	5	2.52
25 x 100mm	m	2.70	5	2.84
Handrail, mopstick				
50 x 50mm	m	4.80	5	5.04
Glazing beads				
13 x 25mm	m	1.60	5	1.68
19 x 36mm	m	1.90	5	2.00
19 x 50mm	m	2.10	5	2.21
Shelving worktops 19mm thick, width				
150mm	m	5.00	5	5.25
225mm	m	6.20	5	6.51
300mm	m	9.80	5	10.29
Shelving bearers				
19 x 50mm	m	1.20	5	1.26
25 x 50mm	m	1.30	5	1.37

WOODWORK

	Unit	Basic Price	Waste %	Total £
Hardboard 3.2mm thick	m2	1.21	5	1.27
Hardboard 6.4mm thick	m2	2.30	5	2.42
Teak faced blockboard 18mm thick	m2	10.05	5	10.55
Chipboard 12mm thick	m2	2.16	5	2.27
Chipboard 15mm thick	m2	2.35	5	2.47
Plywood 4mm thick	m2	3.14	5	3.30
Plywood 6mm thick	m2	4.59	5	4.82
Plywood 9mm thick	m2	5.63	5	5.91
Plywood 12mm thick	m2	7.21	5	7.57
Melamine faced chipboard				
15mm thick	m2	2.84	5	2.98
Insulation board 12.7mm thick	m2	1.66	5	1.74
Insulation board 19mm thick	m2	2.71	5	2.85
Insulation board 25mm thick	m2	3.51	5	3.69

Doors

Standard flush door hardboard both sides

35mm thick size

686 x 1981mm	nr	10.35	1	10.45
762 x 1981mm	nr	10.47	1	10.58

40mm thick size

626 x 2040mm	nr	11.48	1	11.60
726 x 2040mm	nr	11.79	1	11.91
826 x 2040mm	nr	12.31	1	12.43

Standard flush door plywood faced both sides

35mm thick size

686 x 1981mm	nr	14.34	1	14.48
762 x 1981mm	nr	14.41	1	14.55

40mm thick size

626 x 2040mm	nr	14.91	1	15.06
726 x 2040mm	nr	15.15	1	15.30
826 x 2040mm	nr	15.74	1	15.90

Standard flush door sapele faced both sides

35mm thick size

686 x 1981mm	nr	18.46	1	18.64
762 x 1981mm	nr	18.51	1	18.70

WOODWORK

	Unit	Basic Price	Waste %	Total £
40mm thick size				
626 x 2040mm	nr	19.66	1	19.86
726 x 2040mm	nr	19.79	1	19.99
826 x 2040mm	nr	20.51	1	20.72

Standard flush door teak faced both sides

	Unit	Basic Price	Waste %	Total £
35mm thick size				
686 x 1981mm	nr	34.10	1	34.44
762 x 1981mm	nr	34.22	1	34.56
40mm thick size				
626 x 2040mm	nr	34.80	1	35.15
726 x 2040mm	nr	34.92	1	35.27
826 x 2040mm	nr	35.25	1	35.60

Standard flush door half hour fire check hardboard both sides

	Unit	Basic Price	Waste %	Total £
44mm thick size				
686 x 1981mm	nr	28.42	1	28.70
762 x 1981mm	nr	28.42	1	28.70
626 x 2040mm	nr	29.53	1	29.83
726 x 2040mm	nr	29.53	1	29.83
826 x 2040mm	nr	31.02	1	31.33

Standard flush door half hour fire check plywood faced both sides

	Unit	Basic Price	Waste %	Total £
44mm thick size				
686 x 1981mm	nr	27.41	1	27.68
762 x 1981mm	nr	27.41	1	27.68
626 x 2040mm	nr	24.64	1	24.89
726 x 2040mm	nr	28.16	1	28.44
826 x 2040mm	nr	29.59	1	29.89

Standard flush door half hour fire check sapele faced both sides

	Unit	Basic Price	Waste %	Total £
44mm thick size				
686 x 1981mm	nr	38.75	1	39.14
762 x 1981mm	nr	38.75	1	39.14
626 x 2040mm	nr	39.76	1	40.16
726 x 2040mm	nr	39.76	1	40.16
826 x 2040mm	nr	41.25	1	41.66

Framed ledged and braced door 44mm thick with 19mm matchboarding

	Unit	Basic Price	Waste %	Total £
686 x 1981mm	nr	34.74	1	35.09
762 x 1981mm	nr	36.81	1	37.18

WOODWORK

	Unit	Basic Price	Waste %	Total £
Framed ledged and braced door 44mm thick with 25mm matchboarding				
726 x 2040mm	nr	45.19	1	45.64
826 x 2040mm	nr	46.86	1	47.33
Door linings				
32 x 63mm	m	3.39	2½	3.48
32 x 100mm	m	4.41	2½	4.52
32 x 150mm	m	5.68	2½	5.82
50 x 75mm	m	4.80	2½	4.92
Door frames, rebated and rounded				
32 x 100mm	m	5.20	2½	5.33
50 x 75mm	m	4.39	2½	4.50
50 x 100mm	m	6.51	2½	6.67
50 x 125mm	m	7.74	2½	7.93
63 x 100mm	m	8.01	2½	8.21
Door frames, twice rebated and rounded				
32 x 100mm	m	7.58	2½	7.77
50 x 75mm	m	8.00	2½	8.20
50 x 100mm	m	8.76	2½	8.98
50 x 125mm	m	10.12	2½	10.37
63 x 100mm	m	10.25	2½	10.51
Door frame for door size 762 x 1981 with loose stops				
32 x 63 lining	nr	12.81	2½	13.13
32 x 100 lining	nr	15.93	2½	16.33
50 x 75 rebated frame	nr	18.00	2½	18.45
50 x 100 rebated frame	nr	22.51	2½	23.07
63 x 100 rebated frame	nr	27.00	2½	27.68
Door frame for door size 726 x 2040mm with loose stops				
32 x 100 lining	nr	17.01	2½	17.44
50 x 75 rebated frame	nr	18.00	2½	18.45
50 x 100 rebated frame	nr	22.51	2½	23.07
63 x 100 rebated frame	nr	27.00	2½	27.68

WOODWORK

	Unit	Basic Price	Waste %	Total £
Standard softwood windows, with 75 x 150 sills, ironmongery, without glazing bars, type				
N07V	nr	29.65	2½	30.39
N09V	nr	30.98	2½	31.76
N12V	nr	33.65	2½	34.49
107C	nr	35.56	2½	36.45
110C	nr	39.41	2½	40.40
112C	nr	41.36	2½	42.39
110T	nr	53.92	2½	55.27
113T	nr	57.76	2½	59.20
109V	nr	34.60	2½	35.47
112V	nr	36.97	2½	37.89
212DG	nr	33.21	2½	34.04
212W	nr	54.89	2½	56.26
210C	nr	51.83	2½	53.13
212T	nr	66.36	2½	68.02
212CV	nr	68.98	2½	70.71
310CVC	nr	96.43	2½	98.84
413CWC	nr	126.78	2½	129.95
Double hung sash window, spiral balances complete, without glazing bars type				
28S37N	nr	131.62	2½	134.91
28S47N	nr	139.65	2½	143.14
28S57N	nr	149.52	2½	153.26
35S37N	nr	139.65	2½	143.14
35S47N	nr	149.52	2½	153.26
35S57N	nr	156.57	2½	160.48
Double hung sash window, spiral balances complete, with glazing bars type				
GS328S37B	nr	146.07	2½	149.72
GS428S47B	nr	158.49	2½	162.45
GS528S57B	nr	171.15	2½	175.43
GW335S37B	nr	159.41	2½	163.40
GW435S47B	nr	175.43	2½	179.82
GW535S57B	nr	190.14	2½	194.89
Open tread staircase in one flight, 2600 height, consisting of 12 treads and 13 risers, width				
850mm	nr	230.46	-	230.46
910mm	nr	244.01	-	244.01

WOODWORK

	Unit	Basic Price	Waste %	Total £
Closed tread staircase in one flight, 2600 height, consisting of 14 treads and 15 risers, width				
850mm	nr	417.24	-	417.24
910mm	nr	433.14	-	433.14
Waterproof reinforced building paper				
reflective one side	m2	1.13	7½	1.22
reflective both sides	m2	1.63	7½	1.75
Glass fibre quilt 1200mm wide thickness				
80mm	m2	2.68	10	2.95
100mm	m2	3.25	10	3.58
Expanded polystyrene board, thickness				
12mm	m2	0.62	10	0.68
25mm	m2	1.28	10	1.41
50mm	m2	2.55	10	2.81

ALTERATION WORK Labour rate £5.55 per hour	Labour hours	Nett labour £	Nett material £	O'heads /profit £	Unit	Total £
Take down, cut out or demolish and load into skips						
Structural timbers						
- 50 x 100mm	0.10	0.56	-	0.08	m	0.64
- 50 x 150mm	0.11	0.61	-	0.09	m	0.70
- 75 x 100mm	0.14	0.78	-	0.12	m	0.90
- 75 x 150mm	0.17	0.94	-	0.14	m	1.08
- 100 x 150mm	0.20	1.11	-	0.17	m	1.28
- 100 x 200mm	0.22	1.22	-	0.18	m	1.40
Roof boarding	0.28	1.55	-	0.23	m2	1.78
Floor boarding	0.22	1.22	-	0.18	m2	1.40
Stud partition plastered both sides	0.85	4.72	-	0.71	m2	5.43
Skirting and grounds						
- 100mm high	0.07	0.39	-	0.06	m	0.45
- 150mm high	0.08	0.44	-	0.07	m	0.51
- 250mm high	0.10	0.56	-	0.08	m	0.64

ALTERATION WORK	Labour hours	Nett labour £	Nett material £	O'heads /profit £	Unit	Total £
Take down, cut out or demolish and load into skips contd.;						
Rails						
- 50mm high	0.05	0.28	-	0.04	m	0.32
- 75mm high	0.06	0.33	-	0.05	m	0.38
- 100mm high	0.07	0.39	-	0.06	m	0.45
Standard kitchen fittings						
- wall cupboards	0.25	1.39	-	0.21	nr	1.60
- floor units	0.20	1.11	-	0.17	nr	1.28
- sink units	0.25	1.39	-	0.21	nr	1.60
Staircase 900mm wide, single straight flight	3.70	20.54	-	3.08	nr	23.62
Landing	1.20	6.66	-	1.00	nr	7.66
Internal door, and lining	0.35	1.94	-	0.29	nr	2.23
External door and frame	0.45	2.50	-	0.38	nr	2.88
Casement window						
- 1200 x 900mm	0.50	2.78	-	0.42	nr	3.20
- 1800 x 900mm	0.55	3.05	-	0.46	nr	3.51
Sash window						
- 900 x 1500mm	0.75	4.16	-	0.62	nr	4.78
- 1200 x 1800mm	0.90	5.00	-	0.75	nr	5.75
Porch canopy	1.20	6.66	-	1.00	nr	7.66
Ironmongery						
- bolt	0.20	1.11	-	0.17	nr	1.28
- deadlock	0.30	1.67	-	0.25	nr	1.92
- mortice lock	0.40	2.22	-	0.33	nr	2.55
- mortice latch	0.40	2.22	-	0.33	nr	2.55
- cylinder lock	0.25	1.39	-	0.21	nr	1.60
- door closer	0.30	1.67	-	0.25	nr	1.92
- casement stay	0.15	0.83	-	0.13	nr	0.96
- casement fastener	0.15	0.83	-	0.13	nr	0.96
- toilet roll holder	0.15	0.83	-	0.13	nr	0.96
- shelf bracket	0.10	0.56	-	0.08	nr	0.64

ALTERATION WORK	Labour hours	Nett labour £	Nett material £	O'heads /profit £	Unit	Total £

Take down, cut out or demolish and load into skips contd.;

Labour rate £6.44

Cut out defective joists or
rafters and replace with new

- 50 x 75mm	0.35	2.25	0.82	0.46	m	3.53
- 50 x 100mm	0.48	3.09	0.96	0.61	m	4.66
- 50 x 150mm	0.55	3.54	1.44	0.75	m	5.73
- 75 x 100mm	0.60	3.86	1.45	0.80	m	6.11
- 75 x 150mm	0.82	5.28	2.30	1.14	m	8.72

Cut out defective 25mm thick
tongued and grooved boarding and

renew	1.38	8.89	7.32	2.43	m2	18.64

Cut out defective skirting and
fit new

- 75mm high	0.70	4.51	0.80	0.80	m	6.11
- 100mm high	0.88	5.67	1.02	1.00	m	7.69
- 150mm high	1.05	6.76	1.47	1.24	m	9.47

Ease and adjust, oil hardware and
ironmongery

- door	1.00	6.44	-	0.97	nr	7.41
- casement window	0.75	4.83	-	0.73	nr	5.56

Ease and adjust, oil hardware and
ironmongery renew cords to sash

window	2.00	12.88	1.90	2.22	nr	17.00

NEW WORK
Labour rate £5.90 per hour

CARCASSING

Sawn softwood, untreated

Floors

- 50 x 100mm	0.22	1.42	0.96	0.36	m	2.74
- 50 x 125mm	0.25	1.61	1.29	0.44	m	3.34
- 50 x 150mm	0.27	1.74	1.44	0.48	m	3.66

195

CARCASSING	Labour hours	Nett labour £	Nett material £	O'heads /profit £	Unit	Total £
Sawn softwood, untreated contd.;						
- 75 x 125mm	0.28	1.80	1.89	0.55	m	4.24
- 75 x 150mm	0.30	1.93	2.30	0.64	m	4.87
Partitions						
- 38 x 75mm	0.32	2.06	0.66	0.41	m	3.13
- 38 x 100mm	0.34	2.19	0.81	0.45	m	3.45
- 50 x 75mm	0.34	2.19	0.82	0.45	m	3.46
- 50 x 100mm	0.34	2.19	0.96	0.47	m	3.62
Flat roofs						
- 38 x 100mm	0.15	0.97	0.82	0.27	m	2.06
- 50 x 75mm	0.17	1.09	0.82	0.29	m	2.20
- 50 x 100mm	0.18	1.16	0.96	0.32	m	2.44
- 50 x 125mm	0.19	1.22	1.29	0.38	m	2.89
- 50 x 150mm	0.20	1.29	1.44	0.41	m	3.14
- 75 x 100mm	0.20	1.29	1.44	0.41	m	3.14
- 75 x 125mm	0.26	1.67	1.89	0.53	m	4.09
Pitched roofs						
- 38 x 100mm	0.22	1.42	0.82	0.34	m	2.58
- 50 x 75mm	0.24	1.55	0.82	0.36	m	2.73
- 50 x 100mm	0.25	1.61	0.96	0.39	m	2.96
- 50 x 125mm	0.26	1.67	1.29	0.44	m	3.40
- 50 x 150mm	0.27	1.74	1.44	0.48	m	3.66
- 75 x 100mm	0.27	1.74	1.44	0.48	m	3.66
- 75 x 125mm	0.38	2.45	1.89	0.65	m	4.99
- 75 x 150mm	0.45	2.90	2.30	0.78	m	5.98
Kerb, bearer						
- 25 x 75mm	0.12	0.77	0.42	0.18	m	1.37
- 25 x 100mm	0.16	1.03	0.55	0.24	m	1.82
- 25 x 150mm	0.19	1.22	0.81	0.31	m	2.34
- 38 x 75mm	0.15	0.97	0.66	0.25	m	1.88
- 38 x 100mm	0.20	1.29	0.82	0.32	m	2.43
- 50 x 50mm	0.14	0.90	0.52	0.21	m	1.63
- 50 x 75mm	0.20	1.29	0.82	0.32	m	2.43
- 50 x 100mm	0.26	1.67	0.96	0.40	m	3.03
- 75 x 75mm	0.28	1.80	1.23	0.46	m	3.49
- 75 x 100mm	0.34	2.19	1.44	0.55	m	4.18
- 75 x 125mm	0.42	2.71	2.30	0.75	m	5.76

CARCASSING	Labour hours	Nett labour £	Nett material £	O'heads /profit £	Unit	Total £
Sawn softwood, untreated contd.;						
Solid strutting						
- 38 x 100mm	0.45	2.90	0.82	0.56	m	4.28
- 50 x 100mm	0.50	3.22	0.96	0.63	m	4.81
- 50 x 125mm	0.50	3.22	1.29	0.68	m	5.19
- 50 x 150mm	0.50	3.22	1.44	0.70	m	5.36
Herringbone strutting 50 x 50mm						
to joists depth						
- 125mm	0.60	3.86	0.80	0.70	m	5.36
- 150mm	0.60	3.86	0.90	0.71	m	5.47
- 175mm	0.60	3.86	1.00	0.73	m	5.59
- 240mm	0.60	3.86	1.10	0.74	m	5.70
Trimming around rectangular						
openings, joists size						
- 50 x 100mm	1.50	9.66	-	1.45	m	11.11
- 50 x 125mm	1.65	10.63	-	1.60	m	12.23
- 50 x 150mm	1.80	11.59	-	1.74	m	13.33
- 75 x 125mm	2.12	13.65	-	2.05	m	15.70
- 75 x 150mm	2.35	15.13	-	2.27	m	17.40

All the above materials are
untreated. 12½% should be added
for cost of preservative treatment.

FIRST FIXINGS	Labour hours	Nett labour £	Nett material £	O'heads /profit £	Unit	Total £
Labour rate £6.44 per hour						
Flooring						
Butt jointed boarding to joists,						
size						
- 19 x 75mm	1.16	7.47	10.79	2.74	m2	21.00
- 25 x 150mm	1.10	7.08	9.79	2.53	m2	19.40
Tongued and grooved boarding to						
joists, size						
- 19 x 125mm	0.95	6.12	6.56	1.90	m2	14.58
- 25 x 150mm	0.82	5.28	7.32	1.89	m2	14.49

FIRST FIXINGS	Labour hours	Nett labour £	Nett material £	O'heads /profit £	Unit	Total £
Flooring contd.						
Chipboard boarding to floors and roofs, thickness						
- 18mm	0.44	2.83	3.03	0.88	m2	6.74
- 25mm	0.50	3.22	5.14	1.25	m2	9.61
Plywood marine grade to roofs, thickness						
- 12mm	0.42	2.71	8.47	1.68	m2	12.86
- 18mm	0.51	3.28	12.51	2.37	m2	18.16
- 25mm	0.58	3.74	17.85	3.24	m2	24.83
Gutters						
Plywood marine quality in gutters over 300mm wide, thickness						
- 12mm	1.30	8.37	8.47	2.53	m2	19.37
- 18mm	1.58	10.18	12.51	3.40	m2	26.09
- 25mm	1.80	11.59	17.85	4.42	m2	33.86
Plywood marine quality in gutters 150mm wide, thickness						
- 12mm	0.42	2.71	1.40	0.62	m	4.73
- 18mm	0.50	3.22	2.00	0.78	m	6.00
- 25mm	0.58	3.74	2.80	0.98	m	7.52
Plywood marine quality in gutters 300mm wide, thickness						
- 12mm	0.68	4.38	2.70	1.06	m	8.14
- 18mm	0.76	4.89	3.90	1.32	m	10.11
- 25mm	0.85	5.47	5.50	1.65	m	12.62
Softwood bearers, size						
- 25 x 50mm	0.09	0.58	0.63	0.18	m	1.39
- 38 x 50mm	0.11	0.71	0.70	0.21	m	1.62
- 50 x 50mm	0.12	0.77	0.82	0.24	m	1.83

FIRST FIXINGS	Labour hours	Nett labour £	Nett material £	O'heads /profit £	Unit	Total £
Plywood marine grade to eaves, verges, soffits, fascias; thickness						
12mm						
- over 300mm width	1.30	8.37	7.62	2.40	m2	18.39
- 150mm wide	0.42	2.71	1.20	0.59	m	4.50
- 225mm wide	0.53	3.41	1.90	0.80	m	6.11
15mm						
- over 300mm width	1.43	9.21	9.45	2.80	m2	21.46
- 150mm wide	0.47	3.03	1.50	0.68	m	5.21
- 225mm wide	0.58	3.74	2.20	0.89	m	6.83
18mm						
- over 300mm width	1.58	10.18	11.25	3.22	m2	24.65
- 150mm wide	0.50	3.22	1.80	0.75	m	5.77
- 225mm wide	0.59	3.80	2.60	0.96	m	7.36
25mm						
- over 300mm width	1.80	11.59	16.06	4.15	m2	31.80
- 150mm wide	0.58	3.74	2.50	0.94	m	7.18
- 225mm wide	0.68	4.38	3.80	1.23	m	9.41

SECOND FIXINGS
Labour rate £6.44 per hour

Wrought softwood

Architraves, skirtings chamfered						
- 19 x 50mm	0.14	0.90	0.70	0.24	m	1.84
- 19 x 63mm	0.14	0.90	0.79	0.25	m	1.94
- 25 x 50mm	0.15	0.97	0.84	0.27	m	2.08
- 25 x 63mm	0.15	0.97	0.84	0.27	m	2.08
- 25 x 75mm	0.15	0.97	1.18	0.32	m	2.47
- 25 x 100mm	0.17	1.10	1.36	0.37	m	2.83
- 25 x 125mm	0.18	1.16	1.47	0.40	m	3.03
- 25 x 150mm	0.18	1.16	1.83	0.45	m	3.44
Rails, moulded						
- 19 x 50mm	0.14	0.90	0.70	0.24	m	1.84
- 19 x 75mm	0.14	0.90	0.73	0.25	m	1.88
- 19 x 100mm	0.15	0.97	0.78	0.26	m	2.01
- 25 x 50mm	0.15	0.97	0.84	0.27	m	2.08

SECOND FIXINGS	Labour hours	Nett labour £	Nett material £	O'heads /profit £	Unit	Total £
Wrought softwood contd.;						
- 25 x 75mm	0.15	0.97	1.28	0.34	m	2.59
- 25 x 100mm	0.17	1.10	1.36	0.37	m	2.83
Handrail, mopstick						
- 50 x 50mm	0.15	0.97	2.40	0.51	m	3.88
Glazing beads						
- 13 x 25mm	0.10	0.64	0.73	0.21	m	1.58
- 19 x 36mm	0.10	0.64	0.92	0.23	m	1.79
- 19 x 50mm	0.10	0.64	1.02	0.25	m	1.91
Shelving worktops 19mm thick, width						
- 150mm	0.33	2.13	2.46	0.69	m	5.28
- 225mm	0.40	2.58	3.09	0.85	m	6.52
- 300mm	0.45	2.90	6.51	1.41	m	10.82
Shelving bearers						
- 19 x 50mm	0.15	0.97	1.26	0.33	m	2.51
- 25 x 50mm	0.16	1.03	1.36	0.36	m	2.75
Wrought hardwood						
Architraves, skirtings chamfered						
- 19 x 50mm	0.21	1.35	1.52	0.43	m	3.30
- 19 x 63mm	0.21	1.35	1.73	0.46	m	3.54
- 25 x 50mm	0.22	1.42	1.83	0.49	m	3.74
- 25 x 63mm	0.22	1.42	1.99	0.51	m	3.92
- 25 x 75mm	0.22	1.42	2.52	0.59	m	4.53
- 25 x 100mm	0.25	1.61	2.83	0.67	m	5.11
- 25 x 125mm	0.26	1.67	3.15	0.72	m	5.54
- 25 x 150mm	0.26	1.67	3.88	0.83	m	6.38
Rails, moulded						
- 19 x 50mm	0.21	1.35	1.52	0.43	m	3.30
- 19 x 75mm	0.21	1.35	1.62	0.45	m	3.42
- 19 x 100mm	0.22	1.42	1.73	0.47	m	3.62
- 25 x 50mm	0.22	1.42	1.99	0.51	m	3.92
- 25 x 75mm	0.22	1.42	2.52	0.59	m	4.53
- 25 x 100mm	0.25	1.61	2.83	0.67	m	5.11
Handrail, mopstick						
- 50 x 50mm	0.25	1.61	5.04	1.00	m	7.65

SECOND FIXINGS	Labour hours	Nett labour £	Nett material £	O'heads /profit £	Unit	Total £
Wrought softwood contd.;						
Glazing beads						
- 13 x 25mm	0.15	0.97	1.68	0.40	m	3.05
- 19 x 36mm	0.15	0.97	1.99	0.44	m	3.40
- 19 x 50mm	0.15	0.97	2.20	0.48	m	3.65
Shelving worktops 19mm thick, width						
- 150mm	0.47	3.03	5.25	1.24	m	9.52
- 225mm	0.55	3.54	6.51	1.51	m	11.56
- 300mm	0.60	3.86	10.29	2.12	m	16.27
Shelving bearers						
- 19 x 50mm	0.27	1.74	1.26	0.45	m	3.45
- 25 x 50mm	0.25	1.61	1.36	0.45	m	3.42
Sheet linings and casings						
Linings or casings over 300mm wide						
- hardboard 3.2mm thick	0.53	3.41	1.27	0.70	m2	5.38
- hardboard 6.4mm thick	0.55	3.54	2.41	0.89	m2	6.84
- teak faced blockboard 18mm thick	0.60	3.86	10.55	2.16	m2	16.57
- chipboard 12mm thick	0.43	2.77	2.26	0.76	m2	5.79
- chipboard 15mm thick	0.50	3.22	2.46	0.85	m2	6.53
- plywood 4mm thick	0.34	2.19	3.29	0.82	m2	6.30
- plywood 6mm thick	0.36	2.32	4.81	1.07	m2	8.20
- plywood 9mm thick	0.40	2.58	5.91	1.27	m2	9.76
- plywood 12mm thick	0.46	2.96	7.57	1.58	m2	12.11
- melamine faced chipboard 15mm thick	0.58	3.74	2.98	1.01	m2	7.73
- insulation board 12.7mm thick	0.36	2.32	1.74	0.61	m2	4.67
- insulation board 19mm thick	0.38	2.45	2.84	0.79	m2	6.08
- insulation board 25mm thick	0.40	2.58	3.68	0.94	m2	7.20
Linings or casings not exceeding 100mm wide						
- hardboard 3.2mm thick	0.18	1.16	0.25	0.21	m	1.62
- hardboard 6.4mm thick	0.18	1.16	0.48	0.25	m	1.89
- teak faced blockboard 18mm thick	0.20	1.29	2.11	0.51	m	3.91
- chipboard 12mm thick	0.16	1.03	0.45	0.22	m	1.70
- chipboard 15mm thick	0.18	1.16	0.49	0.25	m	1.90

SECOND FIXINGS	Labour hours	Nett labour £	Nett material £	O'heads /profit £	Unit	Total £
Sheet linings and casings contd.;						
- plywood 4mm thick	0.12	0.77	0.66	0.22	m	1.65
- plywood 6mm thick	0.13	0.84	0.96	0.27	m	2.07
- plywood 9mm thick	0.14	0.90	1.18	0.31	m	2.39
- plywood 12mm thick	0.16	1.03	1.51	0.38	m	2.92
- melamine faced chipboard 15mm thick	0.21	1.35	0.60	0.29	m	2.24
- insulation board 12.7mm thick	0.14	0.90	0.35	0.19	m	1.44
- insulation board 19mm thick	0.15	0.97	0.57	0.23	m	1.77
- insulation board 25mm thick	0.18	1.16	0.74	0.29	m	2.19
Linings or casings 100mm to 200mm wide						
- hardboard 3.2mm thick	0.21	1.35	0.38	0.26	m	1.99
- hardboard 6.4mm thick	0.21	1.35	0.72	0.31	m	2.38
- teak faced blockboard 18mm thick	0.24	1.55	3.17	0.71	m	5.43
- chipboard 12mm thick	0.19	1.22	0.68	0.29	m	2.19
- chipboard 15mm thick	0.21	1.35	0.74	0.31	m	2.40
- plywood 4mm thick	0.15	0.97	0.99	0.29	m	2.25
- plywood 6mm thick	0.16	1.03	1.44	0.37	m	2.84
- plywood 9mm thick	0.17	1.10	1.77	0.43	m	3.30
- plywood 12mm thick	0.19	1.22	2.27	0.52	m	4.01
- melamine faced chipboard 15mm thick	0.24	1.55	0.89	0.37	m	2.81
- insulation board 12.7mm thick	0.17	1.10	0.52	0.24	m	1.86
- insulation board 19mm thick	0.18	1.16	0.85	0.30	m	2.31
- insulation board 25mm thick	0.20	1.29	1.10	0.36	m	2.75
Linings or casings 200mm to 300mm wide						
- hardboard 3.2mm thick	0.25	1.61	0.60	0.33	m	2.54
- hardboard 6.4mm thick	0.25	1.61	1.20	0.42	m	3.23
- teak faced blockboard 18mm thick	0.30	1.93	5.25	1.08	m	8.26
- chipboard 12mm thick	0.24	1.55	1.15	0.41	m	3.11
- chipboard 15mm thick	0.25	1.61	1.25	0.43	m	3.29
- plywood 4mm thick	0.20	1.29	1.65	0.44	m	3.38
- plywood 6mm thick	0.21	1.35	2.40	0.56	m	4.31
- plywood 9mm thick	0.22	1.42	2.95	0.66	m	5.03
- plywood 12mm thick	0.24	1.55	3.80	0.80	m	6.15
- melamine faced chipboard 15mm thick	0.28	1.80	1.50	0.50	m	3.80
- insulation board 12.7mm thick	0.24	1.55	1.85	0.51	m	3.91

WOODWORK

SECOND FIXINGS	Labour hours	Nett labour £	Nett material £	O'heads /profit £	Unit	Total £
Sheet linings and casings contd.;						
- insulation board 19mm thick	0.22	1.42	1.40	0.42	m	3.24
- insulation board 25mm thick	0.24	1.55	1.80	0.50	m	3.85
Doors						
Standard flush door hardboard both sides, 35mm thick size						
- 686 x 1981mm	1.00	6.44	10.45	2.53	nr	19.42
- 762 x 1981mm	1.00	6.44	10.57	2.55	nr	19.56
Standard flush door hardboard both sides, 40mm thick size						
- 626 x 2040mm	1.20	7.73	11.59	2.90	nr	22.22
- 726 x 2040mm	1.20	7.73	11.90	2.95	nr	22.58
- 826 x 2040mm	1.20	7.73	12.43	3.02	nr	23.18
Standard flush door plywood faced both sides, 35mm thick size						
- 686 x 1981mm	1.00	6.44	14.48	3.14	nr	24.06
- 762 x 1981mm	1.00	6.44	14.55	3.15	nr	24.14
Standard flush door plywood faced both sides, 40mm thick size						
- 626 x 2040mm	1.20	7.73	15.05	3.42	nr	26.20
- 726 x 2040mm	1.20	7.73	15.30	3.46	nr	26.49
- 826 x 2040mm	1.20	7.73	15.89	3.54	nr	27.16
Standard flush door sapele faced both sides, 35mm thick size						
- 686 x 1981mm	1.00	6.44	18.64	3.76	nr	28.84
- 762 x 1981mm	1.00	6.44	18.69	3.77	nr	28.90
Standard flush door sapele faced both sides, 40mm thick size						
- 626 x 2040mm	1.20	7.73	19.85	4.14	nr	31.72
- 726 x 2040mm	1.20	7.73	19.98	4.16	nr	31.87
- 826 x 2040mm	1.20	7.73	20.71	4.27	nr	32.71
Standard flush door teak faced both sides, 35mm thick size						
- 686 x 1981mm	1.00	6.44	34.44	6.13	nr	47.01
- 762 x 1981mm	1.00	6.44	34.56	6.15	nr	47.15

SECOND FIXINGS	Labour hours	Nett labour £	Nett material £	O'heads /profit £	Unit	Total £
Doors contd.;						
Standard flush door teak faced both sides, 40mm thick size						
- 626 x 2040mm	1.20	7.73	35.14	6.43	nr	49.30
- 726 x 2040mm	1.20	7.73	35.26	6.45	nr	49.44
- 826 x 2040mm	1.20	7.73	35.60	6.50	nr	49.83
Standard flush door, half hour fire check hardboard both sides 44mm thick size						
- 686 x 1981mm	1.20	7.73	28.70	5.47	nr	41.90
- 762 x 1981mm	1.20	7.73	28.70	5.47	nr	41.90
- 626 x 2040mm	1.20	7.73	29.82	5.63	nr	43.18
- 726 x 2040mm	1.20	7.73	29.82	5.63	nr	43.18
- 826 x 2040mm	1.20	7.73	31.33	5.86	nr	44.92
Standard flush door, half hour fire check plywood faced both sides, 44mm thick size						
- 686 x 1981mm	1.20	7.73	27.68	5.31	nr	40.72
- 762 x 1981mm	1.20	7.73	27.68	5.31	nr	40.72
- 626 x 2040mm	1.20	7.73	24.88	4.89	nr	37.50
- 726 x 2040mm	1.20	7.73	28.44	5.43	nr	41.60
- 826 x 2040mm	1.20	7.73	29.88	5.64	nr	43.25
Standard flush door, half hour fire check sapele faced both sides, 44mm thick size						
- 686 x 1981mm	1.20	7.73	39.13	7.03	nr	53.89
- 762 x 1981mm	1.20	7.73	39.13	7.03	nr	53.89
- 626 x 2040mm	1.20	7.73	40.15	7.18	nr	55.06
- 726 x 2040mm	1.20	7.73	40.15	7.18	nr	55.06
- 826 x 2040mm	1.20	7.73	41.66	7.41	nr	56.80
Framed ledged and braced door 44mm thick with 19mm matchboarding						
- 686 x 1981mm	1.30	8.37	35.08	6.52	nr	49.97
- 762 x 1981mm	1.30	8.37	37.17	6.83	nr	52.37

SECOND FIXINGS	Labour hours	Nett labour £	Nett material £	O'heads /profit £	Unit	Total £
Doors contd.;						
Framed ledged and braced door						
44mm thick with 25mm						
matchboarding						
- 726 x 2040mm	1.30	8.37	45.64	8.10	nr	62.11
- 826 x 2040mm	1.30	8.37	47.32	8.35	nr	64.04
Door linings						
- 32 x 63mm	0.30	1.93	3.47	0.81	m	6.21
- 32 x 100mm	0.30	1.93	4.52	0.97	m	7.42
- 32 x 150mm	0.34	2.19	5.82	1.20	m	9.21
- 50 x 75mm	0.30	1.93	4.92	1.03	m	7.88
Door frames, rebated and rounded						
- 32 x 100mm	0.30	1.93	5.33	1.09	m	8.35
- 50 x 75mm	0.30	1.93	4.49	0.96	m	7.38
- 50 x 100mm	0.35	2.25	6.67	1.34	m	10.26
- 50 x 125mm	0.35	2.25	7.93	1.53	m	11.71
- 63 x 100mm	0.40	2.58	8.21	1.62	m	12.41
Door frames twice rebated and						
rounded						
- 32 x 100mm	0.30	1.93	7.76	1.45	m	11.14
- 50 x 75mm	0.30	1.93	8.20	1.52	m	11.65
- 50 x 100mm	0.35	2.25	8.97	1.68	m	12.90
- 50 x 125mm	0.35	2.25	10.37	1.89	m	14.51
- 63 x 100mm	0.40	2.58	10.50	1.96	m	15.04
Door frame for door size 762 x						
1981 with loose stops						
- 32 x 63 lining	0.75	4.83	13.13	2.69	nr	20.65
- 32 x 100 lining	0.75	4.83	16.32	3.17	nr	24.32
- 50 x 75 rebated frame	0.90	5.80	18.45	3.64	nr	27.89
- 50 x 100 rebated frame	1.10	7.08	23.07	4.52	nr	34.67
- 63 x 100 rebated frame	1.15	7.41	27.67	5.26	nr	40.34
Door frame for door size 726 x						
2040mm with loose stops						
- 32 x 100 lining	0.75	4.83	17.43	3.34	nr	25.60
- 50 x 75 rebated frame	0.90	5.80	18.45	3.64	nr	27.89
- 50 x 100 rebated frame	1.10	7.08	23.07	4.52	nr	34.67
- 63 x 100 rebated frame	1.15	7.41	27.67	5.26	nr	40.34

WOODWORK

SECOND FIXINGS	Labour hours	Nett labour £	Nett material £	O'heads /profit £	Unit	Total £
Windows						
Standard soft wood windows with 75 x 150 sills, ironmongery without glazing bars, type						
- N07V	0.75	4.83	30.39	5.28	nr	40.50
- N09V	1.00	6.44	31.75	5.73	nr	43.92
- N12V	1.25	8.05	34.49	6.38	nr	48.92
- 107C	0.75	4.83	36.54	6.21	nr	47.58
- 110C	1.00	6.44	40.39	7.03	nr	53.86
- 112C	1.25	8.05	42.39	7.57	nr	58.01
- 110T	0.75	4.83	55.26	9.01	nr	69.10
- 113T	1.00	6.44	59.20	9.85	nr	75.49
- 109V	1.25	8.05	35.46	6.53	nr	50.04
- 112V	0.75	4.83	37.89	6.41	nr	49.13
- 212DG	1.00	6.44	34.04	6.07	nr	46.55
- 212W	1.25	8.05	56.26	9.65	nr	73.96
- 210C	1.50	9.66	53.12	9.42	nr	72.20
- 212T	1.50	9.66	68.01	11.65	nr	89.32
- 212CV	1.75	11.27	70.06	12.20	nr	93.53
- 310CVC	1.75	11.27	98.84	16.52	nr	126.63
- 413CWC	1.75	11.27	129.94	21.18	nr	162.39
Double hung sash window, spiral balances complete, without glazing bars, type						
- 28S37N 825 x 1094mm	2.70	17.39	134.91	22.85	nr	175.15
- 28S47N 825 x 1394mm	2.80	18.03	143.14	24.18	nr	185.35
- 28S57N 825 x 1694mm	2.90	18.68	153.25	25.79	nr	197.72
- 35S37N 1051 x 1094mm	2.80	18.03	143.14	24.18	nr	185.35
- 35S47N 1051 x 1394mm	2.90	18.68	153.25	25.79	nr	197.72
- 35S57N 1051 x 1694mm	3.00	19.32	160.48	26.97	nr	206.77
Double hung sash window, spiral balances complete, with glazing bars, type						
- GS328S37B 825 x 1094mm	2.70	17.39	149.72	25.07	nr	192.18
- GS428S47B 825 x 1394mm	2.80	18.03	162.45	27.07	nr	207.55
- GS528S57B 825 x 1694mm	2.90	18.68	175.42	29.12	nr	223.22
- GW335S37B 1051 x 1094mm	2.80	18.03	163.47	27.23	nr	208.73
- GW435S47B 1051 x 1394mm	2.90	18.68	179.81	29.77	nr	228.26
- GW535S57B 1051 x 1694mm	3.00	19.32	194.89	32.13	nr	246.34

WOODWORK

SECOND FIXINGS	Labour hours	Nett labour £	Nett material £	O'heads /profit £	Unit	Total £
Standard staircases						
Staircase in one flight, 2600 height, consisting of 12 treads and 13 risers, width						
- 850mm	22.00	141.68	230.46	55.82	nr	427.96
- 910mm	22.00	141.68	244.01	57.85	nr	443.54
Staircase in one flight, 2900 height, consisting of 14 treads and 15 risers, width						
- 850mm	23.00	148.12	417.24	84.80	nr	650.16
- 910mm	23.00	148.12	433.14	87.19	nr	668.45
Kitchen Fittings						
Fittings vary widely in quality and price so fix only rates have been included below						
Fix only kitchen fittings						
Base units 600mm deep						
- 600mm long	0.50	3.22	-	0.48	nr	3.70
- 1000mm long	0.60	3.86	-	0.58	nr	4.44
- 1200mm long	0.70	4.51	-	0.68	nr	5.19
Sink base units 600mm deep						
- 600mm long	0.60	3.86	-	0.58	nr	4.44
- 1000mm long	0.70	4.51	-	0.68	nr	5.19
- 1200mm long	0.80	5.15	-	0.77	nr	5.92
Tall storage units 2100mm high, 600mm deep						
- 600mm long	0.90	5.80	-	0.87	nr	6.67
Walls units 300mm deep						
- 600mm long	1.20	7.73	-	1.16	nr	8.89
- 1000mm long	1.30	8.37	-	1.26	nr	9.63
- 1200mm long	1.40	9.02	-	1.35	nr	10.37

WOODWORK

SECOND FIXINGS	Labour hours	Nett labour £	Nett material £	O'heads /profit £	Unit	Total £
Sundries						
Extra over fixing timber at 1000mm centres for						
- steel screws	0.12	0.77	0.05	0.12	m	0.94
- sinking and pellating heads	0.20	1.29	0.05	0.20	m	1.54
- brass cups and screws	0.18	1.16	0.20	0.20	m	1.56
Plugging softwood at 500mm centres to						
- concrete	0.18	1.16	0.05	0.18	m	1.39
- brickwork	0.16	1.03	0.05	0.16	m	1.24
- blockwork	0.15	0.97	0.05	0.15	m	1.17
Softwood fixing stop built in size						
- 19 x 25 x 50mm	0.10	0.64	0.06	0.11	nr	0.81
- 25 x 50 x 50mm	0.10	0.64	0.07	0.11	nr	0.82
- 50 x 50 x 75mm	0.10	0.64	0.08	0.11	nr	0.83
Waterproof reinforced building paper						
- reflective one side	0.15	0.97	1.21	0.33	m2	2.51
- relective both sides	0.15	0.97	1.75	0.41	m2	3.13
Glass fibre quilt laid over ceiling joists, thickness						
- 80mm	0.15	0.97	2.94	0.59	m2	4.50
- 100mm	0.16	1.03	3.57	0.69	m2	5.29
Glass fibre quilt fixed vertically to softwood, thickness						
- 80mm	0.18	1.16	2.94	0.62	m2	4.72
- 100mm	0.19	1.22	3.57	0.72	m2	5.51
Expanded polystryrene board fixed with adhesive to walls, thickness						
- 12mm	0.60	3.86	0.68	0.68	m2	5.22
- 25mm	0.65	4.19	1.40	0.84	m2	6.43
- 50mm	0.70	4.51	2.80	1.10	m2	8.41

SECOND FIXINGS	Labour hours	Nett labour £	Nett material £	O'heads /profit £	Unit	Total £

Ironmongery

The material costs of ironmongery vary considerable due to wide variations in quality. The following rates are for fixing only.

Fix only to softwood

- casement stay and pin	0.35	2.25	-	0.34	nr	2.59
- casement fastener	0.25	1.61	-	0.24	nr	1.85
- hat and coat hook	0.10	0.64	-	0.10	nr	0.74
- shelf bracket	0.35	2.25	-	0.34	nr	2.59
- push plate	0.15	0.97	-	0.15	nr	1.12
- kicking plate	0.20	1.29	-	0.19	nr	1.48

Sliding door gear

- top track	0.30	1.93	-	0.29	m	2.22
- bottom channel	0.30	1.93	-	0.29	m	2.22
- close ends	0.25	1.61	-	0.24	nr	1.85
- open bracket	0.25	1.61	-	0.24	nr	1.85
- bottom guide	0.25	1.61	-	0.24	nr	1.85
- door stop	0.25	1.61	-	0.24	nr	1.85
- top runner	0.33	2.13	-	0.32	nr	2.45

Steel hinges

- light butts	0.30	1.93	-	0.29	pair	2.22
- medium butts	0.33	2.13	-	0.32	pair	2.45
- heavy butts	0.35	2.25	-	0.34	pair	2.59
- rising butts	0.40	2.58	-	0.39	pair	2.97

Tee band hinges

- 150 to 300mm	0.80	5.15	-	0.77	pair	5.92
- 350 to 600mm	1.30	8.37	-	1.26	pair	9.63

Barrel or tower bolts

- 100 to 300mm	0.55	3.54	-	0.53	nr	4.07
- 350 to 450mm	0.60	3.86	-	0.58	nr	4.44

Helical door spring	0.75	4.83	-	0.73	nr	5.56

Overhead door spring

- medium	1.00	6.44	-	0.97	nr	7.41
- heavy	1.10	7.08	-	1.06	nr	8.14

SECOND FIXINGS	Labour hours	Nett labour £	Nett material £	O'heads /profit £	Unit	Total £
Ironmongery contd.;						
Door spring						
- single action	1.75	11.27	-	1.69	nr	12.96
- double action	2.00	12.88	-	1.93	nr	14.81
Sundries						
Postal knocker and letter plate	1.00	6.44	-	0.97	nr	7.41
Pull handles	0.25	1.61	-	0.24	nr	1.85
Flush pull handles	0.40	2.58	-	0.39	nr	2.97
Suffolk/Norfolk latch	0.70	4.51	-	0.68	nr	5.19
Hasp and staple	0.25	1.61	-	0.24	nr	1.85
Flush						
- 100 to 300mm	1.20	7.73	-	1.16	nr	8.89
- 300 to 450mm	1.80	11.59	-	1.74	nr	13.33
Indicating belt	0.60	3.86	-	0.58	nr	4.44
Panic bolt						
- single door	2.20	14.17	-	2.13	nr	16.30
- double door	3.40	21.90	-	3.29	nr	25.19
Locks and latches						
- cylinder rim night latch	1.00	6.44	-	0.97	nr	7.41
- cylinder mortice night latch	1.25	8.05	-	1.21	nr	9.26
- rim dead lock	0.75	4.83	-	0.73	nr	5.56
- mortice dead lock	1.00	6.44	-	0.97	nr	7.41
- rebated mortice lock	1.20	7.73	-	1.16	nr	8.89
- mortice latch	0.80	5.15	-	0.77	nr	5.92
- mortice sliding door lock	0.90	5.80	-	0.87	nr	6.67
- mortice latch furniture	0.30	1.93	-	0.29	nr	2.22
- cupboard catch	0.30	1.93	-	0.29	nr	2.22

STRUCTURAL STEELWORK

1. Labour

       Craftsman   £6.44 per hour
       Labour   £5.55 per hour

2. Materials

	Unit	Basic Price	Waste %	Total £
Rolled steel joists size				
102 x 76mm	t	490.00	2½	502.25
127 x 76mm	t	490.00	2½	502.25
127 x 114mm	t	490.00	2½	502.25
152 x 89mm	t	490.00	2½	502.25
152 x 127mm	t	490.00	2½	502.25
Universal columns				
152 x 152mm	t	515.00	2½	527.87
203 x 203mm	t	515.00	2½	527.87
254 x 254mm	t	515.00	2½	527.87
Angles				
200 x 150mm	t	510.00	2½	522.75
150 x 90mm	t	510.00	2½	522.75
125 x 75mm	t	510.00	2½	522.75
100 x 65mm	t	510.00	2½	522.75
75 x 50mm	t	510.00	2½	522.75

ALTERATION WORK Labour rate £5.55 per hour	Labour hours	Nett labour £	Nett material £	O'heads /profit £	Unit	Total £

The involvement of a Contractor carrying out small works will probably be limited to rolled steel joists in openings and columns. The following rates are typical for this kind of work but special attention should be paid to the cost of materials which can vary widely

Remove the following (No allowance made for credits)

Beams, lintels, columns or stancheons size						
- 127 x 76mm	0.50	2.77	-	0.42	m	3.19
- 152 x 76mm	0.75	4.16	-	0.62	m	4.78
- 152 x 152mm	1.00	5.55	-	0.83	m	6.38
- 203 x 142mm	1.30	7.21	-	1.08	m	8.29

STRUCTURAL STEELWORK

ALTERATION WORK	Labour hours	Nett labour £	Nett material £	O'heads /profit £	Unit	Total £
Beams, lintels, columns or stancheons size (cont'd)						
- 203 x 203mm	1.80	9.99	-	1.50	m	11.49
- 254 x 114mm	1.75	9.71	-	1.46	m	11.17
- 254 x 146mm	2.00	11.10	-	1.67	m	12.77
- 305 x 165mm	3.50	19.42	-	2.91	m	22.33
Disconnecting ends of adjacent members	1.50	8.32	-	1.25	nr	9.57

NEW WORK
Labour rate £6.44 per hour

Steel to B.S.4360 Grade 43

	Labour hours	Nett labour £	Nett material £	O'heads /profit £	Unit	Total £
Rolled steel joists fixed 2 to 3m above ground level						
- 127 x 76mm	0.90	5.80	8.22	2.10	m	16.12
- 127 x 114mm	1.15	7.41	14.94	3.35	m	25.70
- 152 x 89mm	1.05	6.76	8.58	2.30	m	17.64
- 152 x 127mm	1.25	8.05	18.68	4.00	m	30.73
Universal columns						
- 152 x 152mm	1.30	8.37	19.53	4.18	m	32.08
- 203 x 203mm	1.75	11.27	45.39	8.49	m	65.15
- 254 x 254mm	2.50	16.10	88.10	15.63	m	119.83
Angles fixing up to 3m high above ground level						
- 200 x 150mm	1.35	8.69	30.31	5.85	m	44.85
- 150 x 90mm	0.95	6.12	14.63	3.11	m	23.86
- 125 x 75mm	0.48	3.09	10.97	2.10	m	16.16
- 100 x 65mm	0.35	2.25	6.97	1.38	m	10.60
- 75 x 50mm	0.28	1.80	5.22	1.05	m	8.07

METALWORK

1. Labour

Craftsman	£6.44 per hour	
Labourer	£5.55 per hour	

2. Materials

	Unit	Basic Price	Waste %	Total £
Flat section steel arch bars				
25 x 10mm	m	1.37	5	1.43
50 x 10mm	m	2.61	5	3.05
65 x 10mm	m	3.57	5	3.74
100 x 10mm	m	4.15	5	4.35
Angle section steel arch bar				
50 x 50 x 6mm	m	2.86	5	3.00
100 x 100 x 8mm	m	6.21	5	6.52
150 x 150 x 10mm	m	12.00	5	12.60
100 x 75 x 8mm	m	5.67	5	5.95
Standard galvanised steel lintels for 100mm thick walls, 143mm high				
900mm long	nr	13.64	-	13.64
1500mm long	nr	22.71	-	22.71
2100mm long	nr	31.82	-	31.85
Standard galvanised steel lintels for 256mm thick walls, 143mm high				
900mm long	nr	17.03	-	17.03
1500mm long	nr	29.40	-	29.40
2100mm long	nr	41.98	-	41.98
Standard galvanised steel lintels for 256mm thick walls, 219mm high				
2700mm long	nr	69.50	-	69.50
4200mm long	nr	149.54	-	149.54
Crittalls Duralife Homelight standard galvanised steel windows, type				
NC5	nr	10.76	-	10.76
ND5	nr	12.29	-	12.29
NE13	nr	14.20	-	14.20
NC13	nr	16.63	-	16.63
NE14	nr	25.50	-	25.50
NC14	nr	22.50	-	22.50
ND14	nr	25.50	-	25.50
NC6F	nr	21.79	-	21.79
NC5F	nr	24.96	-	24.96
ND5F	nr	26.54	-	26.54
NC07	nr	64.00	-	64.00
ND2	nr	47.50	-	47.50
ND4	nr	79.80	-	79.80
ND11F	nr	92.00	-	92.00

ALTERATION WORK Labour rate £5.55 per hour	Labour hours	Nett labour £	Nett material £	O'heads /profit £	Unit	Total £
Remove the following						
Metal windows size						
- 600 x 450mm	0.95	5.27	-	0.79	nr	6.06
- 900 x 600mm	1.30	7.21	-	1.08	nr	8.29
- 1500 x 900mm	2.40	13.32	-	2.00	nr	15.32
Metal partition	0.90	4.99	-	0.75	m2	21.06
Tubular handrailing and balustrade	0.30	1.66	-	0.25	m	1.90
Standard metal single garage door complete	3.00	16.65	-	2.50	nr	21.63
NEW WORK						
Bars and Lintels Labour rate £6.44 per hour						
Flat section steel arch bars						
- 25 x 10mm	0.15	0.97	1.43	0.36	m	2.76
- 50 x 10mm	0.18	1.16	3.05	0.63	m	4.84
- 65 x 10mm	0.22	1.42	3.74	0.77	m	5.93
- 100 x 10mm	0.25	1.61	4.35	0.89	m	6.85
Angle section steel arch bars						
- 50 x 50 x 8mm	0.25	1.61	3.00	0.69	m	5.30
- 100 x 100 x 8mm	0.45	2.90	6.52	1.41	m	10.83
- 150 x 150 x 10mm	0.80	5.15	12.60	2.66	m	20.41
- 100 x 75 x 8mm	0.60	3.86	5.95	1.47	m	11.28
Standard galvanised steel lintels to 100mm thick wall, 143mm high						
- 900mm long	0.15	0.97	13.64	2.19	nr	16.80
- 1500mm long	0.20	1.29	22.71	3.60	nr	27.60
- 2100mm long	0.25	1.61	31.85	5.01	nr	38.47
Standard galvanised steel lintels to 256mm thick walls, 143mm high						
- 900mm long	0.20	1.29	17.03	2.74	nr	21.06
- 1500mm long	0.25	1.61	29.40	4.65	nr	35.66
- 2100mm long	0.30	1.93	41.98	6.58	nr	50.49

METALWORK

NEW WORK Labour rate £6.44 per hour	Labour hours	Nett labour £	Nett material £	O'heads /profit £	Unit	Total £
Standard galvanised steel lintels to 256mm thick walls, 219mm high						
- 2700mm long	0.75	4.83	69.50	11.14	nr	85.47
- 4200mm long	1.00	6.44	149.54	23.39	nr	179.37
Crittalls Duralife Homelight standard galvanised steel windows, type						
- NC5	0.75	4.83	10.76	2.33	nr	17.92
- ND5	1.25	8.05	12.29	3.05	nr	23.39
- NE13	1.00	6.44	14.20	3.09	nr	23.73
- NC13	1.00	6.44	16.63	3.46	nr	26.53
- NE14	1.40	9.02	25.50	5.17	nr	39.69
- NC14	1.50	9.66	22.50	4.82	nr	36.98
- ND14	1.70	10.95	25.50	5.46	nr	41.91
- NC6F	0.75	4.83	21.79	3.99	nr	30.61
- NC5F	1.00	6.44	24.96	4.71	nr	36.11
- ND5F	1.25	8.05	26.54	5.18	nr	39.77
- NC07	1.00	6.44	64.00	10.56	nr	81.00
- ND2	1.00	6.44	47.50	8.09	nr	62.03
- ND4	1.25	8.05	79.80	13.17	nr	101.02
- ND11F	2.50	16.10	92.00	16.21	nr	124.31

1. Labour rates- the labour rate
    is calculated on an average
    between an advanced and a
    technical plumber:-
    Advanced plumber   £6.12
    Technical plumber   £6.93
    $$\underline{£13.05}$$
    $$\underline{£\ 6.53}$$

2. Materials
    The basic price of the
    materials in this section
    appear in each individual item
    description after the letters
    'BP'. This is the purchase
    cost, nett of any discounts
    which the Contractor could
    expect to pay across the
    counter. The basic price
    includes for all the principal
    components relevant to the
    item involved e.g. clips,
    brackets and connectors, but
    not for sundry items such as
    flux, solder, screws etc. The
    amount in the material column
    is based upon the basic price
    plus an allowance for waste
    and the sundry items as
    mentioned above. The waste
    factors included for the
    various items are as follows:-

Pipework	5%
Gutterwork	5%
Pipe and gutter fittings	5%
Stopcocks, valves	2½%
Boilers	0%
Tanks, cylinders	2½%
Radiators	1%
Insulation	2½%
Immersion heaters	2½%
Ball valves	2½%
Time switches, programmers	2½%
Pumps	2½%
Sanitary fittings	2½%
Traps	2½%
Showers-valves etc.	2½%
Showers-enclosures, etc	0%

PLUMBING WORK

ALTERATIONS	Plumber hours	Nett plumber £	Nett material £	O'heads /profit £	Unit	Total £
Remove 6ft length of existing gutter; prepare ends and install new length of gutter to existing brackets						
Cast iron; half round						
- 100mm; BP £7.75	2.00	13.06	8.63	3.25	nr	24.94
- 115mm; BP £8.07	2.10	13.71	8.96	3.40	nr	26.07
- 125mm; BP £9.44	2.15	14.04	10.39	3.67	nr	28.10
Remove existing gutter fittings; prepare ends and install new fittings						
Cast iron; half round; 115mm						
- angle; BP £3.32	1.00	6.53	3.92	1.57	nr	12.02
- outlet; BP £3.32	1.00	6.53	3.92	1.57	nr	12.02
- stop end; BP £1.44	0.50	3.27	1.99	0.79	nr	6.05
Remove existing brackets from gutters and replace with galvanised steel repair brackets at 1m maximum centres						
Cast iron; half round						
- 100mm; BP £0.57	0.25	1.63	0.65	0.34	nr	2.62
- 112mm; BP £0.58	0.27	1.76	0.66	0.36	nr	2.78
- 125mm; BP £0.72	0.30	1.96	0.80	0.41	nr	3.17
Remove 6ft length of existing pipe; replace with new						
Cast iron						
- 63mm; BP £14.25	1.80	11.75	15.02	4.02	nr	30.79
- 75mm; BP £14.25	1.90	12.41	15.02	4.12	nr	31.55
- 100mm; BP £19.48	2.05	13.39	20.20	5.04	nr	38.63

217

ALTERATIONS	Plumber hours	Nett plumber £	Nett material £	O'heads /profit £	Unit	Total £
Remove existing pipe fittings; replace with new						
Cast iron shoes						
- 63mm; BP £7.36	0.66	4.31	7.52	1.78	nr	13.61
- 75mm; BP £7.36	0.80	5.22	7.52	1.91	nr	14.65
- 100mm; BP £9.52	0.90	5.88	9.80	2.35	nr	18.03
Cast iron bends						
- 63mm; BP £4.36	0.75	4.90	4.46	1.40	nr	10.76
- 75mm; BP £4.36	0.95	6.20	4.46	1.60	nr	12.26
- 100mm; BP £6.77	1.00	6.53	6.93	2.02	nr	15.48
Cut out 500mm length of pipe; install new length of pipe with new brass compression connections to existing ends						
Copper						
- 15mm; BP £1.51	0.67	4.38	1.68	0.91	nr	6.97
- 22mm; BP £2.64	0.69	4.51	2.91	1.11	nr	8.53
- 28mm; BP £4.68	0.83	5.42	5.17	1.59	nr	12.18
- 35mm; BP £8.95	0.96	6.27	9.87	2.42	nr	18.56
- 42mm; BP £11.50	1.01	6.60	12.69	2.89	nr	22.18
- 54mm; BP £16.76	1.12	7.31	18.51	3.87	nr	29.69
Take off existing radiator valve; replace with new; drain down system prior to removal and bleed after installation						
Single valves						
- standard type; BP £2.77	1.50	9.80	2.83	1.90	nr	14.53
- thermostatic type; BP £10.19	1.50	9.80	10.43	3.04	nr	23.27
Complete systems; 9nr valves						
- standard type; BP £24.96	4.60	30.04	25.50	8.33	nr	63.87
- thermostatic type; BP £91.72	4.60	30.04	93.88	18.59	nr	142.51

PLUMBING WORK

ALTERATIONS	Plumber hours	Nett plumber £	Nett material £	O'heads /profit £	Unit	Total £
Take out existing galvanised steel water storage tank; install new plastic tank complete with ball valve, lid and insulation; allow for cutting holes, tank connectors, make-up pipework and connectors to existing pipework						
- 15 gallon tank; BP £27.55	4.00	26.12	28.22	8.15	nr	62.49
- 25 gallon tank; BP £34.05	4.50	29.39	34.88	9.64	nr	73.91
- 40 gallon tank; BP £52.90	5.50	35.92	54.19	13.52	nr	103.63
Take off and relocate existing radiator; drain down system prior to removal and bleed after installation; allow for new surface mounted pipework and removing and refixing existing brackets; compression connections to existing pipework						
Distance of relocation						
- not exceeding 2m; BP £4.69	2.50	16.33	4.82	3.17	nr	24.32
- 2-3m; BP £6.58	2.75	17.96	6.77	3.71	nr	28.44
- 3-4m; BP £8.49	3.00	19.59	8.73	4.25	nr	32.57
- 4-5m; BP £10.36	3.25	21.22	10.66	4.78	nr	36.66

SANITARY FITTINGS

	Plumber hours	Nett plumber £	Nett material £	O'heads /profit £	Unit	Total £
Take out existing fitting complete including trap; cut back pipework as necessary and prepare to receive new; install new fitting complete with trap pair of pillar taps, waste and plug; make-up pipework as necessary and connections to hot and cold water and waste pipework						
New bath size 1700 x 790mm; BP £121.80	8.00	52.24	121.80	26.11	nr	200.15

PLUMBING WORK

ALTERATIONS	Plumber hours	Nett plumber £	Nett material £	O'heads /profit £	Unit	Total £
New wash basin size 580 x 470mm; BP £70.55	3.75	24.49	74.08	14.79	nr	113.36

Take out existing high level W.C. and connecting pipework including overflow; cut off spigot of cast iron soil pipe; install new low level W.C. suite complete including new overflow through backwall; quickfit connector to soil pipe and connection to cold water supply

New W.C. suite size 780 x 510 x 710mm; BP £129.19	4.50	29.39	132.16	24.23	nr	185.78

RAINWATER INSTALLATION

uPVC; Terrain 2100 half round system; joint bracket joints; to timber with support brackets at 1m maximum centres

110mm; BP £6.97/4m	0.26	1.70	1.84	0.53	m	4.07
Fittings and connections						
- running outlet ref 2153.4.25; BP £1.30	0.26	1.70	1.33	0.46	nr	3.49
- short stop end ref 2155.4; BP £0.64	0.14	0.91	0.66	0.24	nr	1.81
- 90° angle ref 2154.4.90; BP £1.30	0.26	1.70	1.33	0.46	nr	3.49
- adaptors to cast iron half round; uPVC ref 2158.4.45 & 2159.4.45; BP £1.92	0.28	1.83	1.97	0.57	nr	4.37
- gutter outlet guard ref 9915.25; BP £0.53	0.12	0.78	0.56	0.20	nr	1.54

RAINWATER INSTALLATION	Plumber hours	Nett plumber £	Nett material £	O'heads /profit £	Unit	Total £
uPVC; Terrain 2200 square system; joint bracket joints; to timber with support brackets at 1m maximum centres						
120mm; BP £7.29/4m	0.26	1.70	1.92	0.54	m	4.16
Fittings and connections						
- running outlet ref 2253.5.23; BP £1.41	0.26	1.70	1.44	0.47	nr	3.61
- short stop end ref 2255.5; BP £0.70	0.14	0.91	0.72	0.25	nr	1.88
- 90° angle ref 2254.5.90; BP £1.30	0.26	1.70	1.33	0.46	nr	3.49
- adaptors to cast iron ogee ref 2258.5.45 & 2259.5.45; BP £7.05	0.28	1.83	7.22	1.36	nr	10.41
- gutter outlet guard ref 9915.25; BP £0.55	0.12	0.78	0.56	0.20	nr	1.54
uPVC; Osma Roundline system; joint bracket joints; to timber with support brackets at 1m maximum centres						
112mm; BP £4.81/4m	0.26	1.70	1.27	0.45	m	3.42
Fittings and connections						
- running outlet ref OT.624; BP £1.30	0.26	1.70	1.33	0.46	nr	3.49
- internal stop end ref OT.010; BP £0.34	0.14	0.91	0.35	0.19	nr	1.45
- external stop end ref OT.011; BP £0.54	0.14	0.91	0.55	0.22	nr	1.68
- 90° angle ref OT.003; BP £1.26	0.26	1.70	1.29	0.45	nr	3.44
- adaptor to cast iron half round ref OT.008; BP £1.12	0.28	1.83	1.15	0.45	nr	3.43

RAINWATER INSTALLATION	Plumber hours	Nett plumber £	Nett material £	O'heads /profit £	Unit	Total £
uPVC; Osma Squareline system; joint bracket joints; to timber with support brackets at 1m maximum centres						
100mm; BP £5.18/4m	0.26	1.70	1.39	0.46	m	3.55
Fittings and connections						
- running outlet ref 4T.806; BP £1.41	0.26	1.70	1.44	0.47	nr	3.61
- internal stop end ref 4T.810; BP £0.43	0.14	0.91	0.44	0.20	nr	1.55
- 90° angle ref 4T.803; BP £1.32	0.26	1.70	1.35	0.46	nr	3.51
- adaptors to cast iron ogee ref 4T.814 & 4T.815; BP £1.76	0.28	1.83	1.80	0.55	nr	4.18
Cast iron half round; Drainage Castings Ltd.; mastic joints; ready primed; to timber with brackets at 1m maximum centres						
100mm; BP £9.07/1.8m	0.35	2.29	5.36	1.15	m	8.80
Fittings and connections						
- running outlet ref DC2005; BP £2.94	0.35	2.29	3.16	0.82	nr	6.27
- stop end outlets ref DC2006 & DC2007; BP £2.10	0.20	1.31	2.30	0.54	nr	4.15
- stop ends ref DC2008 & DC2009; BP £0.97	0.18	1.18	1.14	0.35	nr	2.67
- angles 90° and 135° ref DC2001 - 2004 inc.; BP £2.94	0.35	2.29	3.16	0.82	nr	6.27
125mm; BP £10.77/1.8m	0.40	2.61	6.35	1.34	m	10.30
Fittings and connections						
- running outlet ref DC2005; BP £3.83	0.40	2.61	4.07	1.00	nr	7.68
- stop end outlets ref DC2006 & DC2007; BP £2.94	0.25	1.63	3.16	0.72	nr	5.51

RAINWATER INSTALLATION	Plumber hours	Nett plumber £	Nett material £	O'heads /profit £	Unit	Total £
- stop ends ref DC2008 & DC2009; BP £1.40	0.23	1.50	1.58	0.46	nr	3.54
- angles 90° and 135° ref DC2001 - 2004 inc.; BP £3.83	0.40	2.61	4.07	1.00	nr	7.68
150mm; BP £17.55/1.8m	0.45	2.94	10.33	1.99	m	15.26
Fittings and connections						
- running outlet ref DC2005; BP £5.11	0.45	2.94	5.38	1.25	nr	9.57
- stop ends ref DC2008 & DC2009; BP £1.85	0.28	1.83	2.04	0.58	nr	4.45
- angles 90° and 135° ref DC2001 - 2004 inc.; BP £5.11	0.45	2.94	5.38	1.25	nr	9.57

UPVC; Terrain 2100 half round system; connector joints; to brickwork with pipe and fitting clips at 2m maximum centres; plugging

	Plumber hours	Nett plumber £	Nett material £	O'heads /profit £	Unit	Total £
69mm diameter; BP £5.36/3m	0.25	1.63	1.90	0.53	m	4.06
Fittings and connections						
- 92½° bend ref 2108.25.92; BP £1.03	0.15	0.98	1.05	0.31	nr	2.34
- branch ref 2109.25.112; BP £2.19	0.20	1.31	2.24	0.53	nr	4.08
- shoe ref 2110.25; BP £0.57	0.30	1.96	0.60	0.38	nr	2.94
- access pipe ref 2137.25; BP £4.37	0.25	1.63	4.47	0.92	nr	7.02
- connection to back inlet gully; cement mortar (1:3)	0.15	0.98	0.20	0.18	nr	1.36
- connection to 102mm diameter drain pipe; adaptor ref 1829.4.25; BP £2.87	0.10	0.65	2.94	0.54	nr	4.13
Sundries						
- rainwater head ref 2111.25; BP £3.57	0.40	2.61	3.66	0.94	nr	7.21

RAINWATER INSTALLATION	Plumber hours	Nett plumber £	Nett material £	O'heads /profit £	Unit	Total £
- balcony outlet ref 2172.3 with adaptor ref 2173.3.25; BP £9.51	0.50	3.27	9.74	1.95	nr	14.96

uPVC; Terrain 2200 square system; connector joints; to brickwork with pipe and fitting clips at 2m maximum centres; plugging

	Plumber hours	Nett plumber £	Nett material £	O'heads /profit £	Unit	Total £
62mm square; BP £6.87/3m	0.25	1.63	2.43	0.61	m	4.67
Fittings and connections						
- 92½° bend ref 2208.23.92; BP £1.01	0.15	0.98	1.03	0.30	nr	2.31
- branch ref 2209.23.112; BP £2.45	0.20	1.31	2.51	0.57	nr	4.39
- shoe ref 2210.23; BP £0.75	0.30	1.96	0.77	0.41	nr	3.14
- offset ref 2214.23; BP £1.53	0.20	1.31	1.57	0.43	nr	3.31
- access pipe ref 2237.23; BP £5.97	0.25	1.63	6.11	1.16	nr	8.90
- change piece square to circular ref 2215.23.25; BP £1.17	0.10	0.65	1.20	0.28	nr	2.13
- connection to back inlet gully; cement mortar (1:3)	0.15	0.98	0.20	0.18	nr	1.36
- connection to 110mm diameter drain pipe; adaptor ref 1829.4.25; change piece ref 2215.23.25; BP £3.99	0.15	0.98	4.09	0.76	nr	5.83
Sundries						
- rainwater head; ref 2211.23; BP £3.50	0.40	2.61	3.58	0.93	nr	7.12

RAINWATER INSTALLATION	Plumber hours	Nett plumber £	Nett material £	O'heads /profit £	Unit	Total £
uPVC; Terrain 2300 large capacity system; connector joints; to brickwork with pipe and fitting clips at 2m maximum centres; plugging						
75mm square; BP £9.16/3m	0.27	1.76	3.22	0.75	m	5.73
Fittings and connections						
- bend ref 2308.33.112; BP £1.85	0.16	1.05	1.89	0.44	nr	3.38
- shoe ref 2310.33; BP £0.91	0.32	2.09	0.96	0.46	nr	3.51
- offset ref 2314.33; BP £4.11	0.22	1.44	4.20	0.85	nr	6.49
- access pipe ref 2337.33; BP £7.11	0.27	1.76	7.28	1.36	nr	10.40
- change piece to 63mm square ref 2315.33.23; BP £1.40	0.12	0.78	1.43	0.33	nr	2.54
- connection to back inlet gully; cement mortar (1:3)	0.17	1.11	0.20	0.20	nr	1.51
- connection to 110mm drain pipe; adaptor square to round ref 1829.4.33 BP £2.84	0.17	1.11	2.91	0.60	nr	4.62
HOT AND COLD WATER AND HEATING INSTALLATION						
Copper pipe to B.S.2871; lead free presoldered capillary joints and fittings to B.S.864; two piece clips at 1250mm maximum centres						
15mm diameter; table X; to timber base; BP £3.04/3m	0.20	1.31	1.07	0.36	m	2.74
Fittings and connections						
- made bend (table X only)	0.10	0.65	-	0.10	nr	0.75
- made offset (table X only)	0.15	0.98	-	0.15	nr	1.13
- elbow; BP £0.25	0.18	1.18	0.28	0.22	nr	1.68
- obtuse elbow; BP £0.79	0.18	1.18	0.83	0.30	nr	2.31
- tee; BP £0.53	0.23	1.50	0.56	0.31	nr	2.37
- stop end; BP £0.53	0.14	0.91	0.56	0.22	nr	1.69

HOT AND COLD WATER AND HEATING INSTALLATION	Plumber hours	Nett plumber £	Nett material £	O'heads /profit £	Unit	Total £
- adaptor to ½" imperial; BP £0.50	0.18	1.18	0.53	0.26	nr	1.97
- reducer to 8mm; BP £0.85	0.18	1.18	0.89	0.31	nr	2.38
- straight ½" tap connector; BP £0.76	0.22	1.44	0.80	0.34	nr	2.58
- bent ½" tap connector; BP £0.94	0.22	1.44	0.96	0.36	nr	2.76
- ½" tank connector with backnut; BP £1.53	0.28	1.83	1.58	0.51	nr	3.92
22mm diameter; table X; to timber base; BP £5.83/3m	0.21	1.37	2.04	0.51	m	3.92
Fittings and connections						
- made bend (table X only)	0.15	0.98	-	0.15	nr	1.13
- made offset (table X only)	0.20	1.31	-	0.20	nr	1.51
- elbow; BP £0.57	0.18	1.18	0.60	0.27	nr	2.05
- tee; BP £1.05	0.23	1.50	1.08	0.39	nr	2.97
- stop end; BP £0.84	0.14	0.91	0.88	0.27	nr	2.06
- adaptor to ¾" imperial; BP £0.53	0.18	1.18	0.57	0.26	nr	2.01
- reducer to 15mm; BP £0.66	0.18	1.18	0.70	0.28	nr	2.16
- straight ¾" tap connector; BP £1.12	0.22	1.44	1.17	0.39	nr	3.00
- bent ¾" tap connector; BP £1.67	0.24	1.57	1.73	0.50	nr	3.80
- ¾" tank connector with backnut; BP £2.28	0.28	1.83	2.35	0.63	nr	4.81
22mm diameter; table Y; laid in trenches; BP £3.59/m	0.12	0.78	1.43	0.33	m	2.54
Fittings and connections						
- made bend	0.06	0.39	-	0.06	nr	0.45
- made offset	0.10	0.65	-	0.10	nr	0.75
- elbow; BP £0.57	0.18	1.18	0.60	0.27	nr	2.05
- tee; BP £1.02	0.23	1.50	1.06	0.38	nr	2.94

HOT AND COLD WATER AND HEATING INSTALLATION	Plumber hours	Nett plumber £	Nett material £	O'heads /profit £	Unit	Total £
Blue polyethylene pipes and fittings; B.S.6572; socket fusion welded joints; laid in trenches						
20mm diameter; BP £0.39/m	0.10	0.65	0.44	0.16	m	1.25
Fittings and connections – connection to copper; compression adaptor; BP £1.36	0.18	1.18	1.41	0.39	nr	2.98
25mm diameter; BP £0.48/m	0.10	0.65	0.54	0.18	m	1.37
Fittings and connections – equal tee; BP £5.14	0.29	1.89	5.26	1.07	nr	8.22
– connection to copper; compression adaptor; BP £2.11	0.24	1.57	2.16	0.56	nr	4.29
32mm diameter; BP £0.83/m	0.16	1.05	0.87	0.29	m	2.21
Fittings and connections – equal tee; BP £3.77	0.35	2.29	3.86	0.92	nr	7.07
– reducer; BP £1.67	0.28	1.83	1.71	0.53	nr	4.07
– connection to copper; compression adaptor; BP £3.70	0.28	1.83	3.80	0.85	nr	6.48
STOPCOCKS, VALVES AND THE LIKE						
Stopcocks; B.S.1010; lead free presolder capillary joints						
Stopcock; gunmetal with brass headwork						
– 15mm; BP £1.89	0.20	1.31	1.94	0.49	nr	3.74
– 22mm; BP £3.45	0.22	1.44	3.54	0.75	nr	5.73
– 28mm; BP £8.97	0.28	1.83	9.18	1.65	nr	12.66

HOT AND COLD WATER AND HEATING INSTALLATION	Plumber hours	Nett plumber £	Nett material £	O'heads /profit £	Unit	Total £
Stopcock; DZR						
- 15mm; BP £4.25	0.20	1.31	4.38	0.85	nr	6.54
- 22mm; BP £7.34	0.22	1.44	7.52	1.34	nr	10.30
- 28mm; BP £12.22	0.28	1.83	12.51	2.15	nr	16.49
Stopcocks; B.S.1010; compression fittings to tables X and Z copper pipe						
Stopcock; gunmetal with brass headwork						
- 15mm; BP £1.84	0.19	1.24	1.84	0.46	nr	3.54
- 22mm; BP £3.20	0.21	1.37	3.27	0.70	nr	5.34
- 28mm; BP £8.36	0.27	1.76	8.56	1.55	nr	11.87
Stopcock; DZR						
- 15mm; BP £4.26	0.19	1.24	4.37	0.84	nr	6.45
- 22mm; BP £7.00	0.21	1.37	7.17	1.28	nr	9.82
- 28mm; BP £11.56	0.27	1.76	11.83	2.04	nr	15.63
Stopcocks; B.S.1010; compression joints to B.S6572 polyethylene pipe						
Stopcock; gunmetal with brass headwork						
- 20mm; BP £4.99	0.21	1.37	5.08	0.97	nr	7.42
- 25mm; BP £7.90	0.24	1.57	8.08	1.45	nr	11.10
Stopcock; DZR						
- 20mm; BP £6.63	0.21	1.37	6.79	1.22	nr	9.38
- 25mm; BP £10.67	0.27	1.76	10.92	1.90	nr	14.58
- 32mm; BP £14.37	0.31	2.02	14.71	2.51	nr	19.24
Washing machine valves						
Straight pattern; hot or cold; chromium plate						
- 15mm; BP £1.43	0.20	1.31	1.46	0.42	nr	3.19
Angle pattern; hot or cold; chromium plated						
- 15mm; BP £1.65	0.20	1.31	1.69	0.45	nr	3.45

HOT AND COLD WATER AND HEATING INSTALLATION	Plumber hours	Nett plumber £	Nett material £	O'heads /profit £	Unit	Total £
Radiator valves; Yorkshire						
Presetting; capillary inlet; union outlet						
- 15mm x ½"; BP £2.84	0.20	1.31	2.90	0.63	nr	4.84
- 15mm x ½"; chrome plated; BP £3.47	0.20	1.31	3.56	0.73	nr	5.60
Radiator valves; Danfoss S series RAVL						
Thermostatic						
- 15mm straight or angle pattern; BP £10.43	0.22	1.44	10.67	1.82	nr	13.93
- 8/10mm angle pattern; BP £10.43	0.22	1.44	10.67	1.82	nr	13.93
Drain fittings; compression joints to copper						
Draw off coupling; gunmetal						
- 15mm; BP £3.64	0.20	1.31	3.72	0.76	nr	5.79
- 22mm; BP £4.24	0.20	1.31	4.34	0.85	nr	6.50
Draw off elbow; brass						
- 15mm; BP £2.71	0.20	1.31	2.77	0.61	nr	4.69
- 22mm; BP £3.10	0.20	1.31	3.17	0.67	nr	5.15
- 28mm; BP £4.80	0.25	1.63	4.91	0.98	nr	7.52
Plastic water storage cisterns to B.S.4213; placing in position; complete with lid						
- Ref PC 20; 20 galls/91 ltrs; BP £16.96	0.75	4.90	17.35	3.34	nr	25.59
- Ref PC 25; 25 galls/114 ltrs; BP £21.06	0.80	5.22	21.55	4.02	nr	30.79
- Ref PC 40; 40 galls/182 ltrs; BP £36.43	0.90	5.88	37.27	6.47	nr	49.62

HOT AND COLD WATER AND HEATING INSTALLATION	Plumber hours	Nett plumber £	Nett material £	O'heads /profit £	Unit	Total £

BOILERS AND WATER HEATERS

Solid fuel boilers; gravity feed
for domestic central heating and
indirect hot water; white stove
enamelled casing; thermostat;
125mm flue socket

- 13.2 kWh output; BP £582.49	4.75	31.02	582.49	92.03	nr	705.54
- 17.6 kWh output; BP £677.83	4.75	31.02	677.83	106.33	nr	815.18

Gas fired boilers; Myson
Marathon range; free standing; for
domestic central heating and
indirect hot water

- Type M40 C; conventional flue; BP £237.45	3.75	24.49	237.45	39.29	nr	301.23
- Type M40B; balanced flue; BP £289.92	4.10	26.77	289.92	47.50	nr	364.19
- Type M70C; conventional flue; BP £298.60	3.75	24.49	298.60	48.46	nr	371.55
- Type M70B; balanced flue; BP £386.29	4.10	26.77	386.29	61.96	nr	475.02
- Pump kit; BP £46.10	1.25	8.16	46.10	8.14	nr	62.40
- Programmer kit; BP £33.78	0.75	4.90	33.78	5.80	nr	44.48

Gas fired boilers; Potterton
Kingfisher range; freestanding;
for domestic central heating and
indirect hot water

- Type CF40; conventional flue; BP £255.25	3.75	24.49	255.25	41.96	nr	321.70
- Type CF60; conventional flue; BP £270.93	3.75	24.49	270.93	44.31	nr	339.73

HOT AND COLD WATER AND HEATING INSTALLATION	Plumber hours	Nett plumber £	Nett material £	O'heads /profit £	Unit	Total £
Gas fired boilers; Glow-worm space saver range; wall mounted; for domestic central heating and indirect hot water						
- Type 30B; balanced flue; BP £221.29	3.75	24.49	221.29	36.87	nr	282.65
- Type 40B; balanced flue; BP £256.66	3.75	24.49	256.66	42.17	nr	323.32
- Type 50B; balanced flue; BP £285.17	3.75	24.49	285.17	46.45	nr	356.11
- Type 60B; balanced flue; BP £345.64	3.75	24.99	345.64	55.52	nr	425.65
Gas water heaters; for domestic whole house hot water						
Britony multipoint including balanced flue set 3/24"; BP £208.36	2.50	16.33	208.36	33.70	nr	258.39
Direct copper cylinders to B.S.699 grade 3; placing in position						
- Ref 7; 26 galls/120 ltrs; BP £36.90	0.55	3.59	36.90	6.07	nr	46.56
- Ref 8; 32 galls/144 ltrs; BP £37.54	0.65	4.25	37.54	6.27	nr	48.06
- Ref 9; 36 galls/166 ltrs; BP £42.96	0.85	5.55	42.96	7.28	nr	55.79
Indirect copper cylinders to B.S.699 grade 3; placing in position						
- Ref 7; 31 galls/140 ltrs; BP £44.09	0.65	4.25	44.09	7.25	nr	55.59
- Ref 8; 36 galls/162 ltrs; BP £50.48	0.70	4.57	50.48	8.26	nr	63.31

PLUMBING WORK

HOT AND COLD WATER AND HEATING INSTALLATION	Plumber hours	Nett plumber £	Nett material £	O'heads /profit £	Unit	Total £
RADIATORS						
Steel panel radiators; Stelrad Accord; plugged and screwed to brickwork with concealed brackets; primer finish						
Type P1; single panel						
450mm high of length						
- 480mm; BP £7.68	1.00	6.53	8.01	2.18	nr	16.72
- 1120mm; BP £17.31	1.15	7.51	17.72	3.79	nr	29.02
- 1920mm; BP £31.15	1.25	8.16	31.69	5.98	nr	45.83
600mm high of length						
- 480mm; BP £9.91	1.05	6.86	10.24	2.57	nr	19.67
- 1120mm; BP £22.30	1.20	7.84	22.76	4.59	nr	35.19
- 1920mm; BP £40.19	1.30	8.49	40.81	7.40	nr	56.70
Type K1; single panel with one convector surface						
450mm high of length						
- 480mm; BP £8.77	1.00	6.53	9.10	2.35	nr	17.98
- 1120mm; BP £20.08	1.15	7.51	20.51	4.20	nr	32.22
- 1920mm; BP £33.28	1.25	8.16	33.84	6.30	nr	48.30
750mm high of length						
- 480mm; BP £14.05	1.10	7.18	14.43	3.24	nr	24.85
- 1120mm; BP £31.47	1.25	8.16	32.01	6.03	nr	46.20
- 1920mm; BP £59.86	1.35	8.82	60.67	10.42	nr	79.91
Type P+; double panel with one convector surface						
450mm high of length						
- 480mm; BP £14.90	1.10	7.18	15.29	3.37	nr	25.84
- 1120mm; BP £34.17	1.25	8.16	35.74	6.59	nr	50.49
- 1920mm; BP £65.76	1.35	8.82	66.61	11.32	nr	86.75

PLUMBING WORK

HOT AND COLD WATER AND HEATING INSTALLATION	Plumber hours	Nett plumber £	Nett material £	O'heads /profit £	Unit	Total £
750mm high of length						
- 480mm; BP £23.24	1.20	7.84	23.71	4.73	nr	36.28
- 1120mm; BP £51.92	1.35	8.82	52.65	9.22	nr	70.69
- 1920mm; BP £102.65	1.45	9.47	103.86	17.00	nr	130.33

INSULATION

Cylinder jackets to B.S.5615;
80mm glass fibre with flame
retardent PVC cover; fixed with
two fixing bands; 8 segments

	Plumber hours	Nett plumber £	Nett material £	O'heads /profit £	Unit	Total £
- 400mm diameter x 900mm high; BP £6.28	0.35	2.29	6.43	1.31	nr	10.03
- 450mm diameter x 1050mm high; BP £8.16	0.50	3.27	8.45	1.76	nr	13.48
- 450mm diameter x 1200mm high; BP £10.04	0.50	3.27	10.28	2.03	nr	15.58

Cistern jackets to B.S.5615, 60mm
glass fibre with polythene cover;
fixed with two fixing bands

Jacket size	Plumber hours	Nett plumber £	Nett material £	O'heads /profit £	Unit	Total £
- 635 x 457 x 483mm; BP £4.30	0.60	3.92	4.40	1.25	nr	9.57
- 686 x 533 x 533mm; BP £5.35	0.70	4.57	6.47	1.66	nr	12.70
- 737 x 584 x 508mm; BP £5.89	0.80	5.22	6.03	1.69	nr	12.94

Preformed pipe insulation;
elastomeric; fixed with tape; 9mm
thick to copper pipes of size:-

	Plumber hours	Nett plumber £	Nett material £	O'heads /profit £	Unit	Total £
- 15mm; BP £0.70	0.08	0.52	0.75	0.19	m	1.46
- 22mm; BP £0.85	0.08	0.52	0.90	0.21	m	1.63
- 28mm; BP £0.94	0.09	0.59	0.99	0.24	m	1.82

HOT AND COLD WATER AND HEATING INSTALLATION	Plumber hours	Nett plumber £	Nett material £	O'heads /profit £	Unit	Total £

SUNDRIES

Immersion heater to B.S.3456; joint to cylinder entry

3kW output complete with thermostat

- 14"; BP £6.33	0.80	5.22	6.57	1.77	nr	13.56
- 27"; BP £6.51	1.00	6.53	6.76	1.99	nr	15.28
- 36"; BP £6.94	1.10	7.18	7.21	2.16	nr	16.55

Dual type complete with thermostat and switch; top element 2kW; bottom element 3kW of length

- 30"; BP £31.30	1.25	8.16	32.13	6.04	nr	46.33

Ball valves to B.S.1212; brass body; connection to tank; excluding float

Piston type

- ½" high pressure; BP £1.62	0.15	0.98	1.76	0.41	nr	3.15
- ¾" high pressure; BP £6.74	0.20	1.31	7.00	1.25	nr	9.56
- ½" low pressure; BP £2.89	0.15	0.98	3.06	0.61	nr	4.65
- ¾" low pressure; BP £6.89	0.20	1.31	7.15	1.27	nr	9.73

Diaphragm type

- ½" high pressure; BP £3.67	0.15	0.98	3.86	0.73	nr	5.57

Ball valve floats; connection to valve

Copper to B.S.1968

- 4½"; BP £1.70	0.05	0.33	1.74	0.31	nr	2.38

Plastic to B.S.2456

- 4½"; BP £0.24	0.05	0.33	0.25	0.09	nr	0.67
- 5"; BP £0.37	0.05	0.33	0.38	0.11	nr	0.82
- 6"; BP £1.05	0.05	0.33	1.07	0.21	nr	1.61

PLUMBING WORK

HOT AND COLD WATER AND HEATING INSTALLATION	Plumber hours	Nett plumber £	Nett material £	O'heads /profit £	Unit	Total £
Time switches and programmers; fixed to brickwork; excluding electrical connections						
- Randall 102 time switch; BP £29.20	0.25	1.63	29.93	4.73	nr	36.29
- Randall 103 time switch; BP £25.98	0.25	1.63	26.63	4.24	nr	32.50
- Randall 922 electronic programmer; BP £38.40	0.30	1.96	39.36	6.20	nr	47.52
Room thermostats; fixing to brickwork; excluding electrical connections						
- Honeywell ref T6160B; BP £7.91	0.25	1.63	8.11	1.46	nr	11.20
Circulator pumps						
- SMC comet 130-45; complete with valves; BP £26.30	0.90	5.88	26.96	4.93	nr	37.77
- SMC commodore 130-60; complete with unions and 22mm valves; BP £30.45	1.10	7.18	31.21	5.76	nr	44.15
- SMC comet 160 bronze; BP £61.77	1.10	7.18	63.31	10.57	nr	81.06
- Grundfos selectric MK2 with unions and 22mm valves; BP £28.81	1.10	7.18	29.53	5.51	nr	42.22
WASTE INSTALLATION						
MUPVC; Terrain system 200; solvent welded connector joints to brickwork with clips at 500mm maximum centres; plugging						
32mm diameter; BP £5.74/4m	0.24	1.57	1.65	0.48	m	3.70

WASTE INSTALLATION	Plumber hours	Nett plumber £	Nett material £	O'heads /profit £	Unit	Total £
Fittings and connections						
- bends ref 201.125.91 & 135; BP £0.77	0.22	1.44	0.89	0.35	nr	2.68
- tee ref 204.125.91; BP £1.10	0.25	1.63	1.27	0.44	nr	3.34
- expansion connector ref 225.125; BP £0.67	0.17	1.11	0.77	0.28	nr	2.16
- connectors; female iron to MUPVC; ref 212.125 & 216.125; BP £0.65	0.22	1.44	0.75	0.33	nr	2.52
- connection to back inlet gully; caulking bush ref 232; BP £0.92; cement mortar (1:3)	0.15	0.98	1.06	0.31	nr	2.35
40mm diameter; BP £6.99/4m	0.27	1.76	2.00	0.56	m	4.32
Fittings and connections						
- bends ref 201.15.91 & 135; BP £0.87	0.24	1.57	1.00	0.39	nr	2.96
- tee ref 204.15.91; BP £1.37	0.28	1.83	1.58	0.51	nr	3.92
- expansion connector ref 225.15 BP £0.83	0.20	1.31	0.95	0.34	nr	2.60
- connectors; female iron to MUPVC; ref 212.15 & 216.15; BP £0.76	0.24	1.57	0.87	0.37	nr	2.81
- connection to back inlet gully; caulking bush ref 232 BP £0.92; cement mortar (1:3)	0.17	1.11	1.06	0.33	nr	2.50
Sundries						
- washing machine stand pipe ref 9250; BP £2.38	0.26	1.70	2.74	0.67	nr	5.11
50mm diameter; BP £11.10/4m	0.30	1.96	3.19	0.77	m	5.92
Fittings and connections						
- bend ref 201.2.91; BP £1.25	0.26	1.70	1.43	0.47	nr	3.60
- tee ref 204.2.135; BP £2.48	0.30	1.96	2.85	0.72	nr	5.53

WASTE INSTALLATION	Plumber hours	Nett plumber £	Nett material £	O'heads /profit £	Unit	Total £
- expansion connector ref 225.2; BP £1.12	0.22	1.44	1.29	0.41	nr	3.14
- connectors; female iron to MUPVC; ref 212.2 & 216.2; BP £1.12	0.26	1.70	1.29	0.45	nr	3.44
- connection to back inlet gully; caulking bush ref 232; BP £0.92; cement mortar (1:3)	0.20	1.31	1.15	0.37	nr	2.83

TRAPS

Polypropylene; Terrain; screwed joint to outlet and to pipe

Bottle P trap						
- 32mm ref 611.125; BP £1.86	0.25	1.63	2.14	0.57	nr	4.34
- 40mm ref 611.15; BP £2.22	0.30	1.96	2.55	0.68	nr	5.19
Bottle S trap						
- 32mm ref 612.125; BP £2.22	0.25	1.63	2.55	0.63	nr	4.81
- 40mm ref 612.15; BP £2.67	0.30	1.96	3.09	0.76	nr	5.81
Tubular P trap						
- 32mm ref 631.125; BP £1.66	0.27	1.76	1.91	0.55	nr	4.22
- 40mm ref 631.15; BP £1.92	0.32	2.09	2.21	0.65	nr	4.95
- 50mm ref 631.2; BP £4.63	0.35	2.29	5.32	1.14	nr	8.75
Tubular S trap						
- 32mm ref 632.125; BP £2.03	0.27	1.76	2.34	0.62	nr	4.72
- 40mm ref 632.15; BP £2.39	0.32	2.09	2.75	0.73	nr	5.57
Tubular bath traps						
- P trap ref 651.15; BP £3.59	0.33	2.16	4.13	0.94	nr	7.23
- P trap assembly including outlets and overflow ref 653.15; BP £6.12	0.50	3.27	7.04	1.55	nr	11.86
- P trap assembly chromed including outlets and overflow ref 655.15; BP £7.33	0.50	3.27	8.43	1.76	nr	13.46

SOIL AND VENT INSTALLATION	Plumber hours	Nett plumber £	Nett material £	O'heads /profit £	Unit	Total £
uPVC; Terrain soil system 100; solvent welded joints; to brickwork with holderbats at 1250mm maximum centres; plugging						
82mm diameter; BP £15.00/4m	0.33	2.16	4.31	0.97	m	7.44
Fittings and connections						
- sweep bends ref 101.3.92 & 135; BP £3.14	0.30	1.96	3.61	0.84	nr	6.41
- W.C. connecting bend ref 102.3.5; BP £3.51	0.25	1.63	4.04	0.85	nr	6.52
- single branches ref 104.3.92 & 135; BP £4.35	0.35	2.29	5.21	1.13	nr	8.63
- expansion boss connectors ref 113.3.15 & 125; BP £2.26	0.25	1.63	2.60	0.64	nr	4.87
- W.C. connector ref 125.3.5; BP £3.48	0.25	1.63	4.00	0.85	nr	6.48
- connection to drain; PVC caulking bush ref 132.3; BP £2.66; cement mortar (1:3)	0.25	1.63	3.06	0.70	nr	5.39
Sundries						
- weathering apron ref 131.3; BP £0.85	0.22	1.44	0.98	0.36	nr	2.78
- weathering slate ref 149.16.00; BP £10.50	0.25	1.63	12.08	2.06	nr	15.77
- cutting holes for boss connectors	0.15	0.98	-	0.15	nr	1.13
110mm diameter; BP £17.58/4m	0.37	2.42	5.05	1.12	m	8.59
Fittings and connections						
- sweep bends ref 101.4.92, 104, 112, & 135; BP £4.29	0.34	2.22	4.93	1.07	nr	8.22
- W.C. connecting bend ref 102.4.5; BP £4.57	0.29	1.89	5.26	1.07	nr	8.22
- single branch with access ref 105.4.92; BP £11.00	0.39	2.55	12.65	2.28	nr	17.48
- expansion boss connectors ref 113.4.2, 15 & 125; BP £2.38	0.29	1.89	2.74	0.70	nr	5.33

PLUMBING WORK

SOIL AND VENT INSTALLATION	Plumber hours	Nett plumber £	Nett material £	O'heads /profit £	Unit	Total £
- connection to drain; metal caulking bush ref 133.4.416; BP £11.94; cement mortar (1:3)	0.29	1.89	13.73	2.34	nr	17.96
Sundries						
- weathering apron ref 131.4; BP £1.03	0.26	1.70	1.19	0.43	nr	3.32
- weathering slate ref 149.16.00; BP £10.46	0.27	1.76	12.03	2.07	nr	15.86
- cutting holes for boss connectors	0.15	0.98	-	0.15	nr	1.13
160mm diameter; BP £39.50/4m	0.42	2.74	11.36	2.12	m	16.22
Fittings and connections						
- sweep bends ref 101.6.92; BP £9.25	0.37	2.42	10.64	1.96	nr	15.02
- single branches ref 104.64.104 and 135; BP £13.04	0.42	2.74	15.00	2.66	nr	20.40
- expansion boss connectors ref 113.6.2, 15 & 125; BP £2.96	0.32	2.09	3.46	0.83	nr	6.38
- connection to drain; metal caulking bush ref 133.6; BP £17.62; cement mortar (1:3)	0.32	2.09	20.26	3.35	nr	25.70
Sundries						
- weathering apron ref 131.6;BP £3.11	0.28	1.83	3.58	0.81	nr	6.22
- weathering slate ref 149.18.22; BP £10.72	0.28	1.83	12.32	2.12	nr	16.27
- cutting holes for boss connectors	0.15	0.98	-	0.15	nr	1.13

OVERFLOW INSTALLATION	Plumber hours	Nett plumber £	Nett material £	O'heads /profit £	Unit	Total £
ABS; Osmaweld system; solvent welded connector joints; to brickwork with clips at 500mm maximum centres; plugging						
19mm diameter; BP £1.86/4m	0.19	1.24	0.53	0.27	m	2.04
Fittings and connections						
- bends ref 10.160 & 10.163;						
BP £0.32	0.17	1.11	0.34	0.22	nr	1.67
- tee ref 10.190; BP £0.34	0.20	1.31	0.36	0.25	nr	1.92
- tank connector ref 10.129;						
BP £0.41	0.20	1.31	0.43	0.26	nr	2.00
- bent tank connector ref						
10.139; BP £0.45	0.20	1.31	0.48	0.27	nr	2.06
BATHS						
Acrylic; reinforced; complete with 2nr chromium plated grips, waste, overflow with chain and plastic plug; excluding taps and trap						
3mm thick; 1700mm long -						
- white; BP £74.74	2.55	16.65	85.95	15.39	nr	117.99
- coloured; BP £77.55	2.55	16.65	89.18	15.88	nr	121.71
5mm thick; 1700mm long						
- white; BP £90.50	2.65	17.31	104.08	18.21	nr	139.60
- coloured; BP £94.46	2.65	17.31	108.63	18.89	nr	144.83
Moulded high impact polystyrene; fixing in position; trimming as required						
- end panel; BP £8.39	0.25	1.63	9.65	1.69	nr	12.97
- side panel; BP £15.79	0.40	2.61	18.16	3.12	nr	23.89
Angle strip						
Polished aluminium; fixing with chromium plated dome headed screws; cutting to length						
- 25 x 25 x 560mm long;						
BP £1.40/m	0.30	1.96	1.55	0.53	m	4.04

SANITARY FITTINGS	Plumber hours	Nett plumber £	Nett material £	O'heads /profit £	Unit	Total £

BASINS AND PEDESTALS

Wash basin; vitreous china;
complete with chromium plated
waste, overflow with chain and
plastic plug; excluding taps and
trap

560 x 430mm; white
- wall mounted on brackets;

	Plumber hours	Nett plumber £	Nett material £	O'heads /profit £	Unit	Total £
BP £20.07	1.75	11.43	21.58	4.95	nr	37.96
- pedestal mounted; bedded in mastic; screwed to wall;						
BP £38.27	2.05	13.39	41.14	8.18	nr	62.71
560 x 430mm; coloured						
- wall mounted on brackets;						
BP £27.07	1.75	11.43	29.10	6.08	nr	46.61
- pedestal mounted; bedded in mastic; screwed to wall;						
BP £47.06	2.05	13.39	50.59	9.60	nr	73.58

SINKS

Stainless steel sink unit sinks;
complete with chromium plated
waste, overflow with chain and
plastic plug; excluding taps and
trap; fixing to sink top with
proprietary clips

	Plumber hours	Nett plumber £	Nett material £	O'heads /profit £	Unit	Total £
- single bowl with single drainer; 1000 x 500mm;						
BP £121.45	1.80	11.75	130.55	21.35	nr	163.65
- single bowl with double drainer; 1500 x 500mm;						
BP £149.45	1.90	12.41	160.66	25.96	nr	199.03
- double bowl with single drainer; 1500 x 500mm;						
BP £190.62	1.95	12.73	204.92	32.65	nr	250.30

SANITARY FITTINGS	Plumber hours	Nett plumber £	Nett material £	O'heads /profit £	Unit	Total £
W.C. SUITES						
Close coupled; vitreous china with plastic seat; comprising 9 litre cistern, ball valve, flush pipe, pan and all brackets; connection to drain						
White						
- washdown type; BP £91.31	2.35	15.35	98.16	17.03	nr	130.54
- syphonic type; BP £174.03	2.35	15.35	187.08	30.37	nr	232.80
Coloured						
- washdown type; BP £118.47	2.35	15.35	127.36	21.41	nr	164.12
- syphonic type; BP £187.99	2.35	15.35	204.24	32.94	nr	252.53
BIDETS						
Freestanding plain rim; vitreous china; excluding fittings						
- white; BP £57.84	1.95	12.73	62.18	11.24	nr	86.15
- coloured; BP £78.80	1.95	12.73	84.71	14.62	nr	112.06
TAPS; IN PAIRS						
Basin and bath pillar taps						
Alpha chromium plated						
- ½"; BP £8.14	0.35	2.29	8.75	1.66	nr	12.70
- ¾"; BP £9.17	0.35	2.29	9.86	1.82	nr	13.97
Swanlux chromium plated						
- ½"; BP £13.70	0.35	2.29	14.73	2.55	nr	19.57
- ¾"; BP £17.18	0.35	2.29	18.47	3.11	nr	23.87
Sink pillar taps						
- Alpha chromium plated; BP £10.17	0.35	2.29	10.93	1.98	nr	15.20
- Swanlux chromium plated; BP £15.92	0.35	2.29	17.11	2.91	nr	22.31

PLUMBING WORK

SANITARY FITTINGS	Plumber hours	Nett plumber £	Nett material £	O'heads /profit £	Unit	Total £
Basin mixer taps						
- Swanlux chromium plated; 3 hole pop up waste with fixed head; BP £42.00	0.50	3.27	45.15	7.26	nr	55.68
- Swanlux chromium plated; monoblock pop up waste with fixed head; BP £35.92	0.50	3.27	38.61	6.28	nr	48.16
Bath mixer taps						
- Alpha chromium plated; deck pattern with hose and handspray; BP £31.03	0.70	4.57	33.36	5.69	nr	43.62
- Swanlux chromium plated; deck pattern; filler only; BP £34.17	0.55	3.59	36.73	6.05	nr	46.37
- Swanlux chromium plated; deck pattern with handspray; BP £42.43	0.70	4.57	45.61	7.53	nr	57.71
Sink mixer taps						
- Fairline chromium plated; deck pattern with swivel spout; BP £20.97	0.40	2.61	22.54	3.77	nr	28.92
- Swanlux chromium plated; monoblock with swivel spout; BP £33.43	0.40	2.61	35.94	5.78	nr	44.33
WASTE DISPOSAL UNITS						
For metal sinks with 89mm waste outlet; excluding electrical connections						
- Tweeny de-lux 125; BP £191.72	2.00	13.06	206.10	32.87	nr	252.03
- Badger 1; BP £79.83	1.50	9.80	85.82	14.34	nr	109.96

SHOWER INSTALLATION	Plumber hours	Nett plumber £	Nett material £	O'heads /profit £	Unit	Total £
Mira; thermostatic mixing valves; fixing to wall						
- type 723; BP £115.53	0.50	3.27	124.20	19.12	nr	146.59
- type 723B; BP £121.08	0.50	3.27	130.16	20.02	nr	153.45
- type 915A; BP £160.20	0.50	3.27	172.22	26.32	nr	201.81
- type 915BA; BP £158.52	0.50	3.27	170.41	26.05	nr	199.73
Mira; mechanical mixing valves; fixing to wall						
- type 88; BP £63.90	0.50	3.27	68.69	10.79	nr	82.75
- type 88B; BP £63.81	0.50	3.27	68.60	10.78	nr	82.65
SHOWER KITS						
Mira; fixing to wall						
- type EF-S; flexible tube with handspray; BP £11.95	0.50	3.27	12.85	2.42	nr	18.54
- type BIF-S; flexible tube with handspray; connector to concealed pipework; concealed pipework to valve; BP £24.00	0.50	3.27	25.80	4.36	nr	33.43
- type EV-S; flexible tube with handspray; sliding bar; BP £25.30	0.75	4.90	27.20	4.82	nr	36.92
- type BIV-S; flexible tube with handspray; sliding bar; connector to concealed pipework; concealed pipework to valve; BP £33.13	0.75	4.90	35.62	6.08	nr	46.60
- type ER-S; exposed rigid riser with fixed head; BP £22.76	0.75	4.90	24.47	4.41	nr	33.78
- type BIR-S; fixed head to concealed riser; BP £12.19	1.00	6.53	13.10	2.95	nr	22.58
Triton; fixing to wall; excluding electrical connections						
- type T50 LX ; BP £39.44	0.75	4.90	42.40	7.10	nr	54.40
- type T50 SLX; BP £47.49	0.75	4.90	51.05	8.39	nr	64.34
- type T80 SLX; BP £66.59	0.75	4.90	71.58	11.47	nr	87.95

SHOWER INSTALLATION	Plumber hours	Nett plumber £	Nett material £	O'heads /profit £	Unit	Total £
TRAYS						
Ceramic stone fixing in position						
760 x 760 x 180mm						
- white; BP £88.22	2.50	16.33	94.84	16.68	nr	127.85
- coloured; BP £88.22	2.50	16.33	94.84	16.68	nr	127.85
Acrylic; fixing in position						
760 x 760 x 180mm						
- white; BP £28.37	1.50	9.90	30.45	6.04	nr	46.29
- coloured; BP £28.37	1.50	9.80	30.45	6.04	nr	46.29
ENCLOSURES						
'Shower glide' shower enclosure; fixing ends to walls; safety glass						
- pivot door; gold; BP £214.16	1.00	6.53	230.22	35.51	nr	272.26
- pivot door; silver; BP £196.95	1.00	6.53	211.72	32.74	nr	250.99
- side panel; gold; BP £165.99	0.70	4.57	178.44	27.45	nr	210.46
- side panel; silver; BP £154.81	0.70	4.57	166.42	25.65	nr	196.64
'Matki bathscreen'; fixing ends to walls; Polython						
- MB 700; silver; BP £126.43	1.00	6.53	135.91	21.37	nr	163.81
- MB700; Gold; BP £143.63	1.00	6.53	154.40	24.14	nr	185.07

LEADWORK	Plumber hours	Nett plumber £	Nett material £	O'heads /profit £	Unit	Total £

The following leadwork is all
calculated on a Basic Price of
lead of £1360/tonne

Flat roofing fixing with copper
nails and brass screws

Not exceeding 10° to the horizontal						
- Code 4	4.00	26.12	27.76	8.08	m2	61.96
- Code 5	4.20	27.43	34.54	9.30	m2	71.27
- Code 6	4.40	28.73	41.48	10.53	m2	80.74
- Code 7	4.60	30.04	49.94	12.00	m2	91.98
- Code 8	4.80	31.34	54.76	12.92	m2	99.02

Flashings; fixing with brass screws

150mm girth						
- Code 4	0.40	2.61	4.16	1.02	m	7.79
- Code 5	0.45	2.94	5.18	1.22	m	9.34

Stepped flashings; fixings with
brass screws

150mm girth						
- Code 4	0.50	3.27	4.16	1.12	m	8.55
- Code 5	0.55	3.59	6.90	1.57	m	12.06

Aprons; fixing with brass screws

200mm girth						
- Code 4	0.55	3.59	5.55	1.37	m	10.51
- Code 5	0.60	3.92	6.90	1.62	m	12.44

Cappings to ridges or hips; fixing
with copper nails

200mm girth						
- Code 4	0.55	3.59	5.55	1.37	m	10.51
- Code 5	0.60	3.92	6.90	1.62	m	12.44

PLUMBING WORK

LEADWORK	Plumber hours	Nett plumber £	Nett material £	O'heads /profit £	Unit	Total £
Slates; 400 x 400mm with 200mm high collar; around pipe						
100mm diameter						
- Code 4	1.50	9.80	7.80	2.64	nr	20.24
- Code 5	1.60	10.45	11.00	3.22	nr	24.67
Soakers; fixing with copper nails and brass screws						
150 x 150mm						
- Code 3	0.25	1.63	0.46	0.31	nr	2.40
- Code 4	0.30	1.96	0.62	0.39	nr	2.97
CAST IRON DRAINAGE						
Cast iron to B.S. 437; Drainage Castings Ltd., spigot and socket caulked lead joints; in trenches prepared by others						
100mm diameter; BP £52.32/3m	0.65	4.25	19.18	3.52	m	26.95
100mm diameter in lengths not exceeding 3m;BP £32.29/1.8m	0.95	6.20	19.73	3.89	m	29.82
100mm diameter vertical; BP £29.11/1.2m	1.00	6.53	26.68	4.98	m	38.19
Fittings and connections						
- bends 10°, $22\frac{1}{2}^o$, 35°, 45° $67\frac{1}{2}^o$ and $87\frac{1}{2}^o$ ref DC 1005; BP £14.69	0.55	3.59	16.16	2.96	nr	22.71
- long radius bend $22\frac{1}{2}^o$ ref DC 1009; BP £25.16	0.60	3.92	27.68	4.74	nr	36.34
- branch 100mm x 100mm ref DC1016; BP £23.22	0.80	5.22	25.54	4.61	nr	35.37

PLUMBING WORK

CAST IRON DRAINAGE	Plumber hours	Nett plumber £	Nett material £	O'heads /profit £	Unit	Total £
Sundries						
- bellmouth gully inlet 225mm high ref DC1271; BP £13.45	0.75	4.90	14.80	2.96	nr	22.66
- P trap low invert ref DC1200; BP £22.87	0.90	5.88	25.16	4.66	nr	35.70
- intercepting trap with clearing arm ref DC1211; BP £86.36	1.20	7.84	98.30	15.92	nr	122.06
- gully trap with square top ref DC1620; BP £56.85	1.20	7.84	62.54	10.56	nr	80.94
- gully grating ref TD612; BP £2.26	0.20	1.31	2.49	0.57	nr	4.37
- inspection chamber ref DC1741111 100mm x 100mm; BP £105.51	1.50	9.80	116.06	18.88	nr	144.74
150mm diameter; BP £89.97/3m	0.90	5.88	32.99	5.83	m	44.70
150mm diameter in lengths not exceeding 3m; BP £49.41/1.8m	1.26	8.23	30.20	5.77	m	44.20
150mm diameter vertical; BP £44.07/1.2m	0.70	4.57	40.40	6.75	m	51.72
Fittings and connections						
- bends 10° and $22\frac{1}{2}^o$ ref DC1005; BP £43.11	0.70	4.57	47.42	7.80	nr	59.79
- long radius bends 10°, and $67\frac{1}{2}^o$ ref DC1009; BP £46.55	0.80	5.22	51.21	8.47	nr	64.90
- branch 150mm x 150mm ref DC1016; BP £46.20	1.05	6.86	50.82	1.90	nr	14.58
Sundries						
- bellmouth gully inlet 300mm high ref DC1281; BP £27.90	0.80	5.22	30.69	5.39	nr	41.30
- intercepting trap with cleaning arm ref DC1211; BP £137.46	1.20	7.84	151.21	23.86	nr	182.91
- inspection chamber ref DC1742212 150mm x 150mm; BP £203.54	2.70	17.63	223.89	36.23	nr	277.75

1. Labour rates. The rates
   are based upon the rate
   for an Approved Technician
   i.e. £6.14 per hour.

2. Materials

   The following allowances for
   waste have been included in
   the materials costs:-

Conduit	5%
Wiring, Fittings and Accessories	5%
Cables	10%
Distribution Equipment	5%
Fire and Intruder detection systems	5%
Telephone and Communication systems	5%

STEEL CONDUIT	Labour hours	Nett labour £	Nett material £	O'heads /profit £	Unit	Total £
Steel conduit, heavy gauge, galvanised, black enamel						
Run on surface						
- 16mm	0.28	1.72	1.62	0.50	m	3.84
- 20mm	0.33	2.03	1.62	0.55	m	4.20
- 25mm	0.42	2.58	2.15	0.71	m	5.44
- 32mm	0.48	2.95	2.98	0.89	m	6.82
Run in wall chase or floor screed						
- 16mm	0.25	1.54	1.62	0.47	m	3.63
- 20mm	0.32	1.97	1.62	0.54	m	4.13
- 25mm	0.35	2.15	2.15	0.65	m	4.95
- 32mm	0.43	2.64	2.98	0.84	m	6.46
Run in floor slab						
- 16mm	0.23	1.41	1.62	0.46	m	3.49
- 20mm	0.25	1.54	1.62	0.47	m	3.63
- 25mm	0.33	2.03	2.15	0.63	m	4.81
- 32mm	0.42	2.58	2.98	0.83	m	6.39

Conduit fittings for PVC

Bends

Normal, heavy gauge

CONDUIT	Labour hours	Nett labour £	Nett material £	O'heads /profit £	Unit	Total £
Black or white						
- 20mm	0.07	0.43	1.44	0.28	nr	2.15
- 25mm	0.07	0.43	1.94	0.36	nr	2.73
- 32mm	0.08	0.49	3.03	0.53	nr	4.05
Normal, light gauge						
White						
- 16mm	0.07	0.43	0.48	0.14	nr	1.05
- 20mm	0.07	0.43	0.54	0.15	nr	1.12
- 25mm	0.08	0.49	0.90	0.21	nr	1.60
- 32mm	0.08	0.49	1.67	0.32	nr	2.48
Inspection						
Black or white						
- 20mm	0.10	0.61	1.23	0.28	nr	2.12
- 25mm	0.12	0.74	2.33	0.46	nr	3.53
<u>Tees</u>						
Inspection, black or white						
- 20mm	0.15	0.92	1.23	0.32	nr	2.47
- 25mm	0.17	1.04	2.48	0.53	nr	4.05
COVERS						
Boxes adaptable, moulded, black or white						
- 75mm x 75mm x 41mm	0.20	1.23	2.24	0.52	nr	3.99
- 75mm x 75mm x 53mm	0.20	1.23	2.99	0.63	nr	4.85
- 100mm x 100mm x 50mm	0.20	1.23	3.59	0.72	nr	5.54
- 100mm x 100mm x 75mm	0.20	1.23	3.79	0.75	nr	5.77
- 100mm x 75mm x 50mm	0.20	1.23	3.69	0.74	nr	5.66
- 150mm x 100mm x 50mm	0.20	1.23	4.42	0.85	nr	6.50
- 150mm x 150mm x 75mm	0.20	1.23	4.84	0.91	nr	6.98
- 225mm x 225mm x 75mm	0.33	2.03	8.21	1.54	nr	11.78
SUNDRIES						
<u>Adhesive</u>						
- 1 litre	-	-	20.00	3.00	nr	23.00

ELECTRICAL WORK

CONDUIT	Labour hours	Nett labour £	Nett material £	O'heads /profit £	Unit	Total £
Draw tapes						
- 10mm	-	-	14.11	2.12	nr	16.23
- 20mm	-	-	23.48	3.52	nr	27.00
Bending springs						
Light gauge						
- 16mm	-	-	7.97	1.20	nr	9.17
- 20mm	-	-	7.97	1.20	nr	9.17
- 25mm	-	-	11.75	1.76	nr	13.51
- 32mm	-	-	22.95	3.44	nr	26.39
Heavy gauge						
- 16mm	-	-	7.97	1.20	nr	9.17
- 20mm	-	-	7.97	1.20	nr	9.17
- 25mm	-	-	11.75	1.76	nr	13.51
- 32mm	-	-	22.95	3.44	nr	26.39

CABLES

Building management
Twin axial 78ohms (100m reel)
Single twisted pair of
7/0.32mm tinned annealed
copper braid and covered
with a blue PVC outer sheath

	Labour hours	Nett labour £	Nett material £	O'heads /profit £	Unit	Total £
Installed in conduit/trunking (net cost of 100m reel £62.71)	0.03	0.18	0.82	0.15	m	1.15

**Single core PVC insulated
cables, non-armoured with
sheath (twin and earth)
BS 6004 (supplied in packs
of 50m)**
Clipped to surface

Size mm2	Labour hours	Nett labour £	Nett material £	O'heads /profit £	Unit	Total £
1.0	0.07	0.43	0.43	0.13	m	0.99
1.5	0.07	0.43	0.57	0.15	m	1.15
2.5	0.07	0.43	0.79	0.18	m	1.40
4	0.07	0.43	1.81	0.34	m	2.58
6	0.08	0.49	2.46	0.44	m	3.39
10	0.08	0.49	4.43	0.74	m	5.66
16	0.08	0.49	6.93	1.11	m	8.53

ELECTRICAL WORK

CABLES	Labour hours	Nett labour £	Nett material £	O'Heads /profit £	Unit	Total £
Fix in chases (covered with galvanised or PVC sheath)						
Size mm2 1.0	0.10	0.61	0.52	0.17	m	1.30
1.5	0.10	0.61	0.67	0.19	m	1.47
2.5	0.10	0.61	0.88	0.22	m	1.71
4	0.10	0.61	1.90	0.38	m	2.89
6	0.12	0.74	2.66	0.51	m	3.91
10	0.12	0.74	4.66	0.81	m	6.21
16	0.12	0.74	7.13	1.18	m	9.05
Single core PVC insulated PVC sheathed cable BS 6004 (supplied in packs of 50m)						
Clipped to Surface						
Size mm2 1.0	0.07	0.43	0.25	0.10	m	0.78
1.5	0.07	0.43	0.33	0.11	m	0.87
2.5	0.07	0.43	0.57	0.15	m	1.15
4	0.07	0.43	0.93	0.20	m	1.56
6	0.08	0.49	1.26	0.26	m	2.01
10	0.08	0.49	2.00	0.37	m	2.86
16	0.08	0.49	2.93	0.51	m	3.93
Fix in chases (covered with galvanised or PVC sheath)						
Size mm2 1.0	0.10	0.61	0.33	0.14	m	1.08
1.5	0.10	0.61	0.43	0.16	m	1.20
2.5	0.10	0.61	0.67	0.19	m	1.47
4	0.10	0.61	1.02	0.25	m	1.88
6	0.12	0.74	1.48	0.33	m	2.55
10	0.12	0.74	2.23	0.45	m	3.42
16	0.12	0.74	3.04	0.57	m	4.35
Single core PVC insulated PVC Sheathed Cable with Integral Earth Wire to BS 6004						
Clipped to Surface						
Size mm2 1.0	0.07	0.43	0.38	0.12	m	0.93
1.5	0.07	0.43	0.48	0.14	m	1.05

ELECTRICAL WORK

CABLES		Labour hours	Nett labour £	Nett material £	O'Heads /profit £	Unit	Total £
Fix in chases (covered with galvanised or PVC sheath)							
Size mm2	1.0	0.07	0.43	0.48	0.14	m	1.05
	1.5	0.07	0.43	0.57	0.15	m	1.15
Earth/bonding conductors PVC insulated - BS 6004							
Clipped to Surface							
Size mm2	1.0	0.07	0.43	0.14	0.09	m	0.66
	1.5	0.07	0.43	0.22	0.10	m	0.75
	2.5	0.07	0.43	0.32	0.11	m	0.86
	4	0.07	0.43	0.54	0.15	m	1.12
	6	0.08	0.49	0.80	0.19	m	1.48
	10	0.08	0.49	1.47	0.29	m	2.25
	16	0.08	0.49	2.21	0.41	m	3.11
Fixed in chases (covered with galvanised or PVC sheath)							
Size mm2	1.0	0.10	0.61	0.24	0.13	m	0.98
	1.5	0.10	0.61	0.31	0.14	m	1.06
	2.5	0.10	0.61	0.42	0.16	m	1.19
	4	0.10	0.61	0.64	0.19	m	1.44
	6	0.12	0.74	0.92	0.25	m	1.91
	10	0.12	0.74	1.62	0.35	m	2.71
	16	0.12	0.74	2.38	0.47	m	3.59

WIRING, FITTING & ACCESSORIES

1 All times allow for cable connections to wiring accessories

2 Material costs are based on split pack prices plus 5% waste allowance

ACCESSORIES
Moulded fittings
switches

	Labour hours	Nett labour £	Nett material £	O'Heads /profit £	Unit	Total £
5 amp switch T gang 1 way	0.17	1.04	1.30	0.35	nr	2.69
5 amp switch T gang 2 way	0.17	1.04	1.53	0.39	nr	2.96
5 amp switch 2 gang 2 way	0.25	1.54	2.68	0.63	nr	4.85

ELECTRICAL WORK

ACCESSORIES	Labour hours	Nett labour £	Nett material £	O'Heads /profit £	Unit	Total £
5 amp switch 3 gang 2 way	0.38	2.33	3.84	0.93	nr	7.10
5 amp switch 4 gang 3 way	0.43	2.64	6.67	1.40	nr	10.71
5 amp switch 1 gang intermediate	0.17	1.04	3.63	0.70	nr	5.37
5 amp switch 1 gang bellpush	0.17	1.04	2.10	0.47	nr	3.61
5 amp switch 1 gang 2 way architrave	0.17	1.04	1.70	0.41	nr	3.15
5 amp switch 2 gang 2 way architrave	0.25	1.54	3.12	0.70	nr	5.36
5 amp switch 1 gang 1 way architrave	0.17	1.04	1.32	0.35	nr	2.71
15 amp switch 1 gang 1 way	0.17	1.04	1.54	0.39	nr	2.97
15 amp switch 1 gang 2 way	0.17	1.04	1.82	0.43	nr	3.29
15 amp switch 2 gang 2 way	0.25	1.54	3.23	0.72	nr	5.49
15 amp switch 3 gang 2 way	0.38	2.33	4.59	1.04	nr	7.96
15 amp switch 4 gang 2 way	0.43	2.64	8.00	1.60	nr	12.24
15 amp switch 1 gang intermediate	0.17	1.04	4.34	0.81	nr	6.19
Sockets						
13 amp to BS 1363 1 gang	0.23	1.41	2.07	0.52	nr	4.00
13 amp to BS 1363 2 gang	0.28	1.72	3.80	0.83	nr	6.35
13 amp to BS 1363 panel mounting	0.23	1.41	2.63	0.61	nr	4.65
5 amp-3 pin unswitched to BS 546	0.23	1.41	3.18	0.69	nr	5.28
15 amp-3 pin unswitched to BS 546	0.23	1.41	3.67	0.76	nr	5.84
13 amp to BS 1363 1 gang DP switched	0.23	1.41	2.66	0.43	nr	3.32
13 amp to BS 1363 2 gang DP switched	0.28	1.72	5.35	1.06	nr	8.13
13 amp to BS 1363 1 gang DP switched with neon	0.23	1.41	4.31	0.86	nr	6.58
13 amp to BS 1263 2 gang DP switched with neon	0.28	1.72	8.68	1.56	nr	11.96
2 amp 3 pin socket	0.23	1.41	2.20	0.54	nr	4.15
5 amp SP switched surface to BS 546	0.23	1.41	4.00	0.81	nr	6.22
15 amp SP switched surface to BS 546	0.23	1.41	5.34	1.01	nr	7.76
5 amp SP switched flush to BS 546	0.23	1.41	3.70	0.77	nr	5.88
15 amp SP switched flush to BS 546	0.23	1.41	4.26	0.85	nr	6.52
5 amp SP switched flush and neon	0.23	1.41	5.31	1.01	nr	7.73
15 amp SP switched flush and neon	0.23	1.41	5.87	1.09	nr	8.37
RCD protected socket (30m)	0.28	1.72	35.20	5.54	nr	42.46
RCD protected socket (10m)	0.28	1.72	36.35	5.71	nr	43.78

ELECTRICAL WORK

ACCESSORIES	Labour hours	Nett labour £	Nett material £	O'Heads /profit £	Unit	Total £
Connection/Control Units						
Fused DP switched	0.42	2.58	4.44	1.05	nr	8.07
Fused DP switched with neon	0.42	2.58	6.35	1.34	nr	10.27
Fused unswitched	0.42	2.58	4.37	1.04	nr	7.99
Flex Outlet Plate	0.23	1.41	2.20	0.54	nr	4.15
3 amp Clock connector	0.23	1.41	5.57	1.05	nr	8.03
Single TV co-axial socket	0.33	2.03	3.61	0.85	nr	6.49
Twin TV co-axial socket	0.42	2.58	4.83	1.11	nr	8.52
Single Telephone cord outlet	0.28	1.72	2.17	0.58	nr	4.47
Twin telephone cord outlet	0.35	2.15	2.35	0.68	nr	5.18
1 gang blank plate	0.20	1.23	0.84	0.31	nr	2.38
2 gang blank plate	0.25	1.54	1.46	0.45	nr	3.45
Shaver supply unit	0.33	2.03	20.60	3.40	nr	26.03
45 amp horizontal cooker control to BS 4177	0.42	2.58	8.44	1.65	nr	12.67
45 amp horizontal cooker control to BS 4177 with neon	0.42	2.58	11.56	2.12	nr	16.26
Cooker outlet unit with cable clamp	0.38	2.33	2.27	0.69	nr	5.29
Cooker outlet unit with terminal block	0.38	2.33	3.33	0.85	nr	6.51

FITTINGS

Lampholders, to BS 5042/T2						
Standard pendant	0.33	2.03	0.90	0.44	nr	3.37
Heat resistant pendant Home Office skirt	0.33	2.03	1.32	0.50	nr	3.85
Heat resistant pendant	0.33	2.03	1.21	0.49	nr	3.73
Batten 2T Home Office skirt	0.30	1.84	1.50	0.50	nr	3.84
Batten 3T Home Office skirt	0.30	1.84	1.77	0.54	nr	4.15
Angle batten 3T Home Office	0.30	1.84	2.28	0.62	nr	4.74
Combined block/batten holder 3T + earth Home Office skirt	0.30	1.84	3.67	0.83	nr	6.34
Batten holder with 100 pin and earth Home Office skirt	0.30	1.84	2.90	0.71	nr	5.45
Batten holder 2 terminal, loop-in and earth with heat resistant connections	0.30	1.84	3.24	0.76	nr	5.84

FITTINGS	Labour hours	Nett labour £	Nett material £	O'Heads /profit £	Unit	Total £
Dimmers						
1 gang 400 watts rotary action	0.23	1.41	13.00	2.16	nr	16.57
1 gang 250 watts Push on/off	0.23	1.41	13.00	2.16	nr	16.57
2 gang 250 watts Push on/off	0.28	1.72	26.10	4.17	nr	31.99
3 gang 250 watts Push on/off	0.38	2.33	40.17	6.38	nr	48.88
4 gang 250 watts Push on/off	0.43	2.64	55.70	8.75	nr	67.09
1 gang 250 watts rotary action	0.23	1.41	8.24	1.45	nr	11.10
Plugs BS 1363/A: 1984						
13 amp fused - sleeved pins	0.20	1.23	1.06	0.34	nr	2.63
3 amp fused - sleeved pins	0.12	0.74	1.06	0.27	nr	2.07
5 amp fused - sleeved pins	0.12	0.74	1.06	0.27	nr	2.07
13 amp three way adaptor	0.03	0.18	4.08	0.64	nr	4.90
Metal Finish Fittings						
Finishes;						
Golden bronze						
Stainless steel						
Stainless steel - highly polished						
Stainless steel - brushed						
5 amp switches						
1 gang 2 way	0.17	1.04	3.95	0.75	nr	5.74
2 gang 2 way	0.25	1.54	5.42	1.04	nr	8.00
3 gang 2 way	0.38	2.33	7.57	1.49	nr	11.39
1 gang intermediate	0.17	1.04	6.57	1.14	nr	8.75
Bell push	0.17	1.04	4.95	0.90	nr	6.89
13 amp sockets						
1 gang unswitched	0.23	1.41	4.65	0.91	nr	6.97
2 gang unswitched	0 28	1.72	8.51	1.54	nr	11.77
1 gang switched	0.23	1.41	5.17	0.99	nr	7.57
2 gang switched	0.28	1.72	9.45	1.68	nr	12.85
1 gang switched and neon	0.23	1.41	7.92	1.40	nr	10.73
2 gang switched and neon	0.28	1.72	14.29	2.40	nr	18.41
13 amp connection units						
switched spur	0.42	2.58	6.86	1.42	nr	10.86
Spur, unswitched	0.42	2.58	6.16	1.31	nr	10.05
Switched spur and cable outlet	0.42	2.58	7.32	1.49	nr	11.39
Switched spur and neon	0.42	2.58	9.42	1.80	nr	13.80
Spur unswitched and cable outlet	0.42	2.58	6.58	1.37	nr	10.53
Switched spur and neon and cable outlet	0.42	2.58	9.87	1.87	nr	14.32

ELECTRICAL WORK

FITTINGS	Labour hours	Nett labour £	Nett material £	O'Heads /profit £	Unit	Total £
20 amp switches double pole						
Switch	0.42	2.58	5.84	1.26	nr	9.68
Switch with neon	0.42	2.58	7.75	1.55	nr	11.88
Switch with neon marked 'Water heater'	0.42	2.58	8.51	1.66	nr	12.75
Switch with cable outlet (not available in polished stainless steel)	0.42	2.58	6.35	1.34	nr	10.27
Switch with neon and cable outlet (not available in polished stainless steel)	0.42	2.58	8.14	1.61	nr	12.33
45 amp switches - Double Pole						
switch	0.42	2.58	8.96	1.73	nr	13.27
Switch with neon	0.42	2.58	10.00	1.89	nr	14.47
Switch marked 'Cooker'	0.42	2.58	9.23	1.77	nr	13.58
Switch marked 'Cooker' with neon	0.42	2.58	10.29	1.93	nr	14.80
TV/Telephone outlets						
TV co-axial 1 gang	0.33	2.03	6.44	1.27	nr	9.74
TV co-axial 2 gang	0.42	2.58	6.86	1.42	nr	10.86
Telephone outlet 1 gang	0.28	1.72	4.00	0.86	nr	6.58
Telephone outlet 2 gang	0.35	2.15	4.27	0.96	nr	7.38
Telephone Line Jack-master	0.25	1.54	6.48	1.20	nr	9.22
Telephone Line jack secondary	0.25	1.54	5.71	1.09	nr	8.34
Shaver supply unit	0.33	2.03	21.94	3.60	nr	27.57
Dimmers						
1 gang 400watts rotary action (all finishes)	0.23	1.41	22.26	3.55	nr	27.22
1 gang 1000watts rotary action (stainless steel brushed only)	0.23	1.41	27.55	4.34	nr	33.30
TV/telephone outlets						
13 amp socket 2 gang switched	0.28	1.72	9.65	1.71	nr	13.08
13 amp socket 1 gang switched with neon	0.23	1.41	7.41	1.32	nr	10.14
13 amp socket 2 gang switched with neon	0.28	1.72	6.56	1.24	nr	9.52
13 amp switched spur	0.38	2.33	5.44	1.17	nr	8.94
13 amp switched spur with cable outlet	0.38	2.33	5.80	1.22	nr	9.35
13 amp switched spur with neon	0.38	2.33	6.79	1.37	nr	10.49

ELECTRICAL WORK

FITTINGS		Labour hours	Nett labour £	Nett material £	O'Heads /profit £	Unit	Total £
13 amp switched spur with neon and cable outlet		0.38	2.33	7.30	1.45	nr	11.08
13 amp spur unswitched		0.38	2.33	5.14	1.12	nr	8.59
13 amp spur,unswitched with cable outlet		0.38	2.33	5.57	1.19	nr	9.09
Telephone line jack master		0.25	1.54	6.26	1.17	nr	8.97
Telephone line jack secondary		0.25	1.54	5.17	1.01	nr	7.72
TV coaxial cable connectors							
Moulded plugs		0.17	1.04	0.44	0.22	nr	1.70
Sockets		0.17	1.04	0.53	0.24	nr	1.81
Aluminium plug		0.17	1.04	0.37	0.21	nr	1.62
Line connector		0.30	1.84	0.63	0.63	nr	2.84
Attenuator		0.30	1.84	2.31	0.62	nr	4.77
Surface mounting outlet		0.25	1.54	1.78	0.50	nr	3.82
Flush mounting outlet							
single		0.40	2.46	2.31	0.72	nr	5.49
twin		0.50	3.07	3.25	0.95	nr	7.27
Aerial splitter/combiner							
low loss		0.20	1.23	5.88	1.07	nr	8.18
resistive		0.20	1.23	4.20	0.82	nr	6.25
V & E Friedland Ltd Bell and chimes							
Chimes							
'Hi-Hi'		0.60	3.68	5.21	1.33	nr	10.22
'Facet'		0.60	3.68	6.21	1.48	nr	11.37
'Cameo'		0.60	3.68	6.44	1.52	nr	11.64
'Ding Dong'		0.60	3.68	6.62	1.55	nr	11.85
'Big Ben'		0.60	3.68	6.94	1.59	nr	12.21
'Seville'		0.60	3.68	9.27	1.94	nr	14.89
'Madrid'		0.60	3.68	9.27	1.94	nr	14.89
'Apollo'		0.60	3.68	9.50	1.98	nr	15.16
'Quartet'		0.60	3.68	9.59	1.99	nr	15.26
'Classic'		0.60	3.68	10.91	2.19	nr	16.78
Standard							
Standard							
'Linwood'	2.0kW	1.00	6.14	83.56	13.46	nr	103.16
'Minstead'	2.0kW	1.00	6.14	98.50	15.70	nr	120.34

258

ELECTRICAL WORK

ACCESSORIES		Labour hours	Nett labour £	Nett material £	O'Heads /profit £	Unit	Total £
Warm air curtains							
	3.0kW	1.25	7.68	92.50	15.03	nr	115.21
	4.0kW	1.25	7.68	111.73	17.91	nr	137.32
Remote control for above		1.00	6.14	31.68	5.67	nr	43.49
Radiant wall fires							
'Studio 2'	2.0kW	1.00	6.14	44.75	7.63	nr	58.52
'Studio 2 Super'	2.0kW	1.00	6.14	64.63	10.62	nr	81.39
'Studio 3 Super'	3.0kW	1.00	6.14	84.70	13.63	nr	104.47
'Studio Super Electronic 2.1kW		1.00	6.14	103.57	16.46	nr	126.17
Electric towel rails							
Chrome							
Wall	90 watts	1.00	6.14	54.80	9.14	nr	70.08
Wall	130 watts	1.00	6.14	67.05	10.98	nr	84.17
Floor	130 watts	0.25	1.54	67.05	10.29	nr	78.88
Wall	150 watts	1.00	6.14	72.45	11.79	nr	90.38
Floor	150 watts	0.25	1.54	72.45	11.10	nr	85.09
White stove enamel							
Wall	120 watts	1.00	6.14	42.71	7.33	nr	56.18
Wall	175 watts	1.00	6.14	48.20	8.15	nr	62.49
Floor	175 watts	0.25	1.54	48.21	7.46	nr	57.21
Wall	200 watts	1.00	6.14	51.62	8.66	nr	66.42
Floor	200 watts	0.25	1.54	51.62	7.97	nr	61.13
Immersion heaters 2¼" BSP head							
(fitting to tank and electrical connection)							
'Gold dot' 11", 14" and 18" long							
1, 2 or 3kW		0.70	4.30	10.50	2.22	nr	17.02
'Gold Dot' 23", 27" and 30" long							
3kW		0.70	4.30	10.82	2.27	nr	17.39
'Superlay' 11", 14", 18", 23",							
27", 30" long 3kW		0.70	4.30	14.60	2.84	nr	21.74
'Twin heat 23", 27" and 30" long							
3kW		0.70	4.30	20.48	3.72	nr	28.50
Hand driers (Heatrae Sadia Heating Ltd)							
Handy Dri 14	1.4kW	1.00	6.14	86.63	13.92	nr	106.69
Handy Dri 19	1.9kW	1.00	6.14	102.90	16.36	nr	125.40

ACCESSORIES	Labour hours	Nett labour £	Nett material £	O'Heads /profit £	Unit	Total £
Ventilation fans (Vent Axia Ltd)						
Extractor fans VA range, small room						
Window						
YA 100 LWW	1.50	9.21	23.70	4.94	nr	37.85
YA 100 LTWW	1.50	9.21	29.38	5.79	nr	44.38
VA 100 XWW	1.50	9.21	29.38	5.79	nr	44.38
VA 100 XEWW	1.50	9.21	38.43	7.15	nr	54.79
Wall						
VA 100 LWL	1.50	9.21	23.70	4.94	nr	37.85
VA 100 LTWL	1.50	9.21	29.38	5.79	nr	44.38
VA 100 XWL	1.50	9.21	29.38	5.79	nr	44.38
VA 100 EXEL	1.50	9.21	38.43	7.15	nr	54.79
Fixing kits for wall or window fans	0.50	3.07	6.06	1.37	nr	10.50
Accessories shutters for						
6" diameter fan	0.25	1.54	18.58	3.02	nr	23.14
7½" diameter fan	0.25	1.54	22.83	3.66	nr	28.03
9" diameter fan	0.25	1.54	29.60	4.67	nr	35.81
12" diameter fan	0.25	1.54	39.30	6.13	nr	46.97
Standard Range Controllers						
R6/7SC	0.50	3.07	26.30	4.41	nr	33.78
R9/125C	0.50	3.07	31.26	5.15	nr	39.48
T-Series Controllers						
TSC surface mounting	0.50	3.07	25.35	4.26	nr	32.68
TSC flush fitting/metal clad	0.50	3.07	27.87	4.64	nr	35.58
TTC timeswitch	0.50	3.07	31.97	5.26	nr	40.30
Domestic extract unit c/w shutter, switch, grille and wall mounting Kit VA150 6" diameter	1.25	7.68	39.20	7.03	nr	53.91

FITTINGS
Luminaires and light fittings
(Philips Lighting Ltd)

ELECTRICAL WORK

FITTINGS	Labour hours	Nett labour £	Nett material £	O'Heads /profit £	Unit	Total £
R77 Area Floodlights						
complete with lamps, gear and						
brackets						
SOX - E66 lamp	1.60	9.82	193.50	30.50	nr	233.82
400W SON/T lamp	1.60	9.82	226.50	35.45	nr	271.77
400W HPI/T lamp	2.60	15.96	264.13	42.01	nr	322.10
Front glass (inc. gasket)	0.20	12.28	16.05	4.25	nr	32.58
Downlighters						
Full recessed complete with lamps						
Model No						
602W white 12 x 50W halogen	1.25	7.68	16.45	3.62	nr	27.75
602G gold 12 x 50W halogen	1.25	7.68	17.55	3.79	nr	29.02
603W white SLD 18 lamp	1.25	7.68	18.24	3.89	nr	29.81
603B brown SLD 18 lamp	1.25	7.68	18.24	3.89	nr	29.81
603G gold SLD 18 lamp	1.25	7.68	20.37	4.21	nr	32.26
604W white 40W R50 lamp	1.25	7.68	4.89	1.89	nr	14.46
604B brown 40W R50 lamp	1.25	7.68	4.89	1.89	nr	14.46
604G gold 40W R50 lamp	1.25	7.68	7.75	2.32	nr	17.75
Semi-Recessed Downlighters						
Model No complete with lamps						
615W white R50 lamps	1.25	7.68	11.04	2.81	nr	21.53
615B brown R50 lamp	1.25	7.68	11.04	2.81	nr	21.53
615G gold R50 lamp	1.25	7.68	14.20	3.28	nr	25.16
618W white R63 lamp	1.25	7.68	13.93	3.24	nr	24.85
618B brown R63 lamp	1.25	7.68	13.93	3.24	nr	24.85
618G gold R63 lamp	1.25	7.68	16.76	3.67	nr	28.11
619W white PAR38E lamp	1.25	7.68	24.00	4.75	nr	36.43
619B brown PAR38E lamp	1.25	7.68	24.00	4.75	nr	36.43
619G gold PAR38E lamp	1.25	7.68	30.50	5.73	nr	43.91
Spotlights						
(includes lamps excluding track)						
Basic series						
White basic spot (DCS)	1.00	6.14	7.50	2.05	nr	15.69
Black basic spot (DCS)	1.00	6.14	7.50	2.05	nr	15.69
Aluminium 2 circuit track PAR38E	1.00	6.14	21.50	4.15	nr	31.79
Aluminium 3 circuit track PAR38E	1.00	6.14	26.60	4.91	nr	37.65
Aluminium wall/ceiling PAR38E	1.00	6.14	22.00	4.22	nr	32.36
White spot 2 circuit track PAR38E	1.00	6.14	21.95	4.21	nr	32.30
Black spot 2 circuit track PAR38E	1.00	6.14	21.95	4.21	nr	32.30
White spot 3 circuit track PAR38E	1.00	6.14	27.75	5.08	nr	38.97
Black spot 3 circuit track PAR38E	1.00	6.14	27.75	5.08	nr	38.97

ELECTRICAL WORK

FIRE AND INTRUDER DETECTION SYSTEMS	Labour hours	Nett labour £	Nett material £	O'heads /profit £	Unit	Total £
FIRE ALARMS						
Halon gas system status indicator with remote lock-off switch	0.75	4.61	91.00	14.34	nr	109.95
For fire resistant cable refer to cable listing						
INTRUDER ALARM SYSTEM						
Single zone panel 229mm high x 152mm wide x 76mm deep	2.50	15.35	82.70	14.71	nr	112.76
Single zone panel to BS4737	2.50	15.35	88.20	15.53	nr	119.08
Two zone panel to BS4737	3.00	18.42	137.80	23.43	nr	179.65
12V 150mm internal alarm siren	1.00	6.14	16.50	3.40	nr	26.04
12V internal alarm siren	1.00	6.14	16.50	3.40	nr	26.04
Stair pressure mat	0.33	2.03	4.13	0.92	nr	7.08
Floor pressure mat	0.33	2.03	6.06	1.21	nr	9.30
Window foil 33m roll	0.08	0.49	0.16	0.10	m	0.75
2 way male off blocks for window foil	0.08	0.49	0.56	0.16	nr	1.21
Panic button	0.50	3.07	6.06	1.37	nr	10.50
Vibration window contact	0.25	1.54	16.00	2.63	nr	20.17
Infra red detectors						
12m range	0.80	4.91	52.35	8.59	nr	65.85
Anti-pet 10m range	0.80	4.91	54.60	8.93	nr	68.44
Anti-pet 25m range	0.80	4.91	60.60	9.83	nr	75.34
By pass switch	0.25	1.54	13.80	2.30	nr	17.64
Door connector loops	0.33	2.03	2.75	0.72	nr	5.50
Terminal block						
8-way	0.08	0.49	1.05	0.23	nr	1.77
6-way	0.08	0.49	0.66	0.17	nr	1.32
"999" police autodial unit	2.50	15.35	209.50	33.73	nr	258.58

ELECTRICAL WORK

FIRE AND INTRUDER DETECTION SYSTEMS	Labour hours	Nett labour £	Nett material £	O'heads /profit £	Unit	Total £
Digital communicator for connection to central monitoring station	3.00	18.42	264.60	42.45	nr	325.47

FLOOR WALL AND CEILING FINISHES

1. Labour rate £8.29 per hour

2. Basic prices of materials

   The basic prices of the materials (including delivery and off loading) used in the calculations are as follows:-

Material	Basic Price
Sand	£10.00/tonne
Browning plaster	£102.25/tonne
Finishing plaster	£82.13/tonne
Bonding plaster	£100.56/tonne
Ordinary portland cement	£61.20/tonne
Universal one coat plaster	£122.43/tonne
Wallboard 9.5mm thick	£1.24/m2
Wallboard 12.5mm thick	£1.48/m2
Baseboard 9.5mm thick	£1.16/m2
Expamet metal lath	
- BB263	£2.38/m2
- BB264	£2.78/m2
- 94G	£4.26/m2
- 269	£3.06/m2
- 271	£3.52/m2
Red quarry tiles 150mm x 150mm x 12.5mm	£170.00/thousand
Red quarry tiles 225mm x 225mm x 25mm	£75.00/hundred
Marley floor tiles	
- Econoflex series 2; 2mm thick	£2.27/m2
- Econoflex series 2; 2.5mm thick	£2.39/m2
- Econoflex series 4; 2mm thick	£2.69/m2
- Econoflex series 4; 2.5mm thick	£2.62/m2
- Marleyflex 2mm thick	£2.93/m2
- Marleyflex 2.5mm thick	£3.42/m2
- Vylon	£3.06/m2
- Marley floor	£3.76/m2
- HD 2mm thick	£5.00/m2
- HD 2.5mm thick	£5.90/m2
Woodblock flooring	
- Iroko	£21.15/m2
- Merbau	£21.38/m2
- European Oak	£24.32/m2
- American Oak	£28.12/m2
- Sapele	£17.97/m2
- Mahogany	£20.91/m2
- Maple	£17.58/m2
Ceramic Universal tiles	
- 152mm x 152mm x 5.5mm; price group	

FLOOR WALL AND CEILING FINISHES

- A	£9.84/m2
- B	£9.10/m2
- B1	£10.01/m2
- C	£11.24/m2
- D	£12.03/m2
- D1	£12.50/m2
- E	£13.89/m2
- F	£14.73/m2
- G	£16.28/m2
- G2	£20.41/m2
- 200mm x 200mm x 6.5mm ; price group	
- A	£11.00/m2
- B	£11.00/m2
- C	£13.79/m2
- D1	£15.15/m2
- F	£17.88/m2
- G2	£24.71/m2
- SP	£29.59/m2

Ceramic Studio tiles

- 152mm x 152mm x 5.5mm; price group	
- B	£31.18/m2
- C	£41.93/m2
- D	£52.14/m2
- D1	£54.83/m2
- D2	£59.66/m2
- D3	£74.18/m2
- 203mm x 152mm x 6.5mm; price group	
- E	£33.00/m2
- 1	£47.85/m2
- 1A	£58.89/m2
- 1B	£75.08/m2
- 2	£95.70/m2
- 200mm x 200mm x 7mm; price group	
- A	£36.25/m2
- B	£48.44/m2
- C	£60.31/m2
- 250mm x 200mm x 7mm; price group	
- 2	£50.25/m2
- 3	£60.25/m2
- 4	£71.00/m2
- 5	£81.75/m2

Paramount partition

- 50mm	£5.01/m2
- 57mm	£5.09/m2
- 63mm	£5.80/m2

FLOOR WALL AND CEILING FINISHES

IN SITU FINISHINGS	Labour hours £	Nett labour £	Nett material £	O'heads /profit £	Unit	Total £
Plaster; 11mm cement and sand (1:3); 2mm Thistle finish						
To concrete, brickwork or blockwork						
Walls						
- over 300mm wide	0.46	3.81	0.71	0.68	m2	5.20
- not exceeding 300mm wide	0.69	5.72	0.71	0.96	m2	7.39
Curved walls						
- over 300mm wide	0.74	6.13	0.71	1.03	m2	7.87
- not exceeding 300mm wide	0.92	7.63	0.71	1.25	m2	9.59
Ceilings						
- over 300mm wide	0.60	4.97	0.71	0.85	m2	6.53
- not exceeding 300mm wide	0.89	7.38	0.71	1.21	m2	9.30
Sides soffits or tops of isolated beams						
- over 300mm wide	0.74	6.13	0.71	1.03	m2	7.87
- not exceeding 300mm wide	1.06	8.79	0.71	1.43	m2	10.93
Sides of isolated columns						
- over 300mm wide	0.50	4.15	0.71	0.73	m2	5.59
- not exceeding 300mm wide	0.63	5.22	0.71	0.89	m2	6.82

Increase the labour element of all items for working in staircase areas or compartments not exceeding 4m2 by 15%

Increase the labour element of ceilings and beams for work over 3.5m high by 10%

IN SITU FINISHINGS	Labour hours £	Nett labour £	Nett material £	O'heads /profit £	Unit	Total £
Plaster; 5mm two coat Thistle board finish						
To plasterboard or concrete						
Walls						
- over 300mm wide	0.40	3.32	0.52	0.58	m2	4.42
- not exceeding 300mm wide	0.60	4.97	0.52	0.82	m2	6.31
Curved walls						
- over 300mm wide	0.63	5.22	0.52	0.86	m2	6.60
- not exceeding 300mm wide	0.79	6.55	0.52	1.06	m2	8.13
Ceilings						
- over 300mm wide	0.51	4.23	0.52	0.71	m2	5.46
- not exceeding 300mm wide	0.77	6.38	0.52	1.04	m2	7.94
Sides soffits or tops of isolated beams						
- over 300mm wide	0.63	5.22	0.52	0.86	m2	6.60
- not exceeding 300mm wide	0.91	7.54	0.52	1.21	m2	9.27
Sides of isolated columns						
- over 300mm wide	0.43	3.56	0.52	0.61	m2	4.69
- not exceeding 300mm wide	0.54	4.48	0.52	0.75	m2	5.75

Increase the labour element of
all items for working in
staircase areas or compartments
not exceeding 4m2 by 15%

Increase the labour element of
ceilings and beams for work
over 3.5m high by 10%

267

IN SITU FINISHINGS	Labour hours £	Nett labour £	Nett material £	O'heads /profit £	Unit	Total £
Plaster; Thistle universal one coat plaster						
10mm thick to concrete						
Walls						
- over 300mm wide	0.33	2.74	1.11	0.58	m2	4.43
- not exceeding 300mm wide	0.50	4.15	1.11	0.79	m2	6.05
Curved walls						
- over 300mm wide	0.53	4.39	1.11	0.83	m2	6.33
- not exceeding 300mm wide	0.66	5.47	1.11	0.99	m2	7.57
Ceilings						
- over 300mm wide	0.43	3.56	1.11	0.70	m2	5.37
- not exceeding 300mm wide	0.64	5.31	1.11	0.96	m2	7.38
Sides soffits or tops of isolated beams						
- over 300mm wide	0.53	4.39	1.11	0.83	m2	6.33
- not exceeding 300mm wide	0.76	6.30	1.11	1.11	m2	8.52
Sides of isolated columns						
- over 300mm wide	0.36	2.98	1.11	0.61	m2	4.70
- not exceeding 300mm wide	0.45	3.73	1.11	0.73	m2	5.57

Increase the labour element of all items for working in staircase areas or compartments not exceeding 4m2 by 15%

Increase the labour element of ceilings and beams for work over 3.5m high by 10%

FLOOR WALL AND CEILING FINISHES

IN SITU FINISHINGS	Labour hours £	Nett labour £	Nett material £	O'heads /profit £	Unit	Total £

Labours on plasterwork

13mm two coat plaster

Rounded internal angles
- not exceeding 10mm radius	0.05	0.41	-	0.06	m	0.47
- 10mm-100mm radius	0.07	0.58	-	0.09	m	0.67

Rounded external angles
- not exceeding 10mm radius	0.06	0.50	-	0.08	m	0.58
- 10mm-100mm radius	0.08	0.66	-	0.10	m	0.76

Making good around pipes and the like
- not exceeding 0.3m girth	0.06	0.50	-	0.08	nr	0.58
- 0.3m-1m girth	0.07	0.58	-	0.09	nr	0.67
- 1m-2m girth	0.08	0.66	-	0.10	nr	0.76

10mm two coat plaster

Rounded internal angles
- not exceeding 10mm radius	0.04	0.33	-	0.05	m	0.38
- 10mm-100mm radius	0.06	0.50	-	0.08	m	0.58

Rounded external angles
- not exceeding 10mm radius	0.05	0.41	-	0.06	m	0.47
- 10mm-100mm radius	0.07	0.58	-	0.09	m	0.67

Making good around pipes and the like
- not exceeding 0.3m girth	0.05	0.41	-	0.06	nr	0.47
- 0.3m-1m girth	0.06	0.50	-	0.08	nr	0.58
- 1m-2m girth	0.07	0.58	-	0.09	nr	0.67

FLOOR WALL AND CEILING FINISHES

IN SITU FINISHINGS	Labour hours	Nett labour £	Nett material £	O'heads /profit £	Unit	Total £
Labour on Plasterwork (cont'd)						
5mm single coat plaster						
Making good around pipes and the like						
- not exceeding 0.3m girth	0.04	0.33	-	0.05	nr	0.38
- 0.3m-1m girth	0.05	0.41	-	0.06	nr	0.47
- 1m-2m girth	0.06	0.50	-	0.08	nr	0.58
2mm single coat plaster						
Making good around pipes and the like						
- not exceeding 0.3m girth	0.03	0.25	-	0.04	nr	0.29
- 0.3m-1m girth	0.04	0.33	-	0.05	nr	0.38
- 1m-2m girth	0.05	0.41	-	0.06	nr	0.47
Plaster stops and the like; Expamet or similar						
Standard angle bead						
- ref 550; 10-13mm plaster	0.12	0.99	0.40	0.21	m	1.60
Thin coat angle bead						
- ref 553; 3mm plaster	0.10	0.83	0.40	0.18	m	1.41
- ref 554; 6mm plaster	0.10	0.83	0.51	0.20	m	1.54
Square nose angle bead						
- ref 559; 10mm plaster	0.12	0.99	0.45	0.22	m	1.66
Thin coat stop beads						
- ref 560; 3mm plaster	0.10	0.83	0.50	0.20	m	1.53
- ref 561; 6mm plaster	0.10	0.83	0.50	0.20	m	1.53

FLOOR WALL AND CEILING FINISHES

IN SITU FINISHINGS	Labour hours	Nett labour £	Nett material £	O'heads /profit £	Unit	Total £
Plaster stops and the like (cont'd)						
Standard stop beads						
- ref 562; 10mm plaster	0.12	0.99	0.48	0.22	m	1.69
- ref 563; 13mm plaster	0.12	0.99	0.48	0.22	m	1.69
- ref 565; 16mm plaster	0.12	0.99	0.61	0.24	m	1.84
- ref 566; 19mm plaster	0.12	0.99	0.61	0.24	m	1.84
Architrave beads						
- ref 585; 10mm plaster	0.12	0.99	0.62	0.24	m	1.85
- ref 586; 10mm plaster	0.12	0.99	0.60	0.24	m	1.83
- ref 579; 13mm plaster	0.12	0.99	0.69	0.25	m	1.93
- ref 580; 13mm plaster	0.12	0.99	0.69	0.25	m	1.93
Movement bead						
- ref 588; 10mm plaster	0.12	0.99	2.08	0.46	m	3.53
Granolithic; cement and granite chippings (1:2½); steel trowelled smooth						
Floors; level and to falls						
25mm thick						
- over 300mm wide	0.38	3.15	3.46	0.99	m2	7.60
- not exceeding 300mm wide	0.57	4.73	3.46	1.23	m2	9.42
32mm thick						
- over 300mm wide	0.42	3.48	4.29	1.17	m2	8.94
- not exceeding 300mm wide	0.63	5.22	4.29	1.43	m2	10.94
38mm thick						
- over 300mm wide	0.45	3.73	5.42	1.37	m2	10.52
- not exceeding 300mm wide	0.68	5.64	5.42	1.66	m2	12.72
50mm thick						
- over 300mm wide	0.48	3.98	7.03	1.65	m2	12.66
- not exceeding 300mm wide	0.72	5.97	7.03	1.95	m2	14.95

FLOOR WALL AND CEILING FINISHES

IN SITU FINISHINGS	Labour hours	Nett labour £	Nett material £	O'heads /profit £	Unit	Total £
Granolithic; cement and granite (1:2½) to floors; level (cont'd)						

Increase the labour element of
all items for working in boiler
rooms and the like or
compartments not exceeding 4m2
by 15%

Landings

	Labour hours	Nett labour	Nett material	O'heads /profit	Unit	Total
25mm thick						
- over 300mm wide	0.42	3.48	3.46	1.04	m2	7.98
- not exceeding 300mm wide	0.63	5.22	3.46	1.30	m2	9.98
32mm thick						
- over 300mm wide	0.46	3.81	4.29	1.22	m2	9.32
- not exceeding 300mm wide	0.69	5.72	4.29	1.50	m2	11.51
38mm thick						
- over 300mm wide	0.50	4.15	5.42	1.44	m2	11.01
- not exceeding 300mm wide	0.75	6.22	5.42	1.75	m2	13.39
50mm thick						
- over 300mm wide	0.53	4.39	7.03	1.71	m2	13.13
- not exceeding 300mm wide	0.79	6.55	7.03	2.04	m2	15.62

Treads; rounded nosing

	Labour hours	Nett labour	Nett material	O'heads /profit	Unit	Total
25mm thick; of width						
- 275mm	0.28	2.32	0.95	0.49	m	3.76
- 350mm	0.35	2.90	1.21	0.62	m	4.73
32mm thick; of width						
- 275mm	0.32	2.65	1.18	0.57	m	4.40
- 350mm	0.39	3.23	1.50	0.71	m	5.44
38mm thick; of width						
- 275mm	0.36	2.98	1.49	0.67	m	5.14
- 350mm	0.43	3.56	1.90	0.82	m	6.28
50mm thick; of width						
- 275mm	0.40	3.32	1.93	0.79	m	6.04
- 350mm	0.47	3.90	2.46	0.95	m	7.31

IN SITU FINISHINGS	Labour hours	Nett labour £	Nett material £	O'heads /profit £	Unit	Total £
Granolithic; cement and granite (1:2½) to floors; level (cont'd)						
Extra over for ends and angles						
- 25/32mm thick; 275mm girth	0.06	0.50	-	0.08	nr	0.58
- 38/50mm thick; 275mm girth	0.07	0.58	-	0.09	nr	0.67
- 25/32mm thick; 350mm girth	0.08	0.66	-	0.10	nr	0.76
- 38/50mm thick; 350mm girth	0.09	0.75	-	0.11	nr	0.86
Extra over for intersections and outlets						
- 25/32mm thick; 275mm girth	0.07	0.58	-	0.09	nr	0.67
- 38/50mm thick; 275mm girth	0.08	0.66	-	0.10	nr	0.76
- 25/32mm thick; 350mm girth	0.09	0.75	-	0.11	nr	0.86
- 38/50mm thick; 350mm girth	0.10	0.83	-	0.12	nr	0.95
Risers; coved junction to tread						
13mm thick; of height						
- 150mm	0.23	1.91	0.27	0.33	m	2.51
- 150mm; undercut	0.27	2.24	0.27	0.38	m	2.89
- 200mm	0.30	2.49	0.36	0.43	m	3.28
- 200mm; undercut	0.34	2.82	0.36	0.48	m	3.66
19mm thick; of height						
- 150mm	0.27	2.24	0.39	0.39	m	3.02
- 150mm; undercut	0.31	2.57	0.39	0.44	m	3.40
- 200mm	0.34	2.82	0.53	0.50	m	3.85
- 200mm; undercut	0.38	3.15	0.53	0.55	m	4.23
Strings or aprons; rounded top edge						
13mm thick; of extreme width						
- 275mm	0.36	2.98	0.50	0.52	m	4.00
- 350mm	0.46	3.81	0.63	0.67	m	5.11
Extra over for ends and angles						
- 275mm	0.10	0.83	-	0.12	nr	0.95
- 350mm	0.12	0.99	-	0.15	nr	1.14

FLOOR WALL AND CEILING FINISHES

IN SITU FINISHINGS	Labour hours	Nett labour £	Nett material £	O'heads /profit £	Unit	Total £
Granolithic; cement and granite (1:2½) to floors; level (cont'd)						
Extra over for ramped and wreathed corners						
- 275mm	0.15	1.24	-	0.19	nr	1.43
- 350mm	0.18	1.49	-	0.22	nr	1.71
19mm thick of extreme width						
- 275mm	0.50	4.15	0.72	0.73	m	5.60
- 350mm	0.63	5.22	0.92	0.92	m	7.06
Extra over for ends and angles						
- 275mm	0.12	0.99	-	0.15	nr	1.14
- 350mm	0.14	1.16	-	0.17	nr	1.33
Extra over for ramped and wreathed corners						
- 275mm	0.18	1.49	-	0.22	nr	1.71
- 350mm	0.20	1.66	-	0.25	nr	1.91
Skirting; rounded top edge; coved junction to paving						
13mm thick; of height						
- 150mm	0.30	2.49	0.27	0.41	m	3.17
- 175mm	0.35	2.90	0.32	0.48	m	3.70
Extra over for ends and angles						
- 150mm	0.12	0.99	-	0.15	nr	1.14
- 175mm	0.14	1.16	-	0.17	nr	1.33
Extra over for ramps						
- 150mm	0.14	1.16	-	0.17	nr	1.33
- 175mm	0.16	1.33	-	0.20	nr	1.53
19mm thick; of height						
- 150mm	0.45	3.73	0.39	0.62	m	4.74
- 175mm	0.53	4.39	0.46	0.73	m	5.58
Extra over for ends and angles						
- 150mm	0.14	1.16	-	0.17	nr	1.33
- 175mm	0.16	1.33	-	0.20	nr	1.53

FLOOR WALL AND CEILING FINISHES

IN SITU FINISHINGS	Labour hours	Nett labour £	Nett material £	O'heads /profit £	Unit	Total £
Granolithic; cement and granite (1:2½) to floors; level (cont'd)						
Extra over for ramps						
- 150mm	0.16	1.33	-	0.20	nr	1.53
- 175mm	0.18	1.49	-	0.22	nr	1.71
Labours and sundry work in connection with granolithic paving						
Making good around pipes and the like						
Not exceeding 0.3m girth; paving thickness						
- 25/32mm	0.10	0.83	-	0.12	nr	0.95
- 38/50mm	0.12	0.99	-	0.15	nr	1.14
0.3m-1m girth; paving thickness						
- 25/32mm	0.13	1.08	-	0.16	nr	1.24
- 38/50mm	0.16	1.33	-	0.20	nr	1.53
1m-2m girth; paving thickness						
- 25/32mm	0.18	1.49	-	0.22	nr	1.71
- 38/50mm	0.20	1.66	-	0.25	nr	1.91
Additives and surface dressings						
Liquid hardening agent; for paving of thickness						
- 25mm	0.10	0.83	0.30	0.17	m2	1.30
- 32mm	0.12	0.99	0.38	0.21	m2	1.58
- 38mm	0.14	1.16	0.46	0.24	m2	1.86
- 50mm	0.16	1.33	0.59	0.29	m2	2.21

FLOOR WALL AND CEILING FINISHES

LATHING AND BASEBOARDING	Labour hours	Nett labour £	Nett material £	O'heads /profit £	Unit	Total £
Baseboarding; Gyproc wallboard square edge; 1200mm x 2400mm; taped butt joints; to receive skim coat; to timber with nails						
9.5mm thick						
Walls						
- over 300mm wide	0.22	1.82	1.55	0.51	m2	3.88
- not exceeding 300mm wide	0.33	2.74	1.61	0.65	m2	5.00
Ceilings						
- over 300mm wide	0.26	2.16	1.55	0.56	m2	4.27
- not exceeding 300mm wide	0.39	3.23	1.61	0.73	m2	5.57
Sides, soffits or tops of isolated beams						
- over 300mm wide	0.33	2.74	1.55	0.64	m2	4.93
- not exceeding 300mm wide	0.50	4.15	1.61	0.86	m2	6.62
Sides of isolated columns						
- over 300mm wide	0.33	2.74	1.55	0.64	m2	4.93
- not exceeding 300mm	0.50	4.15	1.61	0.86	m2	6.62
Add to the previous prices for tapered edge self finished wallboard	0.05	0.41	0.20	0.09	m2	0.70
Add to the previous prices for square edge duplex wallboard	-	-	0.55	0.08	m2	0.63
Add to the previous prices for tapered edge self finished duplex wallboard	0.05	0.41	0.75	0.17	m2	1.33
Add to the previous prices for square edge moisture resistant board	-	-	0.77	0.12	m2	0.89
Add to the previous prices for tapered edge self finished moisture resistant board	0.05	0.41	0.97	0.21	m2	1.59

LATHING AND BASEBOARDING	Labour hours	Nett labour £	Nett material £	O'heads /profit £	Unit	Total £
Baseboarding; wallboard 9.5mm thick (cont'd')						

Increase the labour element
of all items for working in
staircase areas or compartments
not exceeding 4m^2 by 15%

Increase the labour element
of ceilings and beams for work
over 3.5m high by 10%

12.5mm thick

	Labour hours	Nett labour £	Nett material £	O'heads /profit £	Unit	Total £
Walls						
- over 300mm wide	0.26	2.16	1.80	0.59	m2	4.55
- not exceeding 300mm wide	0.40	3.32	1.88	0.78	m2	5.98
Ceilings						
- over 300mm wide	0.31	2.57	1.80	0.66	m2	5.03
- not exceeding 300mm wide	0.47	3.90	1.88	0.87	m2	6.65
Sides, soffits or tops of isolated beams						
- over 300mm wide	0.40	3.32	1.80	0.77	m2	5.89
- not exceeding 300mm wide	0.60	4.97	1.88	1.03	m2	7.88
Sides of isolated columns						
- over 300mm wide	0.40	3.32	1.80	0.77	m2	5.89
- not exceeding 300mm wide	0.60	4.97	1.88	1.03	m2	7.88
Add to the previous prices for tapered edge self finished wallboard	0.05	0.41	0.20	0.09	m2	0.70
Add to the previous prices for square edge duplex wallboard	-	-	0.55	0.08	m2	0.63
Add to the previous prices for tapered edge self finished duplex wallboard	0.05	0.41	0.75	0.17	m2	1.33

FLOOR WALL AND CEILING FINISHES

LATHING AND BASEBOARDING	Labour hours	Nett labour £	Nett material £	O'heads /profit £	Unit	Total £

Metal lathing; galvanised;
Expamet; 700mm x 2500mm;
to timber with galvanised
nails

Reference BB263

	Labour hours	Nett labour £	Nett material £	O'heads /profit £	Unit	Total £
Walls						
- over 300mm wide	0.17	1.41	2.65	0.61	m2	4.67
- not exceeding 300mm wide	0.26	2.16	2.77	0.74	m2	5.67
Ceilings						
- over 300mm wide	0.20	1.66	2.65	0.65	m2	4.96
- not exceeding 300mm wide	0.30	2.49	2.77	0.79	m2	6.05
Sides, soffits or tops of isolated beams						
- over 300mm wide	0.25	2.07	2.65	0.71	m2	5.43
- not exceeding 300mm wide	0.38	3.15	2.77	0.89	m2	6.81
Sides of isolated columns						
- over 300mm wide	0.25	2.07	2.65	0.71	m2	5.43
- not exceeding 300mm wide	0.38	3.15	2.77	0.89	m2	6.81

Add to the previous prices
for fixing with tying

	Labour hours	Nett labour £	Nett material £	O'heads /profit £	Unit	Total £
wire to supporting metalwork	0.04	0.33	-	0.05	m2	0.38

Increase the labour element
of all items for working in
staircase areas or compartments
not exceeding 4m2 by 15%

Increase the labour element
of ceilings and beams for work
over 3.5m high by 10%

Reference BB264

	Labour hours	Nett labour £	Nett material £	O'heads /profit £	Unit	Total £
Walls						
- over 300mm wide	0.19	1.58	3.07	0.70	m2	5.35
- not exceeding 300mm wide	0.28	2.32	3.21	0.83	m2	6.36

LATHING AND BASEBOARDING	Labour hours	Nett labour £	Nett material £	O'heads /profit £	Unit	Total £
Lathing Expamet ref BB264 (cont'd)						
Ceilings						
- over 300mm wide	0.22	1.82	3.07	0.73	m2	5.62
- not exceeding 300mm wide	0.32	2.65	3.21	0.88	m2	6.74
Sides, soffits or tops of isolated beams						
- over 300mm wide	0.27	2.24	3.07	0.80	m2	6.11
- not exceeding 300mm wide	0.40	3.32	3.21	0.98	m2	7.51
Sides of isolated columns						
- over 300mm wide	0.27	2.24	3.07	0.80	m2	6.11
- not exceeding 300mm wide	0.40	3.32	3.21	0.98	m2	7.51

BEDS AND BACKINGS

Cement and sand (1:3) beds screeded finish

Floors; level and to falls

	Labour hours	Nett labour £	Nett material £	O'heads /profit £	Unit	Total £
25mm thick						
- over 300mm wide	0.21	1.74	1.18	0.44	m2	3.36
- not exceeding 300mm wide	0.32	2.65	1.18	0.57	m2	4.40
38mm thick						
- over 300mm wide	0.25	2.07	1.80	0.58	m2	4.45
- not exceeding 300mm wide	0.38	3.15	1.80	0.74	m2	5.69
50mm thick						
- over 300mm wide	0.29	2.40	2.36	0.71	m2	5.47
- not exceeding 300mm wide	0.44	3.65	2.36	0.90	m2	6.91
63mm thick						
- over 300mm wide	0.33	2.74	2.98	0.86	m2	6.58
- not exceeding 300mm wide	0.50	4.15	2.98	1.07	m2	8.20

Increase the labour element of all items for working in boiler rooms or compartments not exceeding 4m2 by 15%

BEDS AND BACKINGS	Labour hours	Nett labour £	Nett material £	O'heads /profit £	Unit	Total £
C & S (1:3) landings (cont'd)						
Landings						
25mm thick						
- over 300mm wide	0.25	2.07	1.30	0.51	m2	3.88
- not exceeding 300mm wide	0.37	3.07	1.30	0.66	m2	5.03
38mm thick						
- over 300mm wide	0.28	2.32	1.98	0.65	m2	4.95
- not exceeding 300mm wide	0.42	3.48	1.98	0.82	m2	6.28
50mm thick						
- over 300mm wide	0.32	2.65	2.60	0.79	m2	6.04
- not exceeding 300mm wide	0.48	3.98	2.60	0.99	m2	7.57
63mm thick						
- over 300mm wide	0.36	2.98	3.28	0.94	m2	7.20
- not exceeding 300mm wide	0.54	4.48	3.28	1.16	m2	8.92
Treads						
25mm thick; of width						
- 275mm	0.21	1.74	0.33	0.31	m	2.38
- 350mm	0.26	2.16	0.41	0.39	m	2.96
38mm thick; of width						
- 275mm	0.25	2.07	0.50	0.39	m	2.96
- 350mm	0.30	2.49	0.63	0.47	m	3.59
50mm thick; of width						
- 275mm	0.28	2.32	0.65	0.45	m	3.42
- 350mm	0.35	2.90	0.83	0.56	m	4.29
Add to the previous prices for floated finish	0.10	0.83	-	0.12	m2	0.95
Add to the previous prices for trowelled finish	0.14	1.16	-	0.17	m2	1.33

FLOOR WALL AND CEILING FINISHES

BEDS AND BACKINGS	Labour hours	Nett labour £	Nett material £	O'heads /profit £	Unit	Total £
Sundry work in connection with C & S (1:3) beds (Cont'd)						

Sundry work in connection with beds
and the like

Additives and surface dressings

	Labour hours	Nett labour £	Nett material £	O'heads /profit £	Unit	Total £
Liquid hardening agent; for beds of thickness						
- 25mm	0.10	0.83	0.30	0.17	m2	1.30
- 38mm	0.14	1.16	0.46	0.24	m2	1.86
- 50mm	0.16	1.33	0.59	0.29	m2	2.21
- 63mm	0.18	1.49	0.74	0.33	m2	2.56
Oil repellent agent; for beds of thickness						
- 25mm	0.10	0.83	0.32	0.17	m2	1.32
- 38mm	0.14	1.16	0.48	0.25	m2	1.89
- 50mm	0.16	1.33	0.62	0.29	m2	2.24
- 63mm	0.18	1.49	0.76	0.34	m2	2.59
Two coats surface hardener						
- all thicknesses	0.15	1.24	0.48	0.26	m2	1.98

TILE SLAB AND BLOCK FINISHINGS

Clay quarry floor tiles; red;
bedding in 12mm cement mortar
(1:3); butt joints straight both
ways

Floors; level and to falls

	Labour hours	Nett labour £	Nett material £	O'heads /profit £	Unit	Total £
150mm x 150mm x 12.5mm thick						
- over 300mm wide	0.90	7.46	8.51	2.40	m2	18.37
- not exceeding 300mm wide	0.90	7.46	8.89	2.45	m2	18.80
225mm x 225mm x 25mm thick						
- over 300mm wide	0.80	6.63	16.13	3.41	m2	26.17
- not exceeding 300mm wide	1.20	9.95	16.87	4.02	m2	30.84

FLOOR WALL AND CEILING FINISHES

TILE SLAB AND BLOCK FINISHINGS	Labour hours	Nett labour £	Nett material £	O'heads /profit £	Unit	Total £
Clay quarries (cont'd)						

Increase the labour element of
all items for working in boiler
rooms or compartments not
exceeding 4m2 by 15%

Floors; to falls, crossfalls and
slopes

150mm x 150mm x 12.5mm thick						
- over 300mm wide	1.05	8.70	8.51	2.58	m2	19.79
- not exceeding 300mm wide	1.58	13.10	8.89	3.30	m2	25.29
225mm x 225mm x 25mm thick						
- over 300mm wide	0.95	7.88	16.13	3.60	m2	27.61
- not exceeding 300mm wide	1.43	11.85	16.87	4.31	m2	33.03

Increase the labour element of
all items for working in boiler
rooms or compartments not
exceeding 4m2 by 15%

Landings

150mm x 150mm x 12.5mm thick						
- over 300mm wide	0.99	8.21	8.51	2.51	m2	19.23
- not exceeding 300mm wide	1.49	12.35	8.89	3.19	m2	24.43
225mm x 225mm x 25mm thick						
- over 300mm wide	0.88	7.30	16.13	3.51	m2	26.94
- not exceeding 300mm wide	1.32	10.94	16.87	4.17	m2	31.98

Treads; rounded nosing

150mm x 150mm x 12.5mm thick; of width						
- 275mm	0.56	4.64	3.06	1.16	m	8.86
- 350mm	0.71	5.89	3.89	1.47	m	11.25
225mm x 225mm x 12.5mm thick; of width						
- 275mm	0.50	4.15	5.80	1.49	m	11.44
- 350mm	0.63	5.22	7.38	1.89	m	14.49

FLOOR WALL AND CEILING FINISHES

TILE SLAB AND BLOCK FINISHINGS	Labour hours	Nett labour £	Nett material £	O'heads /profit £	Unit	Total £
Clay quarries (cont'd)						

Risers

150mm x 150mm x 12.5mm thick; of height						
- 150mm	0.41	3.40	1.67	0.76	m	5.83
- 150mm; undercut	0.46	3.81	1.83	0.85	m	6.49
- 200mm	0.54	4.48	2.22	1.01	m	7.71
- 200mm; undercut	0.59	4.89	2.45	1.10	m	8.44

Strings or aprons; rounded top edge

150mm x 150mm x 12.5mm thick; of width						
- 275mm	0.74	6.13	3.06	1.38	m	10.57
- 350mm	0.95	7.88	3.89	1.77	m	13.54

Skirting; rounded top edge; coved junction to paving

12.5mm thick; of height						
- 150mm	0.25	2.07	1.67	0.56	m	4.30
Extra over for						
- end	0.05	0.41	-	0.06	nr	0.47
- angle	0.07	0.58	1.59	0.33	nr	2.50
- ramp	0.09	0.75	-	0.11	nr	0.86
20mm thick; of height						
- 150mm	0.30	2.49	2.39	0.73	m	5.61
Extra over for						
- end	0.06	0.50	-	0.08	nr	0.58
- angle	0.08	0.66	2.39	0.46	nr	3.51
- ramp	0.10	0.83	-	0.12	nr	0.95

FLOOR WALL AND CEILING FINISHES

TILE SLAB AND BLOCK FINISHINGS	Labour hours	Nett labour £	Nett material £	O'heads /profit £	Unit	Total £
Labours in connection with quarry tiles						
Making good around pipes and the like						
Not exceeding 0.3m girth; paving thickness						
- 12.5mm	0.07	0.58	-	0.09	nr	0.67
- 25mm	0.09	0.75	-	0.11	nr	0.86
0.3m-1m girth; paving thickness						
- 12.5mm	0.10	0.83	-	0.12	nr	0.95
- 25mm	0.12	0.99	-	0.15	nr	1.14
1m-2m girth; paving thickness						
- 12.5mm	0.14	1.16	-	0.17	nr	1.33
- 25mm	0.16	1.33	-	0.20	nr	1.53
Extra over for working into recessed duct covers and the like						
Manhole cover; paving thickness						
- 12.5mm	0.20	1.66	-	0.25	nr	1.91
- 25mm	0.22	1.82	-	0.27	nr	2.09
Duct covers up to 250mm wide; paving thickness						
- 12.5mm	0.12	0.99	-	0.15	m	1.14
- 25mm	0.15	1.24	-	0.19	m	1.43
Duct covers 250mm-500mm wide; paving thickness						
- 12.5mm	0.16	1.33	-	0.20	m	1.53
- 25mm	0.20	1.66	-	0.25	m	1.91
Duct covers over 500mm wide; paving thickness						
- 12.5mm	0.20	1.66	-	0.25	m	1.91
- 25mm	0.25	2.07	-	0.31	m	2.38

TILE SLAB AND BLOCK FINISHINGS	Labour hours	Nett labour £	Nett material £	O'heads /profit £	Unit	Total £

Floor tiles; Marley or similar; 300mm x 300mm; fixing with bitumen adhesive

Floors; level and to falls

Over 300mm wide
- Econoflex

- Series 2; 2mm thick	0.24	1.99	2.88	0.73	m2	5.60
- Series 2; 2.5mm thick	0.26	2.16	3.00	0.77	m2	5.93
- Series 4; 2mm thick	0.24	1.99	3.33	0.80	m2	6.12
- Series 4; 2.5mm thick	0.26	2.16	3.46	0.84	m2	6.46
- Marleyflex; 2mm thick	0.24	1.99	3.57	0.83	m2	6.39
- Marleyflex; 2.5mm thick	0.26	2.16	4.09	0.94	m2	7.19
- Vylon	0.24	1.99	3.71	0.86	m2	6.56
- Marleyflor	0.24	1.99	4.45	0.97	m2	7.41
- HD; 2mm thick	0.24	1.99	5.75	1.16	m2	8.90
- HD; 2.5mm thick	0.26	2.16	6.69	1.33	m2	10.18

Not exceeding 300mm wide
- Econoflex

- Series 2; 2mm thick	0.36	2.98	3.02	0.90	m2	6.90
- Series 2; 2.5mm thick	0.39	3.23	3.15	0.96	m2	7.34
- Series 4; 2mm thick	0.36	2.98	3.50	0.97	m2	7.45
- Series 4; 2.5mm thick	0.39	3.23	3.63	1.03	m2	7.89
- Marleyflex; 2mm thick	0.36	2.98	3.75	1.01	m2	7.74
- Marleyflex; 2.5mm thick	0.39	3.23	4.30	1.13	m2	8.66
- Vylon	0.36	2.98	3.90	1.03	m2	7.91
- Marleyflor	0.36	2.98	4.67	1.15	m2	8.80
- HD; 2mm thick	0.36	2.98	6.04	1.35	m2	10.37
- HD; 2.5mm thick	0.39	3.23	7.03	1.54	m2	11.80

Increase the labour element of
all items for working in boiler
rooms or compartments not
exceeding 4m2 by 15%

FLOOR WALL AND CEILING FINISHES

TILE SLAB AND BLOCK FINISHINGS	Labour hours	Nett labour £	Nett material £	O'heads /profit £	Unit	Total £
Floor tiles; Marley (cont'd.)						

Landings

Over 300mm wide
- Econoflex

- Series 2; 2mm thick	0.26	2.16	2.88	0.76	m2	5.80
- Series 2; 2.5mm thick	0.29	2.40	3.00	0.81	m2	6.21
- Series 4; 2mm thick	0.26	2.16	3.33	0.82	m2	6.31
- Series 4; 2.5mm thick	0.29	2.40	3.46	0.88	m2	6.74
- Marleyflex; 2mm thick	0.26	2.16	3.57	0.86	m2	6.59
- Marleyflex; 2.5mm thick	0.29	2.40	4.09	0.97	m2	7.46
- Vylon	0.26	2.16	3.71	0.88	m2	6.75
- Marleyflor	0.26	2.16	4.45	0.99	m2	7.60
- HD; 2mm thick	0.26	2.16	5.75	1.19	m2	9.10
- HD; 2.5mm thick	0.29	2.40	6.69	1.36	m2	10.45

Treads

275mm wide
- Econoflex

- Series 2; 2mm thick	0.15	1.24	0.83	0.31	m	2.38
- Series 2; 2.5mm thick	0.16	1.33	0.87	0.33	m	2.53
- Series 4; 2mm thick	0.15	1.24	0.96	0.33	m	2.53
- Series 4; 2.5mm thick	0.16	1.33	1.00	0.35	m	2.68
- Marleyflex; 2mm thick	0.15	1.24	1.03	0.34	m	2.61
- Marleyflex; 2.5mm thick	0.16	1.33	1.18	0.38	m	2.89
- Vylon	0.15	1.24	1.07	0.35	m	2.66
- Marleyflor	0.15	1.24	1.28	0.38	m	2.90
- HD; 2mm thick	0.15	1.24	1.66	0.44	m	3.34
- HD; 2.5mm thick	0.16	1.33	1.93	0.49	m	3.75

350mm wide
- Econoflex

- Series 2; 2mm thick	0.19	1.58	1.06	0.40	m	3.04
- Series 2; 2.5mm thick	0.20	1.66	1.10	0.41	m	3.17
- Series 4; 2mm thick	0.19	1.58	1.23	0.42	m	3.23
- Series 4; 2.5mm thick	0.20	1.66	1.27	0.44	m	3.37
- Marleyflex; 2mm thick	0.19	1.58	1.31	0.43	m	3.32
- Marleyflex; 2.5mm thick	0.20	1.66	1.51	0.48	m	3.65
- Vylon	0.19	1.58	1.37	0.44	m	3.39
- Marleyflor	0.19	1.58	1.64	0.48	m	3.70
- HD; 2mm thick	0.19	1.58	2.11	0.55	m	4.24
- HD; 2.5mm thick	0.20	1.66	2.46	0.62	m	4.74

TILE SLAB AND BLOCK FINISHINGS	Labour hours	Nett labour £	Nett material £	O'heads /profit £	Unit	Total £
Floor tiles; Marley (cont'd.)						

Risers

150mm high; plain or undercut
- Econoflex

- Series 2; 2mm thick	0.11	0.91	0.45	0.20	m	1.56
- Series 2; 2.5mm thick	0.12	0.99	0.47	0.22	m	1.68
- Series 4; 2mm thick	0.11	0.91	0.53	0.22	m	1.66
- Series 4; 2.5mm thick	0.12	0.99	0.55	0.23	m	1.77
- Marleyflex; 2mm thick	0.11	0.91	0.56	0.22	m	1.69
- Marleyflex; 2.5mm thick	0.12	0.99	0.65	0.25	m	1.89
- Vylon	0.11	0.91	0.59	0.23	m	1.73
- Marleyflor	0.11	0.91	0.70	0.24	m	1.85
- HD; 2mm thick	0.11	0.91	0.91	0.27	m	2.09
- HD; 2.5mm thick	0.12	0.99	1.06	0.31	m	2.36

200mm high; plain or undercut
- Econoflex

- Series 2; 2mm thick	0.14	1.16	0.60	0.26	m	2.02
- Series 2; 2.5mm thick	0.16	1.33	0.63	0.29	m	2.25
- Series 4; 2mm thick	0.14	1.16	0.70	0.28	m	2.14
- Series 4; 2.5mm thick	0.16	1.33	0.73	0.31	m	2.37
- Marleyflex; 2mm thick	0.14	1.16	0.75	0.29	m	2.20
- Marleyflex; 2.5mm thick	0.16	1.33	0.86	0.33	m	2.52
- Vylon	0.14	1.16	0.78	0.29	m	2.23
- Marleyflor	0.14	1.16	0.93	0.31	m	2.40
- HD; 2mm thick	0.14	1.16	1.21	0.36	m	2.73
- HD; 2.5mm thick	0.16	1.33	1.41	0.41	m	3.15

Skirting; fixing with adhesive to walls

Sit on skirting

- 75mm high ref DCB3	0.11	0.91	0.84	0.26	m	2.01
- 100mm high ref DCB4	0.13	1.08	0.97	0.31	m	2.36

Plain skirting

- 100mm high ref DPB4	0.13	1.08	0.89	0.30	m	2.27

TILE SLAB AND BLOCK FINISHINGS	Labour hours	Nett labour £	Nett material £	O'heads /profit £	Unit	Total £
Floor tiles; Marley (cont'd)						

Labours and sundry work in connection with Marley floor tiles

Making good around pipes and the like

  Not exceeding 0.3m girth; tile thickness

- 2mm	0.04	0.33	-	0.05	nr	0.38
- 2.5mm	0.06	0.50	-	0.08	nr	0.58

  0.3m-1m girth; tile thickness

- 2mm	0.05	0.41	-	0.06	nr	0.47
- 2.5mm	0.07	0.58	-	0.09	nr	0.67

  1m-2m girth; tile thickness

- 2mm	0.06	0.50	-	0.08	nr	0.58
- 2.5mm	0.08	0.66	-	0.10	nr	0.76

Extra over for working into recessed covers and the like

  Manhole covers, tile thickness

- 2mm	0.10	0.83	-	0.12	nr	0.95
- 2.5mm	0.12	0.99	-	0.15	nr	1.14

  Duct covers up to 250mm wide; tile thickness

- 2mm	0.07	0.58	-	0.09	m	0.67
- 2.5mm	0.09	0.75	-	0.11	m	0.86

FLOOR WALL AND CEILING FINISHES

TILE SLAB AND BLOCK FINISHINGS	Labour hours	Nett labour £	Nett material £	O'heads /profit £	Unit	Total £

Wood block flooring; 25mm thick; tongued and grooved; herringbone pattern; fixing with adhesive; sanding

Floors; level and to falls

Over 300mm wide						
- Iroko	1.10	9.12	22.26	4.71	m2	36.09
- Merbau	1.10	9.12	22.50	4.74	m2	36.36
- European oak	1.10	9.12	25.60	5.21	m2	39.93
- American oak	1.10	9.12	29.60	5.81	m2	44.53
- Sapele	1.10	9.12	18.92	4.21	m2	32.25
- Mahogany	1.10	9.12	22.01	4.67	m2	35.80
- Maple	1.10	9.12	18.50	4.14	m2	31.76

Increase the labour elements of all items for working in compartments not exceeding 4m2 by 15%

2 block border; stretcher pattern						
- Iroko	0.25	2.07	2.23	0.65	m	4.95
- Merbau	0.25	2.07	2.25	0.65	m	4.97
- European oak	0.25	2.07	2.56	0.69	m	5.32
- American oak	0.25	2.07	2.96	0.75	m	5.78
- Sapele	0.25	2.07	1.89	0.59	m	4.55
- Mahogany	0.25	2.07	2.20	0.64	m	4.91
- Maple	0.25	2.07	1.85	0.59	m	4.51

Labours and sundry work in connection with wood block flooring

Making good around pipes and the like						
- not exceeding 0.3m girth	0.20	1.66	-	0.25	nr	1.91
- 0.3m-1m girth	0.30	2.49	-	0.37	nr	2.86
- 1m-2m girth	0.40	3.32	-	0.50	nr	3.82

TILE SLAB AND BLOCK FINISHINGS	Labour hours	Nett labour £	Nett material £	O'heads /profit £	Unit	Total £
Wood block flooring (cont'd)						
Extra over for working into recessed duct covers and the like						
- manhole covers	0.30	2.49	-	0.37	nr	2.86
- duct covers						
- up to 250mm wide	0.30	2.49	-	0.37	m	2.86
- 250mm-500mm wide	0.45	3.73	-	0.56	m	4.29
- over 500mm wide	0.60	4.97	-	0.75	m	5.72
Surface treatments						
- one coat sealer; one coat wax polish	0.20	1.66	1.25	0.44	m2	3.35
- three coats polyurethane varnish	0.35	2.90	2.50	0.81	m2	6.21

Glazed ceramic Universal Tiles; Pilkington or similar; plain faced fixing with thin bed adhesive; pointing with matching grout

To walls; 152mm x 152mm x 5.5mm thick

Over 300mm wide; price group						
- A	0.95	7.88	10.73	2.79	m2	21.40
- B	0.95	7.88	9.96	2.68	m2	20.52
- B1	0.95	7.88	10.91	2.82	m2	21.61
- C	0.95	7.88	12.20	3.01	m2	23.09
- D	0.95	7.88	13.03	3.14	m2	24.05
- D1	0.95	7.88	13.53	3.21	m2	24.62
- E	0.95	7.88	14.98	3.43	m2	26.29
- F	0.95	7.88	15.86	3.56	m2	27.30
- G	0.95	7.88	17.49	3.81	m2	29.18
- G2	0.95	7.88	21.83	4.46	m2	34.17

TILE SLAB AND BLOCK FINISHINGS	Labour hours	Nett labour £	Nett material £	O'heads /profit £	Unit	Total £
Universal wall tiles (cont'd)						
Not exceeding 300mm wide; price group						
- A	1.43	11.85	11.22	3.46	m2	26.53
- B	1.43	11.85	10.41	3.34	m2	25.60
- B1	1.43	11.85	11.41	3.49	m2	26.75
- C	1.43	11.85	12.76	3.69	m2	28.30
- D	1.43	11.85	13.63	3.82	m2	29.30
- D1	1.43	11.85	14.15	3.90	m2	29.90
- E	1.43	11.85	15.68	4.13	m2	31.66
- F	1.43	11.85	16.60	4.27	m2	32.72
- G	1.43	11.85	18.30	4.52	m2	34.67
- G2	1.43	11.85	22.85	5.21	m2	39.91
To walls 200mm x 100mm x 6.5mm thick						
Over 300mm wide; price group						
- A	1.10	9.12	11.95	3.16	m2	24.23
- B	1.10	9.12	11.95	3.16	m2	24.23
- C	1.10	9.12	14.88	3.60	m2	27.60
- D1	1.10	9.12	16.31	3.81	m2	29.24
- F	1.10	9.12	19.17	4.24	m2	32.53
- G2	1.10	9.12	26.35	5.32	m2	40.79
- SP	1.10	9.12	31.47	6.09	m2	46.68
Not exceeding 300mm wide; price group						
- A	1.65	13.68	12.50	3.93	m2	30.11
- B	1.65	13.68	12.50	3.93	m2	30.11
- C	1.65	13.68	15.57	4.39	m2	33.64
- D1	1.65	13.68	17.07	4.61	m2	35.36
- F	1.65	13.68	20.06	5.06	m2	38.80
- G2	1.65	13.68	27.58	6.19	m2	47.45
- SP	1.65	13.68	32.95	6.99	m2	53.62

FLOOR WALL AND CEILING FINISHES

TILE SLAB AND BLOCK FINISHINGS	Labour hours	Nett labour £	Nett material £	O'heads /profit £	Unit	Total £

Glazed ceramic Studio Tiles;
Pilkington or similar; fixing
with thin bed adhesive; pointing
with matching grout

To walls; 152mm x 152mm x 5.5mm
thick

	Labour hours	Nett labour £	Nett material £	O'heads /profit £	Unit	Total £
Over 300mm wide; price group						
- Studio B	0.95	7.88	33.13	6.15	m2	47.16
- Studio C	0.95	7.88	44.42	7.85	m2	60.15
- Studio D	0.95	7.88	55.14	9.45	m2	72.47
- Studio D1	0.95	7.88	57.96	9.88	m2	75.72
- Studio D2	0.95	7.88	63.05	10.64	m2	81.57
- Studio D3	0.95	7.88	78.28	12.92	m2	99.08
Not exceeding 300mm wide; price group						
- Studio B	1.43	11.85	34.69	6.98	m2	53.52
- Studio C	1.43	11.85	46.52	8.76	m2	67.13
- Studio D	1.43	11.85	57.75	10.44	m2	80.04
- Studio D1	1.43	11.85	60.71	10.88	m2	83.44
- Studio D2	1.43	11.85	60.03	11.68	m2	89.56
- Studio D3	1.43	11.85	81.99	14.08	m2	107.92

To walls; 203mm x 152mm x 6.5mm
thick

	Labour hours	Nett labour £	Nett material £	O'heads /profit £	Unit	Total £
Over 300mm wide; price group						
- Studio E	0.75	6.22	35.05	6.19	m2	47.46
- Studio 1	0.75	6.22	50.64	8.53	m2	65.39
- Studio 1A	0.75	6.22	62.34	10.28	m2	78.84
- Studio 1B	0.75	6.22	79.23	12.82	m2	98.27
- Studio 2	0.75	6.22	100.89	16.07	m2	123.18
Not exceeding 300mm wide; price group						
- Studio E	1.13	9.37	36.70	6.91	m2	52.98
- Studio 1	1.13	9.37	53.04	9.36	m2	71.77
- Studio 1A	1.13	9.37	65.29	11.20	m2	85.86
- Studio 1B	1.13	9.37	82.98	13.85	m2	106.20
- Studio 2	1.13	9.37	105.67	17.26	m2	132.30

FLOOR WALL AND CEILING FINISHES

TILE SLAB AND BLOCK FINISHINGS	Labour hours	Nett labour £	Nett material £	O'heads /profit £	Unit	Total £
Studio tiles (cont'd)						
To walls; 200mm x 200mm x 7mm thick						
Over 300mm wide; price group						
- Studio A	0.70	5.80	38.46	6.64	m2	50.90
- Studio B	0.70	5.80	51.26	8.56	m2	65.62
- Studio C	0.70	5.80	63.73	10.43	m2	79.96
Not exceeding 300mm wide; price group						
- Studio A	1.05	8.70	40.28	7.35	m2	56.33
- Studio B	1.05	8.70	53.68	9.36	m2	71.74
- Studio C	1.05	8.70	66.74	11.32	m2	86.76
To walls; 250mm x 200mm x 7mm thick						
Over 300mm wide; price group						
- Studio 2	0.65	5.39	53.16	8.78	m2	67.33
- Studio 3	0.65	5.39	63.66	10.36	m2	79.41
- Studio 4	0.65	5.39	74.95	12.05	m2	92.39
- Studio 5	0.65	5.39	86.24	13.74	m2	105.37
Not exceeding 300mm wide; price group						
- Studio 2	0.98	8.12	55.68	9.57	m2	73.37
- Studio 3	0.98	8.12	66.68	11.22	m2	86.02
- Studio 4	0.98	8.12	78.50	12.99	m2	99.61
- Studio 5	0.98	8.12	90.33	14.77	m2	113.22
Labour on ceramic wall tiles						
Cutting around pipes and the like						
Not exceeding 0.3m girth; tile thickness						
- 5.5mm	0.05	0.41	-	0.06	nr	0.47
- 6.5mm	0.06	0.50	-	0.08	nr	0.58
- 7mm	0.07	0.58	-	0.09	nr	0.67

TILE SLAB AND BLOCK FINISHINGS	Labour hours	Nett labour £	Nett material £	O'heads /profit £	Unit	Total £
Studio tiles (cont'd)						
0.3m-1m girth; tile thickness						
- 5.5mm	0.07	0.58	-	0.09	nr	0.67
- 6.5mm	0.08	0.66	-	0.10	nr	0.76
- 7mm	0.09	0.75	-	0.11	nr	0.86
1m-2m girth; tile thickness						
- 5.5mm	0.09	0.75	-	0.11	nr	0.86
- 6.5mm	0.10	0.83	-	0.12	nr	0.95
- 7mm	0.11	0.91	-	0.14	nr	1.05

Vitrified ceramic floor tiles to B.S.6431 part 6; Pilkington Dorset plain; fixing with approved adhesive; pointing with matching grout

Floors; level and to falls; 150mm x 150m x 9mm thick

	Labour hours	Nett labour	Nett material	O'heads /profit	Unit	Total
Over 300mm wide						
- Grey steel, white	0.80	6.63	12.91	2.93	m2	22.47
- Stone, rockface, russet blend	0.80	6.63	10.69	2.60	m2	19.92
- Black	0.80	6.63	11.03	2.65	m2	20.31
- Red	0.80	6.63	9.02	2.35	m2	18.00
Not exceeding 300mm wide						
- Grey steel, white	1.20	9.95	13.50	3.52	m2	26.97
- Stone, rockface, russet blend	1.20	9.95	11.18	3.17	m2	24.30
- Black	1.20	9.95	11.54	3.22	m2	24.71
- Red	1.20	9.95	9.43	2.91	m2	22.29

Increase the labour element of all items for working in compartments not exceeding 4m2 by 15%

294

TILE SLAB AND BLOCK FINISHINGS	Labour hours	Nett labour £	Nett material £	O'heads /profit £	Unit	Total £
Vitrified ceramic floor tiles (cont'd)						
Landings						
over 300mm wide						
- Grey steel, white	0.88	7.30	12.91	3.03	m2	23.24
- Stone, rockface, russet						
blend	0.88	7.30	10.69	2.70	m2	20.69
- Black	0.88	7.30	11.03	2.75	m2	21.08
- Red	0.88	7.30	9.02	2.45	m2	18.77
Treads						
275mm wide						
- Grey steel, white	0.36	2.98	3.71	1.00	m	7.69
- Stone, rockface, russet						
blend	0.36	2.98	3.08	0.10	m	6.97
- Black	0.36	2.98	3.17	0.92	m	7.07
- Red	0.36	2.98	2.59	0.84	m	6.41
350mm wide						
- Grey steel, white	0.46	3.81	4.73	1.28	m	9.82
- Stone, rockface, russet						
blend	0.46	3.81	3.91	1.16	m	8.88
- Black	0.46	3.81	4.04	1.18	m	9.03
- Red	0.46	3.81	3.30	1.07	m	8.18
Risers						
150mm high; plain or undercut						
- Grey steel, white	0.26	2.16	2.03	0.63	m	4.82
- Stone, rockface, russet						
blend	0.26	2.16	1.68	0.58	m	4.42
- Black	0.26	2.16	1.73	0.58	m	4.47
- Red	0.26	2.16	1.42	0.54	m	4.12
200mm high; plain or undercut						
- Grey steel, white	0.35	2.90	2.70	0.84	m	6.44
- Stone, rockface, russet						
blend	0.35	2.90	2.24	0.77	m	5.91
- Black	0.35	2.90	2.31	0.78	m	5.99
- Red	0.35	2.90	1.89	0.72	m	5.51

TILE SLAB AND BLOCK FINISHINGS	Labour hours	Nett labour £	Nett material £	O'heads /profit £	Unit	Total £
Vitrified ceramic floor tiles (cont'd)						
Skirtings; Universal Metricove						
150mm x 109mm x 9mm						
- Grey steel, white	0.25	2.07	5.98	1.21	m	9.26
- Stone, rockface, russet blend	0.25	2.07	3.70	0.87	m	6.64
- Black	0.25	2.07	3.70	0.87	m	6.64
- Red	0.25	2.07	3.70	0.87	m	6.64
Internal/external angles						
- Grey steel, white	0.07	0.58	1.01	0.24	nr	1.83
- Stone, rockface, russet blend	0.07	0.58	0.69	0.19	nr	1.46
- Black	0.07	0.58	0.69	0.19	nr	1.46
- Red	0.07	0.58	0.69	0.19	nr	1.46
Stop ends						
- Grey steel, white	0.05	0.41	1.40	0.27	nr	2.08
- Stone, rockface, russet blend	0.05	0.41	1.02	0.21	nr	1.64
- Black	0.05	0.41	1.02	0.21	nr	1.64
- Red	0.05	0.41	1.02	0.21	nr	1.64
Step nosing						
150mm x 100mm x 18mm						
- Stone	0.25	2.07	3.70	0.87	m	6.64
- Black	0.25	2.07	3.96	0.90	m	6.93
Internal/external angles						
- Stone	0.07	0.58	0.86	0.22	nr	1.66
- Black	0.07	0.58	0.90	0.22	nr	1.70
Labours on vitrified ceramic Floor tiles						
Cutting around pipes and the like						
- not exceeding 0.3m girth	0.07	0.58	-	0.09	nr	0.67
- 0.3m-1m girth	0.10	0.83	-	0.12	nr	0.95
- 1m-2m girth	0.14	1.16	-	0.17	nr	1.33

FLOOR WALL AND CEILING FINISHES

DRY LININGS AND PARTITIONS	Labour hours	Nett labour £	Nett material £	O'heads /profit £	Unit	Total £
Partitions; Paramount dry partition; Gyproc wallboard on cellular core						
50mm thick; 30mm x 37mm jointing battens; grey faced with square butt joints for plastering (not included)						
- over 300mm wide	0.80	6.63	5.35	1.80	m2	13.78
- not exceeding 300mm wide	1.20	9.95	5.62	2.34	m2	17.91
- over 300mm wide in compartments not exceeding 4m2	0.90	7.46	5.35	1.92	m2	14.73
- not exceeding 300mm wide in compartments not exceeding 4m2	1.30	10.78	5.62	2.46	m2	18.86
Add to the previous prices for tapered edge joints taped and filled; one coat of Gyproc drywall topcoat	0.17	1.41	0.53	0.29	m2	2.23
57mm thick; 37mm x 37mm jointing battens; grey faced with square butt joints for plastering (not included)						
- over 300mm wide	0.85	7.05	5.45	1.88	m2	14.38
- not exceeding 300mm wide	1.28	10.61	5.72	2.45	m2	18.78
- over 300mm wide in compartments not exceeding 4m2	0.90	7.46	5.45	1.94	m2	14.85
- not exceeding 300mm wide in compartments not exceeding 4m2	1.33	11.03	5.72	2.51	m2	19.26
Add to the previous prices for tapered edge joints taped and filled; one coat of Gyproc drywall topcoat	0.17	1.41	0.53	0.29	m2	2.23

DRY LININGS AND PARTITIONS	Labour hours	Nett labour £	Nett material £	O'heads /profit £	Unit	Total £
Paramount partition (cont'd)						

63mm thick; 37mm x 37mm jointing battens; grey faced with square butt joints for plastering (not included)

	Labour hours	Nett labour £	Nett material £	O'heads /profit £	Unit	Total £
- over 300mm wide	0.90	7.46	6.15	2.04	m2	15.65
- not exceeding 300mm wide	1.35	11.19	6.46	2.65	m2	20.30
- over 300mm wide in compartments not exceeding 4m2	0.95	7.88	6.15	2.10	m2	16.13
- not exceeding 300mm wide in compartments not exceeding 4m2	1.40	11.61	6.46	2.71	m2	20.78
Add to the previous prices for tapered edge joints taped and filled; one coat of Gyproc drywall topcoat	0.17	1.41	0.53	0.29	m2	2.23
Perimeter fixing batten						
- 30mm x19mm						
- to timber with nails	0.12	0.99	0.27	0.19	m	1.45
- to brickwork or concrete with screws; plugging	0.18	1.49	0.37	0.28	m	2.14
- 37mm x 19mm						
- to timber with nails	0.13	1.08	0.32	0.21	m	1.61
- to brickwork or concrete with screws; plugging	0.19	1.58	0.42	0.30	m	2.30
Right angle junction						
- 50mm thick; 30mm x 37mm and 30mm x 19mm battens	0.40	3.32	0.69	0.59	m	4.50
- 57mm thick; 37mm x 37mm and 37mm x 19mm battens	0.43	3.56	0.85	0.66	m	5.07
- 63mm thick; 37mm x 37mm and 37mm x 19mm battens	0.44	3.65	0.85	0.68	m	5.18
T junction						
- 50mm thick; 30mm x 37mm and 30mm x 19mm battens	0.33	2.74	0.69	0.51	m	3.94
- 57mm thick; 37mm x 37mm and 37mm x 19mm battens	0.34	2.82	0.85	0.55	m	4.22

298

DRY LININGS AND PARTITIONS	Labour hours	Nett labour £	Nett material £	O'heads /profit £	Unit	Total £
Paramount partition (cont'd)						
- 63mm thick; 37mm x 37mm and 37mm x 19mm battens	0.35	2.90	0.85	0.56	m	4.31
Trimming around openings						
- 50mm thick; 30mm x 37mm batten	0.21	1.74	0.42	0.32	m	2.48
- 57mm thick; 37mm x 37mm batten	0.23	1.91	0.53	0.37	m	2.81
- 63mm thick; 37mm x 37mm batten	0.24	1.99	0.53	0.38	m	2.90
Accessories						
- drywall angle bead	0.09	0.75	0.47	0.18	m	1.40
- edge bead	0.09	0.75	0.50	0.19	m	1.44
- 30mm x 37mm softwood batten for fixings	0.14	1.16	0.42	0.24	m	1.82
- 37mm x 37mm softwood batten for fixings	0.15	1.24	0.53	0.27	m	2.04
- 150mm long softwood plugs built in	0.08	0.66	0.16	0.12	nr	0.94
Labours; cutting and fitting around pipes and the like						
- Not exceeding 0.3m girth						
- 50mm thick	0.05	0.41	-	0.06	nr	0.47
- 57mm thick	0.06	0.50	-	0.08	nr	0.58
- 63mm thick	0.07	0.58	-	0.09	nr	0.67
- 0.3m-1m girth						
- 50mm thick	0.07	0.58	-	0.09	nr	0.67
- 57mm thick	0.08	0.66	-	0.10	nr	0.76
- 63mm thick	0.09	0.75	-	0.11	nr	0.86
- 1m-2m girth						
- 50mm thick	0.09	0.75	-	0.11	nr	0.86
- 57mm thick	0.10	0.83	-	0.12	nr	0.95
- 63mm thick	0.12	0.99	-	0.15	nr	1.14
Labours; raking cutting						
- 50mm thick	0.07	0.58	-	0.09	m	0.67
- 57mm thick	0.08	0.66	-	0.10	m	0.76
- 63mm thick	0.09	0.75	-	0.11	m	0.86

FLOOR WALL AND CEILING FINISHES

SUSPENDED CEILINGS	Labour hours	Nett labour £	Nett material £	O'heads /profit £	Unit	Total £
British Gypsum Paraclip metal grid fixing system; comprising ref P502 primary channel sections, ref P506 main supporting sections, and ref P507N cross supporting sections; suspension height 500mm; including all necessary clips and brackets; nailed to timber soffits or wired to steelwork						
Panels comprising Gyproc industrial grade boards						
Horizontal; board size						
- 600mm x 1800mm x 9.5mm thick	0.40	3.32	4.86	1.23	m2	9.41
- 600mm x 1800mm x 12.5mm thick	0.40	3.32	5.17	1.27	m2	9.76
- 600mm x 2400mm x 9.5mm thick	0.38	3.15	4.64	1.17	m2	8.96
- 600mm x 2400mm x 12.5mm thick	0.38	3.15	4.96	1.22	m2	9.33
Add to the previous prices for plugging and screwing to concrete soffits	0.08	0.66	0.16	0.12	m2	0.94
Increase the labour element for working in staircase areas or compartments not exceeding 4m2 by 15%						
Increase the labour element for work over 3.5m high by 10%						
Edging and trims; fixing with screws; plugging						
- angle section ref P510; 25mm x 25mm	0.10	0.83	0.34	0.18	m	1.35
- angle section ref P514; 32mm x 19mm	0.10	0.83	0.34	0.18	m	1.35
Access panels; extra over for; size						
- 600mm x 600mm	0.30	2.49	2.74	0.78	nr	6.01
- 600mm x 900mm	0.35	2.90	2.90	0.87	nr	6.67

SUSPENDED CEILINGS	Labour hours	Nett labour £	Nett material £	O'heads /profit £	Unit	Total £
British Gypsum paraclip metal grid fixing system (cont'd)						
Cutting to profile of openings; including						
- ref P570 trim	0.12	0.99	0.37	0.20	m	1.56
- ref P571 trim	0.12	0.99	0.35	0.20	m	1.54

Treetex Quicklock fire rated
lay-in grid system; comprising
ref Q411M main T sections;
ref Q412M or Q413M cross T
sections; suspension height 500mm;
nailed to timber soffits or wired
to steelwork

Panels comprising M/G pvc faced
boards

Horizontal; boards of size						
- 600mm x 600mm x 9.5mm thick	0.44	3.65	5.36	1.35	m2	10.36
- 1200mm x 600mm x 9.5mm thick	0.42	3.48	5.27	1.31	m2	10.06

Panels comprising Fireline M/G pvc
faced boards

Horizontal; boards of size						
- 600mm x 600mm x 9.5mm thick	0.44	3.65	6.18	1.47	m2	11.30

Add to the previous prices for plugging and screwing to concrete soffits	0.08	0.66	0.16	0.12	m2	0.94

Increase the labour element for
working in staircase areas or
compartments not exceeding 4m2
by 15%

Increase the labour element for
work over 3.5m high by 10%

FLOOR WALL AND CEILING FINISHES

SUSPENDED CEILINGS	Labour hours	Nett labour £	Nett material £	O'heads /profit £	Unit	Total £
Treetex quicklock system (cont'd)						
Edgings and trims; fixing with screws; plugging						
- angle section ref Q414	0.12	0.99	0.40	0.21	m	1.60
- shadowline moulding ref Q415	0.12	0.99	0.61	0.24	m	1.84
Access panels; extra over for; size						
- 600mm x 600mm	0.30	2.49	2.74	0.78	nr	6.01
- 600mm x 900mm	0.35	2.90	2.90	0.87	nr	6.67

GLAZING

1. Labour

    Craftsman £6.44 per hour

2. Materials

	Unit	Basic Price	Waste %	Total £
Clear glass, thickness				
3mm	m2	21.67	5	22.75
4mm	m2	24.56	5	25.79
6mm	m2	39.84	5	41.83
10mm	m2	79.00	5	82.95
Rough cast glass, thickness				
6mm	m2	29.67	5	31.15
10mm	m2	41.00	5	43.05
Georgian wired cast glass, thickness				
7mm	m2	31.33	5	32.90
Georgian wired polished glass, thickness				
6mm	m2	68.31	5	71.73

ALTERATION WORK	Labour hours	Nett labour £	Nett material £	O'heads /profit £	Unit	Total £
Hack out glass and remove	1.00	6.44	-	0.97	m2	7.41
Clean rebates, remove sprigs or clips and prepare for reglazing	0.50	3.22	-	0.48	m	3.70

NEW WORK

Clear glass glazed to wood with putty and sprigs, thickness						
- 3mm	0.60	3.86	22.98	4.03	m2	30.87
- 4mm	0.60	3.86	23.00	4.03	m2	30.89
- 6mm	0.65	4.19	42.06	6.94	m2	53.19
- 10mm	0.70	4.51	83.17	13.15	m2	100.83

NEW WORK	Labour hours	Nett labour £	Nett material £	O'heads /profit £	Unit	Total £
Clear glass glazed to wood with pinned beads, thickness						
- 3mm	0.80	5.15	23.00	4.22	m2	32.37
- 4mm	0.80	5.15	23.03	4.23	m2	32.41
- 6mm	0.90	5.80	42.09	7.18	m2	55.07
- 10mm	1.00	6.44	83.20	13.47	m2	103.09
Clear glass glazed to wood with screwed beads, thickness						
- 3mm	1.10	7.08	23.05	4.52	m2	34.65
- 4mm	1.10	7.08	23.08	4.52	m2	34.68
- 6mm	1.20	7.73	42.14	7.48	m2	57.35
- 10mm	1.30	8.37	83.25	13.74	m2	105.36
Clear glass glazed to metal with putty, thickness						
- 3mm	0.80	5.15	22.98	4.22	m2	32.35
- 4mm	0.80	5.15	23.00	4.22	m2	32.37
- 6mm	0.90	5.80	42.06	7.18	m2	55.04
- 10mm	1.00	6.44	83.17	13.44	m2	103.05
Rough cast glass glazed to wood with putty, thickness						
- 6mm	0.65	4.19	31.38	5.34	m2	40.91
- 10mm	0.70	4.51	43.26	7.17	m2	54.94
Rough cast glass, glazed to wood with pinned beads, thickness						
- 6mm	0.65	4.19	31.41	5.34	m2	40.94
- 10mm	0.70	4.51	43.29	7.17	m2	54.97
Rough cast glass, glazed to wood with screwed beads, thickness						
- 6mm	0.65	4.19	31.46	5.35	m2	41.00
- 10mm	0.70	4.51	43.34	7.18	m2	55.03
Rough cast glass glazed to metal with putty, thickness						
- 6mm	0.65	4.19	31.38	5.34	m2	40.91
- 10mm	0.70	4.51	43.26	7.17	m2	54.94
Georgian wired cast glass, 7mm thick						
- to wood with putty	0.70	4.51	33.12	5.50	m2	42.13
- to wood with pinned beads	0.85	5.47	33.15	5.79	m2	44.41

GLAZING

NEW WORK	Labour hours	Nett labour £	Nett material £	O'heads /profit £	Unit	Total £
Georgian wired cast glass, 7mm thick contd.;						
- to wood with screwed beads	0.95	6.12	33.20	5.90	m2	45.22
- to metal with putty	1.05	6.76	33.12	5.98	m2	45.86
Georgian wired polished glass, 6mm thick						
- to wood with putty	0.65	4.19	71.95	11.42	m	87.56
- to wood with pinned beads	0.90	5.80	71.98	11.67	m	89.45
- to wood with screwed beads	1.20	7.73	72.03	11.96	m	91.72
- to metal with putty	0.90	5.80	71.95	11.66	m	89.41

PAINTING

1. Labour

   Craftsman £6.44 per head

2. Materials

Primers	Unit (litres)	Basic Price £	Waste %	Total £
Wood primer	5	12.37	2½	12.67
Acrylic primer	5	12.26	2½	12.56
Red lead	2½	19.66	2½	20.15
Quick drying metal primer	5	13.65	2½	13.99
Emulsions				
Matt	5	9.35	5	9.81
Oil Based				
Undercoat	5	11.82	2½	12.11
Gloss	5	11.82	2½	12.11
Eggshell	5	12.42	2½	12.73
Stains, Varnishes and Preservatives				
Cuprinol Clear	5	11.72	10	12.89
Cuprinol Oak	5	11.72	10	12.89
Polyurathene Clear	2½	8.85	5	9.29
Solignum Green	5	8.50	5	8.92
Miscellaneous				
'Artex' Preparation	25kg	9.18	10	10.09
'Artex' Sealer	5	10.23	10	11.25
'Artex' finish AX	25kg	9.50	10	10.45
'Artex finish XL	10	15.96	10	17.55
'Blue Circle' Stabilising Solution	5	12.82	5	13.46
'Blue Circle' Sandtex Matt	5	13.14	10	14.45

PAINTING

The unit rates listed under this
head include all the
preparatory work involved in
treating existing surfaces to
receive a new painted finish.
This includes cutting out and
filling cracks, knotting and
stopping where necessary and a
minimum allowance for patch priming.

The unit rates are based upon
brush application and
working in normal conditions on
existing surfaces that could be
described as "in average
condition." The following
adjustments should be made where
necessary:-

1. Working at heights above 3.5m
   - add 15%.

2. Working on surfaces in poor
   condition - add 10%.

3. Spraying - labour 30 to 50%
   saving, material 10 to 20%
   extra.

PAPERHANGING	Painter hours	Nett painter £	Nett material £	O'heads /profit £	Unit	Total £
For removing wallpaper previously painted with emulsion paint - add 10%.						
For removing wallpaper previously painted with oil paint - add 20%.						
Strip off one layer of paper; stop cracks; rub down						
Woodchip						
- wall	0.18	1.16	0.02	0.18	m2	1.36
- walls in staircase areas	0.20	1.29	0.02	0.20	m2	1.51
- ceilings	0.22	1.42	0.02	0.22	m2	1.66
- ceilings in staircase areas	0.24	1.55	0.02	0.24	m2	1.81
Vinyl						
- walls	0.23	1.48	0.02	0.23	m2	1.73
- walls in staircase areas	0.25	1.61	0.02	0.24	m2	1.87
- ceilings	0.27	1.74	0.02	0.26	m2	2.02
- ceilings in staircase areas	0.29	1.87	0.02	0.28	m2	2.17
Standard patterned						
- walls	0.21	1.35	0.02	0.21	m2	1.58
- walls in staircase areas	0.23	1.48	0.02	0.23	m2	1.73
- ceilings	0.25	1.61	0.02	0.24	m2	1.87
- ceilings in staircase areas	0.27	1.74	0.02	0.26	m2	2.02
Lining paper (BP £0.75 per roll)						
Walls and columns						
- generally up to 3.5m high	0.25	1.61	0.17	0.27	m2	2.05
- 3.5 to 5m high	0.28	1.80	0.17	0.30	m2	2.27
- staircase areas	0.28	1.80	0.17	0.30	m2	2.27
Ceilings and beams						
- generally up to 3.5m high	0.30	1.93	0.17	0.32	m2	2.42
- 3.5 to 5m high	0.32	2.06	0.17	0.33	m2	2.56
- staircase areas	0.32	2.06	0.17	0.33	m2	2.56
Woodchip paper (BP £0.90 per roll)						
Walls and columns						
- generally up to 3.5m high	0.26	1.67	0.20	0.28	m2	2.15
- 3.5 to 5m high	0.29	1.87	0.20	0.31	m2	2.38
- staircase areas	0.29	1.87	0.20	0.31	m2	2.38

PAPERHANGING	Painter hours	Nett painter £	Nett material £	O'heads /profit £	Unit	Total £
Woodchip paper (BP £0.90 per roll) contd.;						
Ceilings and beams						
- generally up to 3.5m high	0.31	2.00	0.20	0.33	m2	2.53
- 3.5 to 5m high	0.33	2.13	0.20	0.35	m2	2.68
- staircase areas	0.33	2.13	0.20	0.35	m2	2.68
Flock paper (BP £6.50 per roll)						
Walls and columns						
- generally up to 3.5m high	0.27	1.74	1.39	0.47	m2	3.60
- 3.5 to 5m high	0.30	1.93	1.39	0.50	m2	3.82
- staircase areas	0.30	1.93	1.39	0.50	m2	3.82
Ceilings and beams						
- generally up to 3.5m high	0.32	2.06	1.39	0.52	m2	3.97
- 3.5 to 5m high	0.33	2.13	1.39	0.53	m2	4.05
- staircase areas	0.33	2.13	1.39	0.53	m2	4.05
Anaglypta paper (BP £1.60 per roll)						
Walls and columns						
- generally up to 3.5m high	0.27	1.74	0.34	0.31	m2	2.39
- 3.5 to 5m high	0.30	1.93	0.34	0.34	m2	2.61
- staircase areas	0.30	1.93	0.34	0.34	m2	2.61
Ceilings and beams						
- generally up to 3.5m high	0.32	2.06	0.34	0.36	m2	2.76
- 3.5 to 5m high	0.33	2.13	0.34	0.37	m2	2.84
- staircase areas	0.33	2.13	0.34	0.37	m2	2.84
Vinyl surface paper (BP £4.80 per roll)						
Walls and columns						
- generally up to 3.5m high	0.26	1.67	1.03	0.41	m2	3.11
- 3.5 to 5m high	0.29	1.87	1.03	0.43	m2	3.33
- staircase areas	0.29	1.87	1.03	0.43	m2	3.33
Ceilings and beams						
- generally up to 3.5m high	0.31	2.00	1.03	0.45	m2	3.48
- 3.5 to 5m high	0.33	2.13	1.03	0.47	m2	3.63
- staircase areas	0.33	2.13	1.03	0.47	m2	3.63

PAPERHANGING	Painter hours	Nett painter £	Nett material £	O'heads /profit £	Unit	Total £
Ready pasted paper (BP £4.30 per roll)						
Walls and columns						
- generally up to 3.5m high	0.26	1.67	0.92	0.39	m2	2.98
- 3.5 to 5m high	0.29	1.87	0.92	0.42	m2	3.21
- staircase areas	0.29	1.87	0.92	0.42	m2	3.21
Ceilings and beams						
- generally up to 3.5m high	0.31	2.00	0.92	0.44	m2	3.36
- 3.5 to 5m high	0.33	2.13	0.92	0.46	m2	3.31
- staircase areas	0.33	2.13	0.92	0.46	m2	3.51

INTERNAL WORK

Wash down water painted surfaces over 300mm girth; stop cracks; rub down

Brickwork						
- walls	0.14	0.90	0.02	0.14	m2	0.06
- walls in staircase areas	0.16	1.03	0.02	0.16	m2	1.21
Blockwork						
- walls	0.15	0.97	0.02	0.15	m2	1.14
- walls in staircase areas	0.17	1.09	0.02	0.17	m2	1.28

Wash down previously oil painted wood surfaces; rub down

General surfaces						
- over 300mm girth	0.28	1.80	-	0.27	m2	2.07
- isolated surfaces not exceeding 300mm girth	0.10	0.64	-	0.10	m	0.74
- isolated areas not exceeding 0.5m2	0.12	0.77	-	0.12	nr	0.89
Windows, screens, glazed doors and the like						
- panes area not exceeding 0.1m2	0.40	2.58	-	0.39	m2	2.97
- panes area 0.1 - 0.5m2	0.37	2.38	-	0.36	m2	2.74
- panes area 0.5 - 1m2	0.36	2.32	-	0.35	m2	2.67
- panes area exceeding 1m2	0.30	1.93	-	0.29	m2	2.22

PAINTING

PREPARING EXISTING SURFACES INTERNALLY	Painter hours	Nett painter £	Nett material £	O'heads /profit £	Unit	Total £
Wash down previously oil painted wood surfaces; remove paint with chemical stripper; rub down						
General surfaces						
- over 300mm girth	0.80	5.15	1.31	0.97	m2	7.43
- isolated surfaces not exceeding 300mm girth	0.25	1.61	0.39	0.30	m	2.30
- isolated areas not exceeding 0.5m2	0.30	1.93	0.65	0.39	nr	2.97
Windows, screens,glazed doors and the like						
- panes area not exceeding 0.1m2	1.70	10.95	1.31	1.84	m2	14.10
- panes area 0.1 - 0.5m2	1.60	10.30	1.31	1.74	m2	13.35
- panes area exceeding 0.5 - 1m2	1.50	9.66	1.31	1.65	m2	12.62
- panes area exceeding 1 m2	1.40	9.02	1.31	1.55	m2	11.88
Burn off previously oil painted wood surfaces; rub down						
General surfaces						
- over 300mm girth	1.05	6.76	-	1.01	m2	7.77
- isolated surfaces not exceeding 300mm girth	0.30	1.93	-	0.29	m	2.22
- isolated areas not exceeding 0.5m2	0.50	3.22	-	0.48	nr	3.70
Windows, screens,glazed doors and the like						
- panes area not exceeding 0.1m2	1.70	10.95	-	1.64	m2	12.59
- panes area 0.1 - 0.5m2	1.60	10.30	-	1.55	m2	11.85
- panes area exceeding 0.5 - 1m2	1.50	9.66	-	1.45	m2	11.11
- panes area exceeding 1m2	1.40	9.02	-	1.35	m2	10.37

PRIMERS	Painter hours	Nett painter £	Nett material £	O'heads /profit £	Unit	Total £
One coat emulsion paint as primer; surfaces over 300mm girth						
Brickwork						
- walls	0.20	1.29	0.24	0.23	m2	1.76
- walls in staircase areas	0.22	1.42	0.24	0.25	m2	1.91
Blockwork						
- walls	0.24	1.55	0.33	0.28	m2	2.16
- walls in staircase areas	0.26	1.67	0.33	0.30	m2	2.30
Concrete						
- walls	0.17	1.09	0.20	0.19	m2	1.48
- walls in staircase areas	0.20	1.29	0.20	0.22	m2	1.71
- ceilings	0.21	1.35	0.20	0.23	m2	1.78
- ceilings in staircase areas	0.23	1.48	0.20	0.25	m2	1.93
Plastered						
- walls	0.16	1.03	0.20	0.18	m2	1.41
- walls in staircase areas	0.18	1.16	0.20	0.20	m2	1.56
- ceilings	0.20	1.29	0.20	0.22	m2	1.71
- ceilings in staircase areas	0.21	1.35	0.20	0.23	m2	1.78
Embossed paper						
- walls	0.17	1.09	0.23	0.20	m2	1.52
- walls in staircase areas	0.20	1.29	0.23	0.23	m2	1.75
- ceilings	0.21	1.35	0.23	0.24	m2	1.82
- ceilings in staircase areas	0.23	1.48	0.23	0.26	m2	1.97
One coat wood primer; wood						
General surfaces						
- over 300mm girth	0.28	1.80	0.31	0.32	m2	2.43
- isolated surfaces not exceeding 300mm girth	0.08	0.52	0.10	0.09	m	0.71
- isolated areas; not exceeding 0.5m2	0.13	0.84	0.51	0.20	nr	1.55
Windows, screens, glazed doors and the like						
- panes area not exceeding 0.1m2	0.62	3.99	0.31	0.65	m2	4.95
- panes area 0.1 - 0.5m2	0.52	3.35	0.25	0.54	m2	4.14
- panes area 0.5 - 1m2	0.46	2.96	0.19	0.47	m2	3.62
- panes area exceeding 1m2	0.38	2.45	0.14	0.39	m2	2.98

PRIMERS	Painter hours	Nett painter £	Nett material £	O'heads /profit £	Unit	Total £
One coat acrylic primer; wood						
General surfaces						
- over 300mm girth	0.25	1.61	0.25	0.28	m2	2.14
- isolated surfaces not exceeding 300mm girth	0.08	0.52	0.08	0.09	m	0.69
- isolated areas; not exceeding 0.5m2	0.13	0.84	0.12	0.14	nr	1.10
Windows, screens, glazed doors and the like						
- panes area not exceeding 0.1m2	0.62	3.99	0.25	0.64	m2	4.88
- panes area 0.1 - 0.5m2	0.52	3.35	0.20	0.53	m2	4.08
- panes area 0.5 - 1m2	0.46	2.96	0.17	0.47	m2	3.60
- panes area exceeding 1m2	0.38	2.45	0.12	0.39	m2	2.96
One coat quick drying metal primer						
General surfaces						
- over 300mm girth	0.30	1.93	0.23	0.32	m2	2.48
- isolated surfaces not exceeding 300mm girth	0.10	0.64	0.08	0.11	m	0.83
- isolated areas; not exceeding 0.5m2	0.15	0.97	0.11	0.16	nr	1.24
Windows, screens, glazed doors and the like						
- panes area not exceeding 0.1m2	0.62	3.99	0.24	0.63	m2	4.86
- panes area 0.1 - 0.5m2	0.52	3.35	0.21	0.53	m2	4.09
- panes area 0.5 - 1m2	0.46	2.96	0.17	0.47	m2	3.60
- panes area exceeding 1m2	0.38	2.45	0.14	0.39	m2	2.98
Structural metalwork, general surfaces						
- over 300mm girth	0.35	2.25	0.23	0.37	m2	2.85
- isolated surfaces not exceeding 300mm girth	0.12	0.77	0.08	0.13	m	0.98
- isolated areas not exceeding 0.5m2	0.17	1.09	0.11	0.18	nr	1.38

PRIMERS	Painter hours	Nett painter £	Nett material £	O'heads /profit £	Unit	Total £
One coat quick drying metal primer contd.;						
Structural metalwork, members of roof trusses, lattice girders, purlins and the like						
- over 300mm girth	0.30	1.93	0.23	0.32	m2	2.48
- isolated surfaces not exceeding 300mm girth	0.10	0.64	0.08	0.11	m	0.83
- isolated areas not exceeding 0.5m2	0.15	0.97	0.11	0.16	nr	1.24
Radiators, panel type						
- over 300mm girth	0.30	1.93	0.23	0.32	m2	2.48
- isolated surfaces not exceeding 300mm girth	0.10	0.64	0.08	0.11	m	0.83
- isolated areas not exceeding 0.5m2	0.15	0.97	0.11	0.16	nr	1.24
Radiators, column type						
- over 300mm girth	0.35	2.25	0.23	0.37	m2	2.85
- isolated surfaces not exceeding 300mm girth	0.12	0.77	0.08	0.13	m	0.98
- isolated areas not exceeding 0.5m2	0.17	1.09	0.11	0.18	nr	1.38
UNDERCOATS - INTERNALLY						
One coat emulsion paint; primed surfaces over 300mm girth						
Brickwork						
- walls	0.15	0.97	0.25	0.18	m2	1.40
- walls in staircase areas	0.17	0.97	0.25	0.20	m2	1.54
Blockwork						
- walls	0.19	1.22	0.32	0.23	m2	1.77
- walls in staircase areas	0.21	1.35	0.32	0.25	m2	1.92
Concrete						
- walls	0.12	0.77	0.19	0.14	m2	1.10
- walls in staircase areas	0.15	0.97	0.19	0.17	m2	1.33
- ceilings	0.16	1.03	0.19	0.18	m2	1.40
- ceilings in staircase areas	0.18	1.16	0.19	0.20	m2	1.55

PAINTING

UNDERCOATS INTERNALLY	Painter hours	Nett painter £	Nett material £	O'heads /profit £	Unit	Total £
Plastered						
- walls	0.11	0.71	0.19	0.13	m2	1.03
- walls in staircase areas	0.13	0.84	0.19	0.15	m2	1.18
- ceilings	0.15	0.97	0.19	0.17	m2	1.33
- ceilings in staircase areas	0.16	1.03	0.19	0.18	m2	1.40
Embossed paper						
- walls	0.12	0.77	0.23	0.15	m2	1.15
- walls in staircase areas	0.15	0.97	0.23	0.18	m2	1.38
- ceilings	0.16	1.03	0.23	0.19	m2	1.45
- ceilings in staircase areas	0.18	1.16	0.23	0.21	m2	1.60
Cement rendered						
- walls	0.12	0.77	0.19	0.14	m2	1.10
- walls in staircase areas	0.15	0.97	0.19	0.17	m2	1.33
- ceilings	0.16	1.03	0.19	0.18	m2	1.40
- ceilings in staircase areas	0.18	1.16	0.19	0.20	m2	1.55

One undercoat oil based paint;
primed wood surfaces

	Painter hours	Nett painter £	Nett material £	O'heads /profit £	Unit	Total £
General surfaces						
- over 300mm girth	0.21	1.35	0.20	0.23	m2	1.78
- isolated surfaces not exceeding 300mm girth	0.08	0.52	0.08	0.09	m	0.69
- isolated areas; not exceeding 0.5m2	0.10	0.64	0.10	0.11	nr	0.85

One undercoat oil based paint;
primed wood surfaces

	Painter hours	Nett painter £	Nett material £	O'heads /profit £	Unit	Total £
Windows, screens, glazed doors and the like						
- panes area not exceeding 0.1m2	0.50	3.22	0.20	0.51	m2	3.93
- panes area 0.1 - 0.5m2	0.43	2.77	0.17	0.44	m2	3.38
- panes area 0.5 - 1m2	0.37	2.38	0.13	0.38	m2	2.89
- panes area exceeding 1m2	0.30	1.93	0.10	0.30	m2	2.33

315

UNDERCOATS INTERNALLY	Painter hours	Nett painter £	Nett material £	O'heads /profit £	Unit	Total £
One undercoat oil based paint; primed metal surfaces						
General surfaces						
- over 300mm girth	0.21	1.35	0.20	0.23	m2	1.78
- isolated surfaces not exceeding 300mm girth	0.08	0.52	0.08	0.09	m	0.69
- isolated areas; not exceeding 0.5m2	0.10	0.64	0.10	0.11	nr	0.85
Windows, screens, glazed doors and the like						
- panes area not exceeding 0.1m2	0.50	3.22	0.20	0.51	m2	3.93
- panes area 0.1 - 0.5m2	0.43	2.77	0.17	0.44	m2	3.38
- panes area 0.5 - 1m2	0.37	2.38	0.13	0.38	m2	2.89
- panes area exceeding 1m2	0.30	1.93	0.10	0.30	m2	2.33
Structural metalwork, general surfaces						
- over 300mm girth	0.21	1.35	0.20	0.23	m2	1.78
- isolated surfaces not exceeding 300mm girth	0.08	0.52	0.08	0.09	m	0.69
- isolated areas not exceeding 0.5m2	0.10	0.64	0.10	0.11	nr	0.85
Structural metalwork, members of roof trusses, lattice girders, purlins and the like						
- over 300mm girth	0.35	2.25	0.20	0.37	m2	2.82
- isolated surfaces not exceeding 300mm girth	0.12	0.77	0.08	0.13	m	0.98
- isolated areas not exceeding 0.5m2	0.17	1.09	0.10	0.18	nr	1.37

FINISHING COATS INTERNALLY	Painter hours	Nett painter £	Nett material £	O'heads /profit £	Unit	Total £
One coat matt emulsion paint; undercoated surfaces over 300mm girth						
Brickwork						
- walls	0.15	0.97	0.24	0.18	m2	1.39
- walls in staircase areas	0.17	1.09	0.24	0.20	m2	1.53
Blockwork						
- walls	0.19	1.22	0.30	0.23	m2	1.75
- walls in staircase areas	0.21	1.35	0.30	0.25	m2	1.90
Concrete						
- walls	0.12	0.77	0.30	0.16	m2	1.23
- walls in staircase areas	0.15	0.97	0.30	0.19	m2	1.46
- ceilings	0.16	1.03	0.30	0.20	m2	1.53
- ceilings in staircase areas	0.18	1.16	0.30	0.22	m2	1.68
Plastered						
- walls	0.11	0.71	0.20	0.14	'm2	1.05
- walls in staircase areas	0.13	0.84	0.20	0.16	m2	1.20
- ceilings	0.15	0.97	0.20	0.18	m2	1.35
- ceilings in staircase areas	0.16	1.03	0.20	0.18	m2	1.41
Embossed paper						
- walls	0.12	0.77	0.22	0.15	m2	1.14
- walls in staircase areas	0.15	0.97	0.22	0.18	m2	1.37
- ceilings	0.16	1.03	0.22	0.19	m2	1.44
- ceilings in staircase areas	0.18	1.16	0.22	0.21	m2	1.59
Cement rendered						
- walls	0.12	0.77	0.27	0.16	m2	1.20
- walls in staircase areas	0.15	0.97	0.27	0.19	m2	1.43
- ceilings	0.16	1.03	0.27	0.20	m2	1.50
- ceilings in staircase areas	0.18	1.16	0.27	0.21	m2	1.64
One coat eggshell finish; undercoated surfaces over 300mm girth						
Brickwork						
- walls	0.15	0.97	0.25	0.18	m2	1.40
- walls in staircase areas	0.17	1.09	0.25	0.20	m2	1.54

PAINTING

FINISHING COATS INTERNALLY	Painter hours	Nett painter £	Nett material £	O'heads /profit £	Unit	Total £
One coat eggshell finish; undercoated surfaces over 300mm girth contd.;						
Blockwork						
- walls	0.19	1.22	0.32	0.23	m2	1.77
- walls in staircase areas	0.21	1.35	0.32	0.25	m2	1.92
Concrete						
- walls	0.12	0.77	0.32	0.16	m2	1.25
- walls in staircase areas	0.15	0.97	0.32	0.19	m2	1.48
- ceilings	0.16	1.03	0.32	0.20	m2	1.55
- ceilings in staircase areas	0.18	1.16	0.32	0.22	m2	1.70
Plastered						
- walls	0.11	0.71	0.21	0.14	m2	1.06
- walls in staircase areas	0.13	0.84	0.21	0.16	m2	1.21
- ceilings	0.15	0.97	0.21	0.18	m2	1.36
- ceilings in staircase areas	0.16	1.03	0.21	0.19	m2	1.43
Embossed paper						
- walls	0.12	0.77	0.23	0.15	m2	1.15
- walls in staircase areas	0.15	0.97	0.23	0.18	m2	1.38
- ceilings	0.16	1.03	0.23	0.19	m2	1.45
- ceilings in staircase areas	0.18	1.16	0.23	0.21	m2	1.60
Cement rendered						
- walls	0.12	0.77	0.28	0.16	m2	1.21
- walls in staircase areas	0.15	0.97	0.28	0.19	m2	1.44
- ceilings	0.16	1.03	0.28	0.20	m2	1.51
- ceilings in staircase areas	0.18	1.16	0.28	0.22	m2	1.66
One coat gloss finish; undercoated surfaces over 300mm girth						
Brickwork						
- walls	0.15	0.97	0.24	0.18	m2	1.39
- walls in staircase areas	0.17	1.09	0.24	0.20	m2	1.53
Blockwork						
- walls	0.19	1.22	0.30	0.23	m2	1.75
- walls in staircase areas	0.21	1.35	0.30	0.25	m2	1.90

PAINTING

FINISHING COATS INTERNALLY	Painter hours	Nett painter £	Nett material £	O'heads /profit £	Unit	Total £
One coat gloss finish; undercoated surfaces over 300mm girth contd.;						
Concrete						
- walls	0.12	0.77	0.30	0.16	m2	1.23
- walls in staircase areas	0.15	0.97	0.30	0.19	m2	1.46
- ceilings	0.16	1.03	0.30	0.20	m2	1.53
- ceilings in staircase areas	0.18	1.16	0.30	0.22	m2	1.68
Plastered						
- walls	0.11	0.71	0.20	0.14	m2	1.05
- walls in staircase areas	0.13	0.84	0.20	0.16	m2	1.20
- ceilings	0.15	0.97	0.20	0.18	m2	1.35
- ceilings in staircase areas	0.16	1.03	0.20	0.18	m2	1.41
Embossed paper						
- walls	0.12	0.77	0.22	0.15	m2	1.14
- walls in staircase areas	0.15	0.97	0.22	0.18	m2	1.37
- ceilings	0.16	1.03	0.22	0.19	m2	1.44
- ceilings in staircase areas	0.18	1.16	0.22	0.21	m2	1.59
Cement rendered						
- walls	0.12	0.77	0.27	0.16	m2	1.20
- walls in staircase areas	0.15	0.97	0.27	0.19	m2	1.43
- ceilings	0.16	1.03	0.27	0.20	m2	1.50
- ceilings in staircase areas	0.18	1.16	0.27	0.21	m2	1.64
One coat gloss finish; undercoated wood						
General surfaces						
- over 300mm girth	0.23	1.48	0.20	0.25	m2	1.93
- isolated surfaces not exceeding 300mm girth	0.10	0.64	0.08	0.11	m	0.83
- isolated surfaces; not exceeding 0.5m2	0.13	0.84	0.10	0.14	nr	1.08
Windows, screens, glazed doors and the like						
- panes area not exceeding 0.1m2	0.54	3.48	0.20	0.55	m2	4.23
- panes area 0.1 - 0.5m2	0.48	3.09	0.17	0.50	m2	3.75
- panes area 0.5 - 1m2	0.40	2.58	0.13	0.41	m2	3.12
- panes area exceeding 1m2	0.33	2.13	0.1C	0.33	m2	2.56

FINISHING COATS INTERNALLY	Painter hours	Nett painter £	Nett material £	O'heads /profit £	Unit	Total £
One coat gloss finish; undercoated metal						
General surfaces						
- over 300mm girth	0.23	1.48	0.20	0.25	m2	1.93
- isolated surfaces not exceeding 300mm girth	0.11	0.71	0.08	0.12	m	0.91
- isolated areas not exceeding 0.5m2	0.14	0.90	0.10	0.15	m	1.15
Windows, screens, glazed doors and the like						
- panes area not exceeding 0.1m2	0.54	3.48	0.20	0.55	m2	4.23
- panes area 0.1 - 0.5m2	0.48	3.09	0.17	0.49	m2	3.75
- panes area 0.5 - 1m2	0.40	2.58	0.13	0.41	m2	3.12
- panes area exceeding 1m2	0.33	2.13	0.10	0.33	m2	2.56
Structural metalwork, general surfaces						
- over 300mm girth	0.28	1.80	0.20	0.30	m2	2.30
- isolated surfaces not exceeding 300mm girth	0.11	0.71	0.08	0.12	m	0.91
- isolated areas not exceeding 0.5m2	0.14	0.90	0.10	0.15	nr	1.15
Structural metalwork, members of roof trusses, lattice girders purlins and the like						
- over 300mm girth	0.32	2.06	0.20	0.34	m2	2.60
- isolated surfaces not exceeding 300mm girth	0.13	0.84	0.08	0.14	m	1.06
- isolated areas not exceeding 0.5m2	0.17	1.09	0.10	0.18	nr	1.37
Radiators, panel type						
- over 300mm girth	0.28	1.80	0.20	0.30	m2	2.30
- isolated surfaces not exceeding 300mm girth	0.11	0.71	0.08	0.12	m	0.91
- isolated areas not exceeding 0.5m2	0.14	0.90	0.10	0.15	nr	1.15

FINISHING COATS INTERNALLY	Painter hours	Nett painter £	Nett material £	O'heads /profit £	Unit	Total £
One coat gloss finish; undercoated metal						
Radiators, column type						
- over 300mm girth	0.33	2.13	0.20	0.35	m2	2.68
- isolated surfaces not exceeding						
300mm girth	0.14	0.90	0.08	0.15	m	1.13
- isolated areas not exceeding						
0.5m2	0.18	1.16	0.10	0.19	nr	1.45

STAINS AND VARNISHES

Prepare; two coats 'Cuprinol' oak preserver; wood wrought surfaces

General surfaces						
- over 300mm girth	0.35	2.25	0.48	0.41	m2	3.14
- isolated surfaces not exceeding						
300mm girth	0.15	0.97	0.18	0.17	m	1.32
- isolated areas not exceeding						
0.5m2	0.18	1.16	0.25	0.21	nr	1.62

Prepare; two coats 'Cuprinol' clear preserver; wood wrought surfaces

General surfaces						
- over 300mm girth	0.35	2.25	0.48	0.41	m2	3.14
- isolated surfaces not exceeding						
300mm girth	0.15	0.97	0.18	0.17	m	1.32
- isolated areas not exceeding						
0.5m2	0.18	1.16	0.25	0.21	nr	1.62

Prepare; apply two coats clear polyurethane; wood

General surfaces						
- over 300mm girth	0.36	2.32	0.36	0.40	m2	3.08
- isolated surfaces not exceeding						
300mm girth	0.16	1.03	0.14	0.18	m	1.35
- isolated areas not exceeding						
0.5m2	0.19	1.22	0.20	0.21	nr	1.63

STAINS AND VARNISHES	Painter hours	Nett painter £	Nett material £	O'heads /profit £	Unit	Total £
Prepare; apply two coats clear polyurethane; wood contd.						
Windows, screens, glazed doors and the like						
- panes area not exceeding 0.1m2	0.80	5.15	0.36	0.83	m2	6.34
- panes area 0.1 - 0.5m2	0.72	4.64	0.30	0.74	m2	5.68
- panes area 0.5 - 1m2	0.64	4.12	0.24	0.65	m2	5.01
- panes area not exceeding 1m2	0.56	3.61	0.18	0.57	m2	4.36

ARTEX

Prepare, one coat 'Artex' sealer one coat 'Artex AX' finish; surfaces over 300mm girth

	Painter hours	Nett painter £	Nett material £	O'heads /profit £	Unit	Total £
Brickwork						
- walls	0.40	2.58	0.50	0.46	m2	3.54
- walls in staircase areas	0.42	2.70	0.50	0.48	m2	3.68
Blockwork						
- walls	0.40	2.58	0.55	0.47	m2	3.60
- walls in staircase areas	0.42	2.70	0.55	0.49	m2	3.74
Concrete						
- walls	0.40	2.58	0.50	0.46	m2	3.54
- walls in staircase areas	0.42	2.70	0.50	0.48	m2	3.68
- ceilings	0.44	2.83	0.50	0.50	m2	3.83
- ceilings in staircase areas	0.46	2.96	0.50	0.52	m2	3.98
Plastered						
- walls	0.35	2.25	0.40	0.40	m2	3.05
- walls in staircase areas	0.37	2.38	0.40	0.42	m2	3.20
- ceilings	0.39	2.51	0.40	0.44	m2	3.35
- ceilings in staircase areas	0.41	2.64	0.40	0.46	m2	3.50
Plasterboard						
- walls	0.35	2.25	0.40	0.40	m2	3.05
- walls in staircase areas	0.37	2.38	0.40	0.42	m2	3.20
- ceilings	0.39	2.51	0.40	0.44	m2	3.35
- ceilings in staircase areas	0.41	2.64	0.40	0.46	m2	3.50

ARTEX	Painter hours	Nett painter £	Nett material £	O'heads /profit £	Unit	Total £
Prepare, one coat 'Artex' sealer one coat 'Artex AX' finish; surfaces over 300mm girth (cont'd)						
Cement rendered						
– walls	0.36	2.32	0.50	0.42	m2	3.24
– walls in staircase areas	0.38	2.45	0.50	0.44	m2	3.39
– ceilings	0.39	2.51	0.50	0.45	m2	3.46
– ceilings in staircase areas	0.41	2.64	0.50	0.47	m2	3.61
Prepare, one coat 'Artex XL' finish; surfaces over 300mm girth						
Concrete						
– walls	0.40	2.58	1.20	0.57	m2	4.35
– walls in staircase areas	0.42	2.70	1.20	0.59	m2	4.49
– ceilings	0.44	2.83	1.20	0.61	m2	4.63
– ceilings in staircase areas	0.46	2.96	1.20	0.62	m2	4.78
Plastered						
– walls	0.35	2.25	0.93	0.48	m2	3.66
– walls in staircase areas	0.37	2.38	0.93	0.50	m2	3.81
– ceilings	0.39	2.51	0.93	0.52	m2	3.96
– ceilings in staircase areas	0.41	2.64	0.93	0.54	m2	4.11
Plasterboard						
– walls	0.35	2.25	0.93	0.48	m2	3.66
– walls in staircase areas	0.37	2.38	0.93	0.50	m2	3.81
– ceilings	0.39	2.51	0.93	0.52	m2	3.96
– ceilings in staircase areas	0.41	2.64	0.93	0.54	m2	4.11
Cement rendered						
– walls	0.36	2.32	1.20	0.53	m2	4.05
– walls in staircase areas	0.38	2.45	1.20	0.55	m2	4.20
– ceilings	0.39	2.51	1.20	0.56	m2	4.27
– ceilings in staircase areas	0.41	2.64	1.20	0.58	m2	4.42

MULTICOLOUR - INTERNALLY	Painter hours	Nett painter £	Nett material £	O'heads /profit £	Unit	Total £
Note: In the following multicolour work the basecoat is applied by brush and the finishing coats sprayed.						
One coat 'Basecoat', one coat 'Multiflek'; surfaces over 300mm girth						
Brickwork						
- walls	0.28	1.80	3.02	0.72	m2	5.54
- walls in staircase areas	0.37	2.38	3.02	0.81	m2	6.21
Concrete						
- walls	0.28	1.80	3.02	0.72	m2	5.54
- walls in staircase areas	0.37	2.38	3.02	0.81	m2	6.21
- ceilings	0.36	2.32	3.02	0.80	m2	6.14
- ceilings in staircase areas	0.45	2.90	3.02	0.89	m2	6.81
Plastered						
- walls	0.25	1.61	2.92	0.68	m2	5.21
- walls in staircase areas	0.34	2.19	2.92	0.77	m2	5.88
- ceilings	0.33	2.13	2.92	0.76	m2	5.81
- ceilings in staircase areas	0.42	2.70	2.92	0.84	m2	6.46
Cement rendered						
- walls	0.46	2.96	3.17	0.92	m2	7.05
- walls in staircase areas	0.55	3.54	3.17	1.01	m2	7.72
Blockwork						
- walls	0.48	3.09	3.17	0.94	m2	7.20
- walls in staircase areas	0.57	3.67	3.17	1.03	m2	7.87

PAINTING

MULTICOLOUR - INTERNALLY	Painter hours	Nett painter £	Nett material £	O'heads /profit £	Unit	Total £
One coat 'Basecoat' one coat 'Multiflek' one 'Glazecoat' surfaces over 300mm girth						
Brickwork						
- walls	0.38	2.45	3.21	0.86	m2	6.52
- walls in staircase areas	0.47	3.03	3.21	0.94	m2	7.18
Concrete						
- walls	0.38	2.45	3.21	0.86	m2	6.52
- walls in staircase areas	0.47	3.03	3.21	0.94	m2	7.18
- ceilings	0.46	2.96	3.21	0.93	m2	7.10
- ceilings in staircase areas	0.55	3.54	3.21	1.01	m2	7.76
Plastered						
- walls	0.35	2.25	2.89	0.77	m2	5.91
- walls in staircase areas	0.44	2.83	2.89	0.86	m2	6.58
- ceilings	0.43	2.77	2.89	0.85	m2	6.51
- ceilings in staircase areas	0.52	3.35	2.89	0.94	m2	7.18
Cement rendered						
- walls	0.56	3.61	3.37	1.05	m2	8.03
- walls in staircase areas	0.65	4.19	3.37	1.13	m2	8.69
Blockwork						
- walls	0.58	3.74	3.37	1.07	m2	8.18
- walls in staircase areas	0.67	4.32	3.37	1.15	m2	8.84
Signwriting; up to 25mm high						
Gloss paint						
- capital letters	0.14	0.90	0.02	0.14	nr	1.06
- lower case letters	0.12	0.77	0.02	0.12	nr	0.91
- numerals	0.14	0.90	0.02	0.14	nr	1.06
Gold leaf						
- capital letters	0.14	0.90	0.12	0.15	nr	1.17
- lower case letters	0.12	0.77	0.12	0.13	nr	1.02
- numerals	0.14	0.90	1.12	0.30	nr	2.32

PREPARING EXISTING SURFACES EXTERNALLY	Painter hours	Nett painter £	Nett material £	O'heads /profit £	Unit	Total £
Wash down masonry painted surfaces over 300mm girth; stop cracks; rub down						
Brickwork						
- walls	0.19	1.22	0.02	0.19	m2	1.43
Blockwork						
- walls	0.20	1.29	0.02	0.20	m2	1.51
Concrete						
- walls	0.14	0.90	0.02	0.14	m2	1.06
Cement rendered						
- walls	0.14	0.90	0.02	0.14	m2	1.06
Rough cast						
- walls	0.22	1.42	0.02	0.22	m2	1.66
Wash down previously oil painted wood surfaces; rub down						
General surfaces						
- over 300mm girth	0.32	2.06	-	0.31	m2	2.37
- isolated surfaces not exceeding 300mm girth	0.12	0.77	-	0.12	m	0.89
- isolated areas not exceeding 0.5m2	0.16	1.03	-	0.16	nr	1.19
Windows, screens, glazed doors and the like						
- panes area not exceeding 0.1m2	0.42	2.71	-	0.41	m2	3.12
- panes area 0.1 - 0.5m2	0.39	2.51	-	0.38	m2	2.89
- panes area 0.5 - 1m2	0.36	2.32	-	0.35	m2	2.67
- panes area not exceeding 1m2	0.32	2.06	-	0.31	m2	2.37

PREPARING EXISTING SURFACES EXTERNALLY	Painter hours	Nett painter £	Nett material £	O'heads /profit £	Unit	Total £
Wash down previously oil painted wood surfaces; remove paint with chemical stripper; rub down						
General surfaces						
- over 300mm girth	0.85	5.47	1.31	1.02	m2	7.80
- isolated surfaces not exceeding 300mm girth	0.30	1.93	0.39	0.35	m	2.67
- isolated areas not exceeding 0.5m2	0.35	2.25	0.65	0.44	nr	3.34
Windows, screens, glazed doors and the like						
- panes area not exceeding 0.1m2	1.80	11.59	1.31	1.94	m2	14.84
- panes area 0.1 - 0.5m2	1.70	10.95	1.31	1.84	m2	14.10
- panes area 0.5 - 1m2	1.55	9.98	1.31	1.69	m2	12.98
- panes area not exceeding 1m2	1.45	9.34	1.31	1.60	m2	12.25
Burn off previously oil painted wood surfaces; rub down						
General surfaces						
- over 300mm girth	1.12	7.21	-	1.08	m2	8.29
- isolated surfaces not exceeding 300mm girth	0.30	2.25	-	0.34	m	2.59
- isolated areas not exceeding 0.5m2	0.40	2.58	-	0.39	nr	2.97
Windows, screens, glazed doors and the like						
- panes area not exceeding 0.1m2	2.12	13.65	-	2.05	m2	15.70
- panes area 0.1 - 0.5m2	2.00	12.88	-	1.93	m2	14.81
- panes area 0.5 - 1m2	1.85	11.91	-	1.79	m2	13.70
- panes area not exceeding 1m2	1.75	11.27	-	1.69	m2	12.96

PRIMERS - EXTERNALLY	Painter hours	Nett painter £	Nett material £	O'heads /profit £	Unit	Total £
One coat masonry sealer; surfaces over 300mm girth						
Brickwork						
- walls	0.27	1.74	0.38	0.32	m2	2.44
Blockwork						
- walls	0.31	2.00	0.51	0.38	m2	2.89
Concrete						
- walls	0.24	1.55	0.45	0.30	m2	2.30
Cement rendered						
- walls	0.25	1.61	0.45	0.31	m2	2.37
Rough cast						
- walls	0.34	2.19	0.65	0.43	m2	3.27
One coat wood primer; wood						
General surfaces						
- over 300mm girth	0.26	1.67	0.31	0.30	m2	2.28
- isolated surfaces not exceeding 300mm girth	0.10	0.64	0.10	0.11	m	0.85
- isolated areas not exceeding 0.5m2	0.13	0.84	0.51	0.20	nr	1.55
Windows, screens, glazed doors and the like						
- panes area not exceeding 0.1m2	0.66	4.25	0.31	0.68	m2	5.24
- panes area 0.1 - 0.5m2	0.58	3.74	0.25	0.60	m2	4.59
- panes area 0.5 - 1m2	0.50	3.22	0.19	0.51	m2	3.92
- panes area not exceeding 1m2	0.42	2.71	0.14	0.43	m2	3.28
One coat red lead primer; metal						
General surfaces						
- over 300mm girth	0.26	1.67	0.67	0.35	m2	2.69
- isolated surfaces not exceeding 300mm girth	0.13	0.84	0.22	0.16	m	1.22
- isolated areas not exceeding 0.5m2	0.17	1.10	0.35	0.22	nr	1.67

PRIMERS - EXTERNALLY	Painter hours	Nett painter £	Nett material £	O'heads /profit £	Unit	Total £
One coat red lead primer; metal contd.;						
Windows, screens, glazed doors and the like						
- panes area not exceeding 0.1m2	0.62	3.99	0.67	0.70	m2	5.36
- panes area 0.1 - 0.5m2	0.52	3.35	0.58	0.59	m2	4.52
- panes area 0.5 - 1m2	0.46	2.96	0.46	0.51	m2	3.93
- panes area exceeding 1m2	0.38	2.45	0.35	0.42	m2	3.22
Structural metalwork, general surfaces						
- over 300mm girth	0.30	1.93	0.67	0.39	m2	2.99
- isolated surfaces not exceeding 300mm girth	0.10	0.64	0.23	0.13	m	1.00
- isolated areas not exceeding 0.5m2	0.15	0.97	0.34	0.20	nr	1.51
Structural metalwork, members of roof trusses, lattice girders, purlins and the like						
- over 300mm	0.35	2.25	0.67	0.44	m2	3.36
- isolated surfaces not exceeding 300mm girth	0.10	0.64	0.23	0.13	m	1.00
- isolated areas not exceeding 0.5m2	0.17	1.10	0.34	0.22	nr	1.66
Gutters eaves						
- over 300mm girth	0.27	1.74	0.67	0.36	m2	2.77
- isolated surfaces not 300mm girth	0.10	0.64	0.23	0.13	m	1.00
- isolated areas not exceeding 0.5m2	0.13	0.84	0.34	0.18	nr	1.36
Services, rainwater pipes						
- over 300mm girth	0.27	1.74	0.67	0.36	m2	2.77
- isolated surfaces not exceeding 300mm girth	0.10	0.64	0.23	0.13	m	1.00
- isolated areas not exceeding 0.5m2	0.13	0.84	0.34	0.18	nr	1.36

PAINTING

PRIMERS - EXTERNALLY	Painter hours	Nett painter £	Nett material £	O'heads /profit £	Unit	Total £
One coat red lead primer; metal contd.;						
Rails, fences and gates						
plain open type						
- over 300mm girth	0.30	1.93	0.67	0.39	m2	2.99
- isolated surfaces not exceeding						
300mm girth	0.15	0.97	0.23	0.18	m	1.38
- isolated areas not exceeding						
0.5m2	0.19	1.22	0.34	0.23	nr	1.79
Ornamental type						
- over 300mm girth	0.26	1.67	0.67	0.35	m2	2.69
- isolated surfaces not exceeding						
300mm girth	0.13	0.84	0.23	0.16	m	1.23
- isolated areas not exceeding						
0.5m2	0.17	1.09	0.34	0.22	nr	1.65
UNDERCOATS - EXTERNALLY						
One undercoat oil based paint; primed wood surfaces						
General surfaces						
- over 300mm girth	0.26	1.67	0.20	0.28	m2	2.15
- isolated surfaces not exceeding						
300mm girth	0.10	0.64	0.08	0.11	m	0.83
- isolated areas not exceeding						
0.5m2	0.13	0.84	0.10	0.14	nr	1.08
Windows, screens, glazed doors and the like						
- panes area not exceeding 0.1m2	0.66	4.25	0.20	0.67	m2	5.12
- panes area 0.1-0.5m2	0.50	3.22	0.17	0.51	m2	3.90
- panes area 0.5-1m2	0.50	3.22	0.13	0.50	m2	3.85
- panes area exceeding 1m2	0.40	2.58	0.10	0.40	m2	3.08

UNDERCOATS EXTERNALLY	Painter hours	Nett painter £	Nett material £	O'heads /profit £	Unit	Total £

One undercoat oil based paint;
primed wood surfaces (cont'd)

Rails, fences and gates

Plain open type

	Painter hours	Nett painter £	Nett material £	O'heads /profit £	Unit	Total £
- over 300mm girth	0.30	1.93	0.20	0.32	m2	2.45
- isolated surfaces not exceeding 300mm girth	0.10	0.64	0.08	0.11	m	0.83
- isolated areas not exceeding 0.5m2	0.09	0.58	0.10	0.10	nr	0.78

Close boarded type

- over 300mm girth	0.26	1.67	0.20	0.28	m2	2.16
- isolated surfaces not exceeding 300mm girth	0.10	0.64	0.08	0.11	m	0.83
- isolated areas not exceeding 0.5m2	0.17	1.10	0.10	0.18	nr	1.38

One undercoat oil based paint;
primed metal surfaces

General surfaces

- over 300mm girth	0.26	1.67	0.20	0.28	m2	2.15
- isolated surfaces not exceeding 300mm girth	0.10	0.64	0.08	0.11	m	0.83
- isolated areas not exceeding 0.5m2	0.13	0.84	0.10	0.14	nr	1.08

Windows, screens, glazed doors
and the like

- panes area not exceeding 0.1m2	0.66	4.25	0.20	0.67	m2	5.12
- panes area 0.1-0.5m2	0.58	3.74	0.17	0.59	m2	4.50
- panes area 0.5-1m2	0.50	3.22	0.13	0.50	m2	3.85
- panes area not exceeding 1m2	0.40	2.58	0.10	0.40	m2	3.08

Structural metalwork, general
surfaces

- over 300mm girth	0.28	1.80	0.20	0.30	m2	2.30
- isolated surfaces not exceeding 300mm girth	0.12	0.77	0.08	0.13	m	0.98
- isolated areas not exceeding 0.5m2	0.15	0.97	0.10	0.16	nr	1.23

UNDERCOATS EXTERNALLY	Painter hours	Nett painter £	Nett material £	O'heads /profit £	Unit	Total £
One undercoat oil based paint; primed metal surfaces contd.;						
Structural metalwork, members of roof trusses, lattice girders, purlins and the like						
- over 300mm	0.32	2.06	0.20	0.34	m2	2.80
- isolated surfaces not exceeding 300mm girth	0.10	0.64	0.08	0.11	m	0.83
- isolated areas not exceeding 0.5m2	0.16	1.03	0.10	0.17	nr	1.30
Gutters, eaves						
- over 300mm girth	0.27	1.74	0.20	0.29	m2	2.23
- isolated surfaces not exceeding 300mm girth	0.10	0.64	0.08	0.11	m	0.83
- isolated areas not exceeding 0.5m2	0.17	1.10	0.10	0.18	nr	1.38
Services, rainwater pipes						
- over 300mm girth	0.27	1.74	0.20	0.29	m2	2.23
- isolated surfaces not exceeding 300mm girth	0.10	0.64	0.08	0.11	m	0.83
- isolated areas not exceeding 0.5m2	0.17	1.10	0.10	0.18	nr	1.38
Rails, fences and gates						
Plain open type						
- over 300mm girth	0.30	1.93	0.20	0.32	m2	2.45
- isolated surfaces not exceeding 300mm girth	0.12	0.77	0.08	0.13	m	0.98
- isolated areas not exceeding 0.5m2	0.19	1.22	0.10	0.20	nr	1.52
Ornamental type						
- over 300mm girth	0.32	2.06	0.20	0.34	m2	2.60
- isolated surfaces not exceeding 300mm girth	0.15	0.97	0.08	0.16	m	1.21
- isolated areas not exceeding 0.5m2	0.20	1.29	0.10	0.21	nr	1.60

FINISHING COATS EXTERNALLY	Painter hours	Nett painter £	Nett material £	O'heads /profit £	Unit	Total £
One coat gloss finish;						
undercoated wood						
General surfaces						
- over 300mm girth	0.28	1.80	0.20	0.30	m2	2.30
- isolated surfaces not exceeding						
300mm girth	0.12	0.77	0.08	0.13	m	0.98
- isolated areas not exceeding						
0.5m2	0.15	0.97	0.10	0.16	nr	1.23
Windows, screens, glazed doors						
and the like						
- panes area not exceeding 0.1m2	0.66	4.25	0.20	0.67	m2	5.12
- panes area 0.1 - 0.5m2	0.58	3.74	0.17	0.59	m2	4.50
- panes area 0.5 - 1m2	0.50	3.22	0.13	0.50	m2	3.85
- panes area exceeding 1m2	0.40	2.58	0.10	0.40	m2	3.08
Rails, fences and gates						
Plain open type						
- over 300mm girth	0.30	1.93	0.20	0.32	m2	2.45
- isolated surfaces not exceeding						
300mm girth	0.10	0.64	0.08	0.11	m	0.83
- isolated areas not exceeding						
0.5m2	0.09	0.58	0.10	0.10	nr	0.78
Close boarded type						
- over 300mm girth	0.26	1.67	0.20	0.28	m2	2.16
- isolated surfaces not exceeding						
300mm girth	0.10	0.64	0.08	0.11	m	0.83
- isolated areas not exceeding						
0.5m2	0.17	1.10	0.10	0.18	nr	1.38
One coat gloss finish;						
undercoated metal						
General surfaces						
- over 300mm girth	0.28	1.80	0.20	0.30	m2	2.30
- isolated surfaces not exceeding						
300mm girth	0.12	0.77	0.08	0.13	m	0.98
- isolated areas not exceeding						
0.5m2	0.15	0.97	0.10	0.16	nr	1.23

FINISHING COATS EXTERNALLY	Painter hours	Nett painter £	Nett material £	O'heads /profit £	Unit	Total £
One coat gloss finish; undercoated metal contd.;						
Windows, screens, glazed doors and the like						
- panes area not exceeding 0.1m2	0.66	4.25	0.20	0.67	m2	5.12
- panes area 0.1 - 0.5m2	0.58	3.74	0.17	0.59	m2	4.50
- panes area 0.5-1m2	0.50	3.22	0.13	0.50	m2	3.85
- panes area exceeding 1m2	0.40	2.58	0.10	0.40	m2	3.08
Structural metalwork, general surfaces						
- over 300mm girth	0.28	1.80	0.20	0.30	m2	2.30
- isolated surfaces not exceeding 300mm girth	0.12	0.77	0.08	0.13	m	0.98
- isolated areas not exceeding 0.5m2	0.15	0.97	0.10	0.16	nr	1.23
Structural metalwork, members of roof trusses, lattice girders, purlins and the like						
- over 300mm	0.32	2.06	0.20	0.34	m2	2.60
- isolated surfaces not exceeding 300mm girth	0.10	0.64	0.08	0.11	m	0.83
- isolated areas not exceeding 0.5m2	0.16	1.03	0.10	0.17	nr	1.30
Gutters, eaves						
- over 300mm girth	0.27	1.74	0.20	0.29	m2	2.23
- isolated surfaces not exceeding 300mm girth	0.10	0.64	0.08	0.11	m	0.83
- isolated areas not exceeding 0.5m2	0.17	1.10	0.10	0.18	nr	1.38
Services, rainwater pipes						
- over 300mm girth	0.27	1.74	0.20	0.29	m2	2.23
- isolated surfaces not exceeding 300mm girth	0.10	0.64	0.08	0.11	m	0.83
- isolated areas not exceeding 0.5m2	0.17	1.10	0.10	0.18	nr	1.38

FINISHING COATS EXTERNALLY	Painter hours	Nett painter £	Nett material £	O'heads /profit £	Unit	Total £

One coat gloss finish;
undercoated metal contd.;

Rails, fences and gates

Plain open type

- over 300mm type	0.30	1.93	0.20	0.32	m2	2.45
- isolated surfaces not exceeding						
300mm girth	0.12	0.77	0.08	0.13	m	0.98
- isolated areas not exceeding						
0.5m2	0.19	1.22	0.10	0.20	nr	1.52

Ornamental type

- over 300mm girth	0.32	2.06	0.20	0.34	m2	2.60
- isolated surfaces not exceeding						
300mm girth	0.15	0.97	0.08	0.16	m	1.21
- isolated areas not exceeding						
0.5m2	0.20	1.29	0.10	0.21	nr	1.60

Two coats 'Solignum' green
preservative; wood surfaces

General wrought surfaces

- over 300mm girth	0.36	2.32	0.32	0.40	m2	3.04
- isolated surfaces not exceeding						
300mm girth	0.19	1.22	0.10	0.20	m	1.52
- isolated areas not exceeding						
0.5m2	0.25	1.61	0.15	0.26	nr	2.02

General sawn surfaces

- over 300mm girth	0.38	2.45	0.38	0.43	m2	3.26
- isolated surfaces not exceeding						
300mm girth	0.20	1.29	0.14	0.22	m	1.65
- isolated areas not exceeding						
0.5m2	0.26	1.67	0.17	0.28	nr	2.12

FINISHING COATS EXTERNALLY	Painter hours	Nett painter £	Nett material £	O'heads /profit £	Unit	Total £
Prepare, apply two coats 'Cuprinol' green preserver; wood surfaces						
General wrought surfaces						
- over 300mm girth	0.38	2.45	0.48	0.44	m2	3.37
- isolated surfaces not exceeding 300mm girth	0.20	1.29	0.16	0.22	m	1.67
- isolated areas not exceeding 0.5m2	0.26	1.67	0.24	0.29	nr	2.20
General sawn surfaces						
- over 300mm girth	0.40	2.58	0.54	0.47	m2	3.59
- isolated surfaces not exceeding 300mm girth	0.21	1.35	0.18	0.23	m	1.76
- isolated areas not exceeding 0.5m2	0.27	1.74	0.26	0.30	nr	2.30
Rails, fences and gates						
Plain open type						
- over 300mm type	0.40	2.58	0.54	0.47	m2	3.59
- isolated surfaces not exceeding 300mm girth	0.21	1.35	0.18	0.23	m	1.76
- isolated areas not exceeding 0.5m2	0.27	1.74	0.26	0.30	nr	2.30
Close boarded type						
- over 300mm girth	0.38	2.45	0.54	0.45	m2	3.44
- isolated surfaces not exceeding 300mm girth	0.15	0.97	0.18	0.17	m	1.32
- isolated areas not exceeding 0.5m2	0.20	1.29	0.26	0.23	nr	1.78
Prepare, apply two coats medium dark creosote; wood surfaces						
General wrought surfaces						
- over 300mm girth	0.38	2.45	0.29	0.41	m2	3.15
- isolated surfaces not exceeding 300mm girth	0.20	1.29	0.10	0.21	m	1.60
- isolated areas not exceeding 0.5m2	0.26	1.67	0.15	0.27	nr	2.09

FINISHING COATS EXTERNALLY	Painter hours	Nett painter £	Nett material £	O'heads /profit £	Unit	Total £
Prepare, apply two coats medium dark creosote; wood surfaces contd.;						
General sawn surfaces						
- over 300mm girth	0.40	2.58	0.33	0.44	m2	3.35
- isolated surfaces not exceeding 300mm girth	0.22	1.42	0.12	0.23	m	1.77
- isolated areas not exceeding 0.5m2	0.28	1.80	0.17	0.30	nr	2.27
Rails, fences and gates						
Plain open type						
- over 300mm type	0.40	2.58	0.33	0.44	m2	3.35
- isolated surfaces not exceeding 300mm girth	0.22	1.42	0.12	0.23	m	1.77
- isolated areas not exceeding 0.5m2	0.28	1.80	0.17	0.30	nr	2.27
Close boarded type						
- over 300mm girth	0.38	2.45	0.33	0.42	m2	3.20
- isolated surfaces not exceeding 300mm girth	0.15	0.97	0.12	0.16	m	1.25
- isolated areas not exceeding 0.5m2	0.20	1.29	0.17	0.22	nr	1.68
Prepare, apply three coats clear polyurethane; wood surfaces						
General surfaces						
- over 300mm girth	0.54	3.48	0.54	0.60	m2	4.62
- isolated surfaces not exceeding 300mm girth	0.24	1.55	0.18	0.26	m	1.99
- isolated areas not exceeding 0.5m2	0.28	1.80	0.27	0.31	nr	2.38

FINISHING COATS EXTERNALLY	Painter hours	Nett painter £	Nett material £	O'heads /profit £	Unit	Total £

Prepare, apply three coats clear
polyurethane; wood surfaces
contd.;

Windows, screens, glazed doors
and the like

- panes area not exceeding 0.1m2	0.85	5.47	0.54	0.90	m2	6.91
- panes area 0.1 - 0.5m2	0.75	4.83	0.46	0.79	m2	6.08
- panes area 0.5 - 1m2	0.68	4.38	0.38	0.71	m2	5.47
- panes area exceeding 1m2	0.60	3.86	0.28	0.62	m2	4.76

MASONRY PAINTS - EXTERNALLY

One coat 'Blue Circle'
Stabilising Solution; two coats
'Snowcem' finish, surfaces over
300mm girth

Brickwork
- walls	0.48	3.09	0.49	0.54	m2	4.12

Blockwork
- walls	0.54	3.48	0.59	0.61	m2	4.68

Concrete
- walls	0.45	2.90	0.49	0.51	m2	3.90

Cement rendered
- walls	0.42	2.71	0.59	0.50	m2	3.80

Rough cast
- walls	0.57	3.67	0.70	0.66	m2	5.03

PAINTING

MASONRY PAINTS EXTERNALLY	Painter hours	Nett painter £	Nett material £	O'heads /profit £	Unit	Total £
One coat 'Blue Circle' Stabilising Solution; two coats 'Sandtex Matt' finish; surfaces over 300mm girth						
Brickwork						
- walls	0.60	3.86	1.17	0.76	m2	5.79
Blockwork						
- walls	0.66	4.25	1.40	0.85	m2	6.50
Concrete						
- walls	0.57	3.67	1.17	0.73	m2	5.57
Cement rendered						
- walls	0.54	3.48	1.40	0.73	m2	5.61
Rough cast						
- walls	0.69	4.44	2.33	1.02	m2	7.79
Prepare, one coat Artex 'Force 8' masonry paint surfaces over 300mm girth						
Brickwork						
- walls	0.32	2.06	0.80	0.43	m2	3.29
Blockwork						
- walls	0.36	2.32	0.80	0.47	m2	3.59
Concrete						
- walls	0.30	1.93	0.70	0.40	m2	3.03
Cement rendered						
- walls	0.30	1.93	0.70	0.40	m2	3.03
Rough cast						
- walls	0.40	2.58	0.93	0.53	m2	4.04

MASONRY PAINTS EXTERNALLY	Painter hours	Nett painter £	Nett material £	O'heads /profit £	Unit	Total £
Prepare, one coat Artex 'Hyclad' finish, surfaces over 300mm girth						
Brickwork						
- walls	0.40	2.58	1.90	0.67	m2	5.15
Blockwork						
- walls	0.45	2.90	1.90	0.72	m2	5.52
Concrete						
- walls	0.38	2.45	1.80	0.64	m2	4.89
Cement rendered						
- walls	0.38	2.45	1.80	0.64	m2	4.89
Rough cast						
- walls	0.40	2.58	2.43	0.75	m2	5.76

COMPOSITE RATES

The following composite rates are intended to help the estimator where rates are required for items involving more than one painting operation. The rates are generally based upon the information given in the previous pages and the comments made in the early part of this chapter still apply.

INTERNALLY

Two coats matt emulsion paint; surfaces over 300mm girth

	Painter hours	Nett painter £	Nett material £	O'heads /profit £	Unit	Total £
Brickwork						
- walls	0.30	1.93	0.49	0.36	m2	2.78
- walls in staircase areas	0.34	2.19	0.49	0.40	m2	3.08
Blockwork						
- walls	0.38	2.45	0.65	0.47	m2	3.57
- walls in staircase areas	0.42	2.71	0.65	0.50	m2	3.86

INTERNALLY	Painter hours	Nett painter £	Nett material £	O'heads /profit £	Unit	Total £
Two coats matt emulsion paint; surfaces over 300mm girth contd.;						
Concrete						
- walls	0.24	1.55	0.39	0.29	m2	2.23
- walls in staircase areas	0.30	1.93	0.39	0.35	m2	2.67
- ceilings	0.32	2.06	0.39	0.37	m2	2.82
- ceilings in staircase areas	0.36	2.32	0.39	0.41	m2	3.12
Plastered						
- walls	0.22	1.42	0.39	0.27	m2	2.08
- walls in staircase areas	0.26	1.67	0.39	0.31	m2	2.37
- ceilings	0.30	1.93	0.39	0.35	m2	2.67
- ceilings in staircase areas	0.32	2.06	0.39	0.37	m2	2.82
Embossed paper						
- walls	0.24	1.55	0.42	0.30	m2	2.27
- walls in staircase areas	0.30	1.93	0.42	0.35	m2	2.70
- ceilings	0.32	2.06	0.42	0.37	m2	2.85
- ceilings in staircase areas	0.36	2.32	0.42	0.41	m2	3.15
One coat alkali resisting primer; two coats of silk emulsion paint surfaces over 300mm girth						
Brickwork						
- walls	0.54	3.48	0.84	0.65	m2	4.97
- walls in staircase areas	0.60	3.86	0.84	0.71	m2	5.41
Blockwork						
- walls	0.66	4.25	1.10	0.80	m2	6.15
- walls in staircase areas	0.72	4.64	1.10	0.86	m2	6.60
Concrete						
- walls	0.46	2.96	0.88	0.58	m2	4.42
- walls in staircase areas	0.55	3.54	0.88	0.66	m2	5.08
- ceilings	0.58	3.74	0.88	0.69	m2	5.31
- ceilings in staircase areas	0.64	4.12	0.88	0.75	m2	5.75
Plastered						
- walls	0.43	2.77	0.68	0.52	m2	3.97
- walls in staircase areas	0.50	3.22	0.68	0.59	m2	4.49
- ceilings	0.58	3.74	0.68	0.66	m2	5.08
- ceilings in staircase areas	0.63	4.06	0.68	0.71	m2	5.45

PAINTING

INTERNALLY	Painter hours	Nett painter £	Nett material £	O'heads /profit £	Unit	Total £
One coat aluminum wood primer;						
one oil based undercoat;						
one coat eggshell finish;						
wood						
General surfaces						
- over 300mm girth	0.72	4.64	0.70	0.80	m2	6.14
- isolated surfaces not exceeding						
300mm girth	0.26	1.67	0.19	0.28	m	2.14
- isolated areas not exceeding						
0.5m2	0.36	2.32	0.35	0.40	nr	3.07
Windows, screens, glazed doors						
and the like						
- panes area not exceeding 0.1m2	1.66	10.69	0.70	1.71	m2	13.10
- panes area 0.1 - 0.5m2	1.43	9.21	0.58	1.47	m2	11.26
- panes area 0.5 - 1m2	1.23	7.92	0.47	1.26	m2	9.65
- panes area exceeding 1m2	1.01	6.50	0.35	1.03	m2	7.88
One coat aluminum wood primer;						
One oil based undercoat;						
One coat gloss finish; wood						
General surfaces						
- over 300mm girth	0.72	4.64	0.68	0.80	m2	6.12
- isolated surfaces not exceeding						
300mm girth	0.26	1.67	0.26	0.29	m	2.22
- isolated areas not exceeding						
0.5m2	0.36	2.32	0.34	0.40	nr	3.06
Windows, screens, glazed doors						
and the like						
- panes area not exceeding 0.1m2	1.66	10.69	0.68	1.71	m2	13.08
- panes area 0.1 - 0.5m2	1.43	9.21	0.57	1.47	m2	11.25
- panes area 0.5 - 1m2	1.23	7.92	0.54	1.27	m2	9.73
- panes area exceeding 1m2	1.06	6.83	0.33	1.07	m2	8.23

INTERNALLY	Painter hours	Nett painter £	Nett material £	O'heads /profit £	Unit	Total £
One coat quick drying metal primer; one oil based undercoat; one eggshell finish; metal						
General surfaces						
- over 300mm girth	0.74	4.77	0.67	0.82	m2	6.26
- isolated surfaces not exceeding 300mm girth	0.28	1.80	0.25	0.31	m	2.36
- isolated areas not exceeding 0.5m2	0.38	2.45	0.32	0.42	nr	3.19
Windows, screens, glazed doors and the like						
- panes area not exceeding 0.1m2	1.66	10.69	0.66	1.70	m2	13.05
- panes area 0.1 - 0.5m2	1.43	9.21	0.56	1.47	m2	11.24
- panes area 0.5 - 1m2	1.23	7.92	0.44	1.25	m2	9.61
- panes area exceeding 1m2	1.06	6.83	0.35	1.08	m2	8.26
Structural metalwork, general surfaces						
- over 300mm girth	0.84	5.41	0.65	0.91	m2	6.97
- isolated surfaces not exceeding 300mm girth	0.31	2.00	0.25	0.34	m	2.59
- isolated areas not exceeding 0.5m2	0.41	2.64	0.32	0.44	nr	3.40
Structural metalwork, members of roof trusses, lattice girders, purlins and the like						
- over 300mm girth	0.97	6.25	0.65	1.04	m2	7.94
- isolated surfaces not exceeding 300mm girth	0.35	2.25	0.25	0.38	m	2.88
- isolated areas not exceeding 0.5m2	0.39	2.51	0.32	0.43	nr	3.26
Radiators, panel type						
- over 300mm girth	0.98	6.31	0.65	1.04	m2	8.00
- isolated surfaces not exceeding 300mm girth	0.31	2.00	0.25	0.34	m	2.59
- isolated areas not exceeding 0.5m2	0.44	2.83	0.32	0.47	nr	3.62

INTERNALLY	Painter hours	Nett painter £	Nett material £	O'heads /profit £	Unit	Total £
One coat quick drying metal primer; one oil based undercoat; one eggshell finish; metal contd.;						
Radiators, column type						
- over 300mm girth	1.03	6.63	0.65	1.09	m2	8.37
- isolated surfaces not exceeding 300mm girth	0.38	2.45	0.25	0.41	m	3.11
- isolated areas not exceeding 0.5m2	0.52	3.35	0.32	0.55	nr	4.22
One coat quick drying metal primer; one oil based undercoat; one coat gloss finish; metal						
General surfaces						
- over 300mm girth	0.78	5.02	0.64	0.85	m2	6.51
- isolated surfaces not exceeding 300mm girth	0.28	1.80	0.24	0.31	m	2.35
- isolated areas not exceeding 0.5m2	0.38	2.45	0.31	0.41	nr	3.17
Windows, screens, glazed doors and the like						
- panes area not exceeding 0.1m2	1.66	10.69	0.64	1.70	m2	13.03
- panes area 0.1 - 0.5m2	1.43	9.21	0.54	1.46	m2	11.21
- panes area 0.5 - 1m2	1.23	7.92	0.42	1.25	m2	9.59
- panes area exceeding 1m2	1.06	6.83	0.33	1.07	m2	8.23
Structural metalwork, general surfaces						
- over 300mm girth	0.84	5.41	0.63	0.91	m2	6.95
- isolated surfaces not exceeding 300mm girth	0.31	2.00	0.24	0.34	m	2.58
- isolated areas not exceeding 0.5m2	0.41	2.64	0.32	0.44	nr	3.40

INTERNALLY	Painter hours	Nett painter £	Nett material £	O'heads /profit £	Unit	Total £
One coat quick drying metal primer; one oil based undercoat; one coat gloss finish; metal contd						
Structural metalwork, members of roof trusses, lattice girders, purlins and the like						
- over 300mm girth	0.97	6.25	0.63	1.03	m2	7.91
- isolated surfaces not exceeding 300mm girth	0.35	2.25	0.25	0.37	m	2.86
- isolated areas not exceeding 0.5m2	0.39	2.51	0.31	0.42	nr	3.24
Radiators, panel type						
- over 300mm girth	0.98	6.31	0.63	1.04	m2	7.98
- isolated surfaces not exceeding 300mm girth	0.31	2.00	0.24	0.34	m	2.58
- isolated areas not exceeding 0.5m2	0.44	2.83	0.31	0.47	nr	3.61
Radiators, column type						
- over 300mm girth	1.03	6.63	0.63	1.09	m2	8.35
- isolated surfaces not exceeding 300mm girth	0.38	2.45	0.24	0.40	m	3.09
- isolated areas not exceeding 0.5m2	0.52	3.35	0.31	0.55	nr	4.21
One coat calcium plumbate primer; one oil based undercoat; one coat gloss finish; metal						
General surfaces						
- over 300mm girth	0.70	4.51	0.66	0.78	m2	5.95
- isolated surfaces not exceeding 300mm girth	0.28	1.80	0.26	0.31	m	2.37
- isolated areas not exceeding 0.5m2	0.36	2.32	0.33	0.40	nr	3.05

INTERNALLY	Painter hours	Nett painter £	Nett material £	O'heads /profit £	Unit	Total £
One coat chlorinated rubber primer; one undercoat: one finish coat; surfaces over 300mm girth						
Brickwork						
- walls	0.99	6.38	1.37	1.16	m2	8.91
- walls in staircase areas	1.06	6.83	1.44	1.24	m2	9.51
Blockwork						
- walls	1.16	7.47	1.45	1.34	m2	10.26
- walls in staircase areas	1.29	8.31	1.70	1.50	m2	11.51
Concrete						
- walls	0.88	5.67	1.37	1.06	m2	8.10
- walls in staircase areas	1.01	6.50	1.39	1.18	m2	9.07
- ceilings	1.08	6.96	1.46	1.26	m2	9.68
- ceilings in staircase areas	1.17	7.54	1.45	1.35	m2	10.34
Plastered						
- walls	0.81	5.22	1.13	0.95	m2	7.30
- walls in staircase areas	0.93	5.99	1.24	1.09	m2	8.32
- ceilings	1.05	6.76	1.36	1.22	m2	9.34
- ceilings in staircase areas	1.17	7.54	1.48	1.35	m2	10.37

DRAINAGE

1. Labour

   Craftsman £6.44 per hour
   Labourer   £5.55 per hour

2. Materials

	Unit	Basic Price	Waste %	Total £
Sand filling	t	7.70	10	8.47
Granular filling	t	9.75	10	10.73
Ready mixed concrete mix A				
(1:3:6)	m3	50.96	5	53.51
100mm v.c. spigot and socket pipe	m	2.54	5	2.67
bend	nr	1.90	2½	1.95
rest bend	nr	4.70	2½	4.82
single junction	nr	5.40	2½	5.54
double junction	nr	12.40	2½	12.71
150mm v.c. spigot and socket pipe	m	4.57	5	4.80
bend	nr	4.20	2½	4.31
rest bend	nr	8.10	2½	8.30
single junction	nr	8.40	2½	8.61
double junction	nr	16.40	2½	16.81
100mm Hepsleve pipe	m	2.32	5	2.44
bend	nr	2.40	2½	2.46
rest bend	nr	3.80	2½	3.90
single junction	nr	4.90	2½	5.02
150mm Hepsleve pipe	m	5.72	5	6.01
bend	nr	5.00	2½	5.13
rest bend	nr	6.10	2½	6.25
single junction	nr	8.20	2½	8.41
100mm Hepseal pipe	m	4.26	5	4.47
bend	nr	6.00	2½	6.15
rest bend	nr	7.50	2½	7.69
single junction	nr	7.80	2½	8.00
150mm Hepseal pipe	m	5.62	5	5.90
bend	nr	8.75	2½	8.97
rest bend	nr	11.50	2½	11.79
single junction	nr	28.00	2½	28.70
225mm Hepseal pipe	m	11.44	5	12.01
bend	nr	19.00	2½	19.48
rest bend	nr	30.80	2½	31.57
single junction	nr	31.00	2½	31.78
V.C. 100mm gulley and grid	nr	11.80	5	12.39
Yard gulley and grid	nr	17.00	5	17.85
Site mixed concrete A	m3	54.44	5	57.16
Site mixed concrete B	m3	56.42	5	59.24
Common bricks	1000	130.00	5	136.50

347

	Unit	Basic Price	Waste %	Total £
Class 'B' Engineering bricks	1000	235.00	5	246.75
Step iron	nr	4.30	5	4.52
Cast iron manhole covers				
grade C size 600 x 450mm	nr	32.41	5	34.03
grade B size 600 x 450mm	nr	88.61	5	93.04
grade B single seal 550mm dia.	nr	88.42	5	92.84
Best quality vitrified clay channels				
straight main channel				
100mm	m	2.98	5	3.13
150mm	m	6.30	5	6.62
Tapered main channel				
150 - 100mm	m	14.20	5	14.91
Channel bend				
100mm	nr	3.74	5	3.93
150mm	nr	6.30	5	6.62
Tapered channel bend				
150 - 100mm	nr	22.00	5	23.10
Branched channel bends				
100mm	nr	4.30	5	4.52
150mm	nr	7.20	5	7.56

HAND EXCAVATION
Labour rate £5.55 per hour

	Labour hours	Nett labour £	Nett material £	O'heads /profit £	Unit	Total £
Excavate trench for drain, support sides, grade and ram bottom, backfill and consolidate with excavated material and remove surplus to skip for pipes not exceeding 200mm diameter, average depth of trench						
- 0.50m	1.20	6.66	-	1.00	m	7.66
- 0.75m	1.95	10.82	-	1.62	m	12.44
- 1.00m	2.58	14.32	-	2.15	m	16.47
- 1.25m	4.05	22.48	-	3.37	m	25.85
- 1.50m	5.10	28.31	-	4.25	m	32.56
- 1.75m	5.90	32.75	-	4.91	m	37.66
- 2.00m	6.30	34.97	-	5.25	m	40.22
- 2.25m	8.25	45.79	-	6.87	m	52.66
- 2.50m	9.45	52.45	-	7.87	m	60.32
- 2.75m	10.75	59.66	-	8.95	m	68.61
- 3.00m	12.00	66.60	-	9.99	m	76.59

DRAINAGE

HAND EXCAVATION	Labour hours	Nett labour £	Nett material £	O'heads /profit £	Unit	Total £
Excavate trench for drain, support sides, grade and ram bottom, backfill and consolidate with excavated material and remove surplus to skip for pipes 225mm diameter, average depth of trench						
- 0.50m	1.32	7.33	-	1.10	m	8.43
- 0.75m	2.10	11.66	-	1.75	m	13.41
- 1.00m	2.84	15.76	-	2.36	m	18.12
- 1.25m	4.45	24.70	-	3.71	m	28.41
- 1.50m	5.60	31.08	-	4.66	m	35.74
- 1.75m	6.50	36.08	-	5.41	m	41.49
- 2.00m	6.95	38.57	-	5.79	m	44.36
- 2.25m	9.00	49.95	-	7.49	m	57.44
- 2.50m	10.40	57.72	-	8.66	m	66.38
- 2.75m	11.85	65.77	-	9.87	m	75.64
- 3.00m	13.20	73.26	-	10.99	m	84.25
Excavate trench for drain, support sides, grade and ram bottom, backfill and consolidate with excavated material and remove surplus to skip for pipes 300mm diameter, average depth of trench						
- 0.50m	1.50	8.33	-	1.25	m	9.58
- 0.75m	2.30	12.77	-	1.92	m	14.69
- 1.00m	3.05	16.93	-	2.54	m	19.47
- 1.25m	4.90	27.20	-	4.08	m	31.28
- 1.50m	6.15	34.13	-	5.12	m	39.25
- 1.75m	7.15	39.68	-	5.95	m	45.63
- 2.00m	7.65	42.46	-	6.37	m	48.83
- 2.25m	9.90	54.94	-	8.24	m	63.18
- 2.50m	11.40	63.27	-	9.49	m	72.76
- 2.75m	13.05	72.43	-	10.87	m	83.30
- 3.00m	14.50	80.48	-	12.07	m	92.55
Extra for breaking up						
- concrete 100mm thick	0.90	5.00	-	0.75	m2	5.75
- tarmacadam 75mm thick	0.50	2.78	-	0.42	m2	3.20
- hardcore 100mm thick	0.60	3.33	-	0.50	m2	3.83
- plain concrete	7.00	38.85	-	5.83	m3	44.68
- reinforced concrete	8.00	44.40	-	6.66	m3	51.06
- soft rock	10.00	55.50	-	8.33	m3	63.83

349

DRAINAGE

HAND EXCAVATION	Labour hours	Nett labour £	Nett material /plant £	O'heads /profit £	Unit	Total £
Extra for breaking up contd.;						
- hard rock	11.00	61.05	-	9.16	m3	70.21

MACHINE EXCAVATION

Excavate trench for drain, support sides, grade and ram bottom, backfill and consolidate with excavated material and remove surplus to skip for pipes not exceeding 200mm diameter, average depth of trench

- 0.50m	0.80	4.44	0.45	0.73	m	5.62
- 0.75m	1.20	6.66	0.60	1.09	m	8.35
- 1.00m	1.60	8.88	0.75	1.45	m	11.08
- 1.25m	1.80	9.99	0.90	1.63	m	12.52
- 1.50m	2.00	11.10	1.10	1.83	m	14.03
- 1.75m	2.40	13.32	1.25	2.19	m	16.76
- 2.00m	2.80	15.54	1.40	2.54	m	19.48
- 2.25m	3.10	17.21	1.55	2.81	m	21.57
- 2.50m	3.40	18.87	1.70	3.09	m	23.66
- 2.75m	3.70	20.54	1.85	3.36	m	25.75
- 3.00m	4.00	22.20	2.00	3.63	m	27.83

Excavate trench for drain, support sides, grade and ram bottom, backfill and consolidate with excavated material and remove surplus to skip for pipes 225mm diameter, average depth of trench

- 0.50m	0.40	2.22	0.50	0.41	m	3.13
- 0.75m	1.30	7.22	0.65	1.18	m	9.05
- 1.00m	1.75	9.71	0.80	1.58	m	12.09
- 1.25m	1.95	10.82	0.95	1.77	m	13.54
- 1.50m	2.20	12.21	1.15	2.00	m	15.36
- 1.75m	2.60	14.43	1.30	2.36	m	18.09
- 2.00m	3.00	16.65	1.45	2.72	m	20.82
- 2.25m	3.30	18.32	1.66	3.00	m	22.98
- 2.50m	3.60	19.98	1.80	3.27	m	25.05
- 2.75m	4.00	22.20	1.95	3.62	m	27.77
- 3.00m	4.40	24.42	2.15	3.99	m	30.56

MACHINE EXCAVATION	Labour hours	Nett labour £	Nett material /plant £	O'heads /profit £	Unit	Total £

Excavate trench for drain,
support sides, grade and ram
bottom, backfill and consolidate
with excavated material and
remove surplus to skip for pipes
300mm diameter, average depth of
trench

	Labour hours	Nett labour £	Nett material /plant £	O'heads /profit £	Unit	Total £
- 0.50m	1.00	5.55	0.55	0.92	m	7.02
- 0.75m	1.45	8.05	0.70	1.31	m	10.06
- 1.00m	1.90	10.55	0.85	1.71	m	13.11
- 1.25m	2.15	11.93	1.10	1.96	m	14.99
- 1.50m	2.40	13.32	1.25	2.19	m	16.76
- 1.75m	2.85	15.82	1.40	2.58	m	19.80
- 2.00m	3.30	18.32	1.70	3.00	m	23.02
- 2.25m	3.65	20.26	1.85	3.32	m	25.43
- 2.50m	4.00	22.20	2.00	3.63	m	27.83
- 2.75m	4.40	24.42	2.20	3.99	m	30.61
- 3.00m	4.90	27.20	2.35	4.43	m	33.98
Extra for breaking up						
- concrete 100mm thick	0.40	2.22	1.60	0.57	m2	4.39
- tarmacadam 75mm thick	0.24	1.33	1.00	0.35	m2	2.68
- hardcore 100mm thick	0.28	1.55	1.10	0.40	m2	3.05
- plain concrete	2.30	12.77	15.00	4.17	m3	31.94
- reinforced concrete	3.50	19.43	18.00	5.62	m3	43.05
- soft rock	4.00	22.20	10.00	4.83	m3	37.03
- hard rock	4.00	22.20	18.00	6.03	m3	46.23

BEDS AND COVERINGS

Sand bed in trench under 100mm
diameter pipe, thickness

	Labour hours	Nett labour £	Nett material /plant £	O'heads /profit £	Unit	Total £
- 100mm	0.10	0.56	0.43	0.15	m	1.41
- 150mm	0.12	0.67	0.64	0.20	m	1.51

Sand bed in trench under 150mm
diameter pipe, thickness

	Labour hours	Nett labour £	Nett material /plant £	O'heads /profit £	Unit	Total £
- 100mm	0.11	0.61	0.51	0.17	m	1.29
- 150mm	0.13	0.72	0.76	0.22	m	1.70

BEDS AND COVERINGS	Labour hours	Nett labour £	Nett material £	O'heads /profit £	Unit	Total £
Sand bed in trench under 225mm diameter pipe, thickness						
- 100mm	0.14	0.78	0.64	0.21	m	1.63
- 150mm	0.16	0.89	0.95	0.28	m	2.12
Granular filling to bed in trench under 100mm diameter pipe, thickness						
- 100mm	0.12	0.67	0.53	0.18	m	1.38
- 150mm	0.14	0.78	0.81	0.24	m	1.83
Granular filling to bed in trench under 150mm diameter pipe, thickness						
- 100mm	0.13	0.72	0.64	0.20	m	1.56
- 150mm	0.15	0.83	0.97	0.27	m	2.07
Granular filling to bed in trench under 225mm diameter pipe, thickness						
- 100mm	0.16	0.89	0.81	0.26	m	1.96
- 150mm	0.18	1.00	1.21	0.33	m	2.54
Concrete Mix A bed in trench under 100mm diameter pipe, thickness						
- 100mm	0.24	1.33	2.74	0.61	m	4.68
- 150mm	0.28	1.55	4.11	0.85	m	6.51
Concrete Mix A bed in trench under 150mm diameter pipe, thickness						
- 100mm	0.26	1.44	3.29	0.71	m	5.44
- 150mm	0.30	1.67	4.93	0.99	m	7.59
Concrete Mix A bed in trench under 225mm diameter pipe, thickness						
- 100mm	0.32	1.78	4.11	0.88	m	6.77
- 150mm	0.36	2.00	6.03	1.21	m	9.24

BEDS AND COVERINGS	Labour hours	Nett labour £	Nett material £	O'heads /profit £	Unit	Total £
Granular filling in bed and benching to 100mm diameter pipe, bed thickness						
- 100mm	0.24	1.33	1.07	0.36	m	2.76
- 150mm	0.28	1.55	1.34	0.43	m	3.32
Granular filling in bed and benching to 150mm diameter pipe, bed thickness						
- 100mm	0.26	1.44	1.61	0.46	m	3.51
- 150mm	0.30	1.67	1.93	0.54	m	4.14
Granular filling in bed and benching to 225mm diameter pipe bed thickness						
- 100mm	0.32	1.78	2.58	0.65	m	5.01
- 150mm	0.36	2.00	3.00	0.75	m	5.75
Concrete Mix A in bed and benching to 100mm diameter pipe, bed thickness						
- 100mm	0.48	2.66	5.48	1.22	m	9.36
- 150mm	0.56	3.11	6.85	1.49	m	11.45
Concrete Mix A in bed and benching to 150mm diameter pipe, bed thickness						
- 100mm	0.52	2.89	8.22	1.67	m	12.78
- 150mm	0.60	3.33	9.86	1.98	m	15.17
Concrete Mix A in bed and benching to 225mm diameter pipe, bed thickness						
- 100mm	0.60	3.33	13.16	2.47	m	18.96
- 150mm	0.65	3.61	15.35	2.84	m	21.80
Granular filling in bed and surround to 100mm diameter pipe, bed thickness						
- 100mm	0.36	2.00	1.93	0.59	m	4.52
- 150mm	0.42	2.33	2.15	0.67	m	5.15

BEDS AND COVERINGS	Labour hours	Nett labour £	Nett material £	O'heads /profit £	Unit	Total £
Granular filling in bed and surround to 150mm diameter pipe, bed thickness						
- 100mm	0.39	2.17	2.58	0.71	m	5.46
- 150mm	0.45	2.50	2.90	0.81	m	6.21
Granular filling in bed and surround to 225mm diameter pipe, bed thickness						
- 100mm	0.48	2.66	3.86	0.98	m	7.50
- 150mm	0.54	3.00	4.19	1.08	m	8.27
Concrete Mix A in bed and surround to 100mm diameter pipe, bed thickness						
- 100mm	0.72	4.00	9.87	2.08	m	15.95
- 150mm	0.84	4.66	10.96	2.34	m	17.96
Concrete Mix A in bed and surround to 150mm diameter pipe, bed thickness						
- 100mm	0.78	4.33	13.16	2.62	m	20.11
- 150mm	1.20	6.66	14.80	3.22	m	24.68
Concrete Mix A in bed and surround to 225mm diameter pipe, bed thickness						
- 100mm	0.90	5.00	19.74	3.71	m	28.45
- 150mm	0.98	5.44	21.38	4.02	m	30.84

Pipework

	Labour hours	Nett labour £	Nett material £	O'heads /profit £	Unit	Total £
Vitrified clay spigot and socket drain pipes, joints in cement mortar 100mm diameter						
- laid in trenches	0.50	2.78	2.67	0.82	m	6.27
- in lengths not exceeding 3m	0.75	4.16	2.67	1.03	m	7.86
- bends	0.40	2.22	1.95	0.63	nr	4.80
- rest bend	0.40	2.22	4.82	1.06	nr	8.10

DRAINAGE

	Labour hours	Nett labour £	Nett material £	O'heads /profit £	Unit	Total £
Pipework contd.;						
- single junction	0.40	2.22	5.54	1.16	nr	8.92
- double junction	0.50	2.78	12.71	2.32	nr	17.81
Vitrified clay spigot and socket drain pipes, joints in cement mortar 150mm diameter						
- laid in trenches	0.60	3.33	4.80	1.22	m	9.35
- in lengths not exceeding 3m	0.90	5.00	4.80	1.47	m	11.27
- bends	0.45	2.50	4.31	1.02	nr	7.83
- rest bend	0.45	2.50	8.30	1.62	nr	12.42
- single junction	0.45	2.50	8.61	1.67	nr	12.78
- double junction	0.60	3.33	16.81	3.02	nr	23.16
Hepworths Supersleve vitrified clay drain pipes, spigot and socket joints with sealing rings 100mm diameter						
- laid in trenches	0.36	2.00	2.44	0.67	m	5.11
- in lengths not exceeding 3m	0.54	3.00	2.44	0.82	m	6.26
- bends	0.30	1.67	2.46	0.62	nr	4.75
- rest bend	0.30	1.67	3.90	0.84	nr	6.41
- single junction	0.30	1.67	5.02	1.00	nr	7.69
Hepworths Supersleve vitrified clay drain pipes, spigot and socket joints with sealing rings 150mm diameter						
- laid in trenches	0.40	2.22	6.01	1.24	m	9.47
- in lengths not exceeding 3m	0.60	3.33	6.01	1.40	m	10.74
- bends	0.35	1.94	5.13	1.06	nr	8.13
- rest bend	0.35	1.94	6.25	1.23	nr	9.42
- single junction	0.35	1.94	8.41	1.55	nr	11.90
Hepworths Hepseal vitrified clay drain pipes, spigot and socket joints with sealing rings 100mm diameter						
- laid in trenches	0.36	2.00	4.47	0.97	m	7.44
- in lengths not exceeding 3m	0.54	3.00	4.47	1.12	m	8.59
- bends	0.30	1.67	6.15	1.17	nr	8.99
- rest bend	0.30	1.67	7.69	1.40	nr	10.76
- single junction	0.30	1.67	8.00	1.45	nr	11.12

DRAINAGE

	Labour hours	Nett labour £	Nett material /plant £	O'heads /profit £	Unit	Total £
Pipes contd.;						
Hepworths Hepseal vitrified clay drain pipes, spigot and socket joints with sealing rings 150mm diameter						
- laid in trenches	0.40	2.22	5.90	1.22	m	9.34
- in lengths not exceeding 3m	0.60	3.33	5.90	1.39	m	10.62
- bends	0.35	1.94	8.97	1.64	nr	12.55
- rest bend	0.35	1.94	11.79	2.06	nr	15.79
- single junction	0.35	1.94	28.70	4.60	nr	35.24
Hepworths Hepseal vitrified clay drain pipes, spigot and socket joints with sealing rings 225mm diameter						
- laid in trenches	0.60	3.33	12.01	2.30	m	17.64
- in lengths not exceeding 3m	0.90	5.00	12.01	2.55	m	19.56
- bends	0.45	2.50	19.48	3.30	nr	25.28
- rest bend	0.45	2.50	31.57	5.11	nr	39.18
- single junction	0.45	2.50	31.78	5.14	nr	39.42
Gullies						
Vitrified clay gully with 100mm diameter outlet, 150mm square gully grid jointed to drain, surrounding in concrete	1.50	8.33	17.39	3.86	nr	29.58
Yard gulley, trapped, 150mm diameter with 100mm outlet, 200mm square gulley grid, surrounded in concrete	1.50	8.33	22.85	4.68	nr	35.86
Manholes						
Excavate by hand for manhole not exceeding						
- 1m deep	4.00	22.20	-	3.33	m3	25.53
- 2m deep	4.50	24.98	-	3.75	m3	28.73
- 3m deep	5.65	31.36	-	4.70	m3	36.06
Excavate by machine for manhole not exceeding						
- 1m deep	0.25	1.39	4.80	0.93	m3	7.12

DRAINAGE

	Labour hours	Nett labour £	Nett material /plant £	O'heads /profit £	Unit	Total £
Manholes contd.;						
- 2m deep	0.28	1.55	5.40	1.04	m3	7.99
- 3m deep	0.50	2.78	6.00	1.32	m3	10.10
Earthwork support not exceeding 2m between opposing faces not exceeding						
- 1m deep	0.40	2.22	0.90	0.47	m2	3.59
- 2m deep	0.45	2.50	1.00	0.53	m2	4.03
- 3m deep	0.55	3.05	1.10	0.62	m2	4.77
Load excavated material into barrows, wheel average 50m and load into skip	2.80	15.54	-	2.33	m3	17.87
Site mixed concrete A in manhole bed thickness						
- 100 - 150mm	2.00	11.10	57.16	10.24	m3	78.50
- 150 - 300mm	1.70	9.44	59.24	10.30	m3	78.98
Site mixed concrete B in benching to manholes average 225mm thick	3.40	18.87	59.24	11.72	m3	89.83
Common bricks in cement mortar walls to manholes one brick thick	4.25	23.59	20.50	6.61	m2	50.70
Class 'B' Engineering bricks in cement mortar in walls to manholes one brick thick	4.40	24.42	33.05	8.62	m2	66.09
Extra for fair face and flush pointing	0.25	1.39	-	0.21	m2	1.60
Build in ends of pipes to one brick wall and make good						
- small pipe	0.15	0.83	-	0.13	nr	0.96
- large pipe	0.20	1.11	-	0.17	nr	1.28
Galvanised step irons built into brickwork	0.25	1.39	4.52	0.89	nr	6.80

	Labour hours	Nett labour £	Nett material £	O'heads /profit £	Unit	Total £
Manholes contd.;						
Cast iron manhole covers, frame bedded in cement mortar						
- grade C light duty size 600 x 450mm	1.50	8.33	34.03	6.35	nr	48.71
- grade B medium duty single seal size 600 x 450mm	2.40	13.32	93.04	15.95	nr	122.31
- grade B medium duty single seal, circular 550mm diameter	2.40	13.32	92.84	15.92	nr	122.08
Best quality vitrified clay channels, bedded and jointed in cement mortar						
Half section straight main channel, diameter						
- 100mm	1.10	6.11	3.13	1.39	m	10.63
- 150mm	1.25	6.94	6.62	2.03	m	15.59
Half section tapered main channel, diameter						
- 150 - 100mm	1.25	6.94	14.91	3.28	m	25.13
Half section 90° main channel bends, diameter						
- 100mm	1.10	6.11	3.93	1.51	nr	11.55
- 150mm	1.25	6.94	6.62	2.03	nr	15.59
Half section 90° tapered main channel bend, diameter						
- 150 - 100mm	1.25	6.94	23.10	4.51	nr	34.55
Three quarter section branch channel bend, diameter						
- 100mm	1.10	6.11	4.52	1.60	nr	12.23
- 150mm	1.25	6.94	7.56	2.18	nr	16.68

FENCING

	Unit	Specialist Prices £
The following prices have been supplied by a specialist fencing firm and represent the cost of carrying out small fencing works in average conditions.		
Chainlink fencing, (B.S.1722 Part 1) galvanised steel mesh, three strained line wires, concrete posts at 3m centres, height		
- 1.20m	m	12.00
- 1.80m	m	14.00
Chainlink fencing, (B.S.1722 Part 1) plastic coated mesh, three strained line wires, concrete posts at 3m centres		
- 1.20m	m	14.25
- 1.80m	m	16.30
Extra for one line of barbed wire to top line wire	m	0.12
Strained wire fence (B.S.1722 Part 3), concrete intermediate posts at 3m centres, holed for wire, height		
- 1.00m (5 wires)	m	8.10
- 1.20m (6 wires)	m	8.55
- 1.40m (8 wires)	m	9.10
Cleft chestnut fencing (B.S.1722 Part 4), timber posts average 2.5m centres, pales average 75mm apart, height		
- 0.90m	m	6.90
- 1.05m	m	7.35
- 1.20m	m	8.00
- 1.35m	m	8.40
- 1.80m	m	12.00

FENCING   Unit   Specialist
                                                           Prices
                                                             £

Close boarded fence (B.S.1722
Part 5), pales lapped at 13mm
centres, treated softwood
intermediate posts at 3m centres,
height

- 1.00m	m	19.20
- 1.20m	m	19.50
- 1.40m	m	21.00
- 1.60m	m	23.00
- 1.80m	m	25.00

Wooden palisade fence (B.S.1722
Part 6), pales spaced 75mm apart,
intermediate concrete posts at 3m
centres, height

- 1.00m	m	17.00
- 1.20m	m	18.00
- 1.40m	m	19.00
- 1.60m	m	21.00
- 1.80m	m	23.00

1. Labour

    Craftsman   £6.44 per hour
    Labourer   £5.55 per hour

2. Materials

	Unit	Basic Price	Waste %	Total £
Imported topsoil	m3	14.50	2½	14.86
Fertilizer	25kg	15.00	7½	16.13
Grass seed	kg	3.00	5	3.15
Meadow turf	m2	2.10	5	2.21
Granular fill	m3	9.75	10	10.73
Sand	t	7.70	10	8.47
Hardcore	m3	10.50	10	11.55
Ready mix concrete mix B	m3	53.72	5	56.41
'Korkpak' fibre joint filler				
10mm thick x 78mm wide	m	1.35	5	1.42
Fabric reinforcement (A142)	m2	1.38	10	1.52
P.C. paving flags natural colour, size				
600 x 600 x 50mm	m2	6.41	5	6.73
750 x 600 x 50mm	m2	6.30	5	6.62
900 x 600 x 50mm	m2	5.10	5	5.36
P.C. paving flags coloured, size				
600 x 600 x 50mm	m2	7.80	5	8.19
750 x 600 x 50mm	m2	7.60	5	7.98
900 x 600 x 50mm	m2	6.30	5	6.62
'Pennine' P.C. paving flags 38mm thick buff, brown or red				
225 x 450mm	m2	11.30	5	11.87
450 x 450mm	m2	11.00	5	11.55
675 x 450mm	m2	10.10	5	10.61
Charcon Europa P.C. paving blocks, thickness				
65mm natural	m2	8.15	5	8.56
80mm brindle	m2	8.00	5	8.40
P.C. edgings, 50 x 150mm				
flat top	m	2.45	5	2.57
round top	m	2.50	5	2.63
bullnosed	m	2.50	5	2.63

EXCAVATION	Labour	Nett	Nett	O'heads	Unit	Total
Labour rate £5.55 per hour	hours	labour £	material /plant £	/profit £		£

For cutting down trees and
general excavation see EARTHWORKS
section

FILLING (HAND)

Make up levels, compact and grade, thickness

Over 250mm

- surplus excavated material	1.38	7.66	-	1.15	m3	8.81
- imported topsoil	1.47	8.16	14.86	3.45	m3	26.47

Average 100mm

- surplus excavated material	0.24	1.33	-	0.20	m2	1.53
- imported topsoil	0.28	1.55	1.50	0.46	m2	3.51

Average 150mm

- surplus excavated material	0.28	1.55	-	0.23	m2	1.78
- imported topsoil	0.32	1.78	2.23	0.60	m2	4.61

Average 225mm

- surplus excavated material	0.38	2.11	-	0.32	m2	2.43
- imported topsoil	0.42	2.33	3.34	0.85	m2	6.52

FILLING (MACHINE)

Make up levels, compact and grade, thickness

Over 250mm

∟ surplus excavated material	0.33	1.83	-	0.28	m3	2.10
- imported topsoil	0.33	1.83	14.86	2.50	m3	19.19

Average 100mm

- surplus excavated material	0.11	0.61	-	0.09	m2	0.70
- imported topsoil	0.12	0.67	1.70	0.36	m2	2.73

Average 150mm

- surplus excavated material	0.14	0.78	-	0.12	m2	0.90
- imported topsoil	0.15	0.83	2.50	0.50	m2	3.83

FILLING (MACHINE)	Labour hours	Nett labour £	Nett material /plant £	O'heads /profit £	Unit	Total £
Make up levels, compact and grade, thickness contd.;						
Average 225mm						
- surplus excavated material	0.18	1.00	-	0.15	m2	1.15
- imported topsoil	0.21	1.17	4.00	0.78	m2	5.95
Prepare existing or filled vegetable soil for cultivation, remove stones and weeds						
- hand digging	0.40	2.22	-	0.33	m2	2.55
- rotovating	0.14	0.78	1.10	0.28	m2	2.16
Apply fertilizer by hand to prepared ground	0.03	0.17	0.08	0.04	m2	0.29
Apply grass seed to prepared ground, water, roll, cut and re-seed where necessary	0.05	0.28	0.20	0.07	m2	0.55
Imported meadow turf laid on prepared ground						
- horizontal	0.40	2.22	2.25	0.67	m2	5.14
- sloping	0.45	2.50	2.25	0.71	m2	5.46

BEDS AND BASES

Beds and bases, compacting in layers where necessary, grading thickness

Average 100mm						
- granular fill	0.10	0.56	1.07	0.25	m2	1.88
- sand	0.12	0.67	0.85	0.23	m2	1.75
- hardcore	0.15	0.83	1.16	0.30	m2	2.29
Average 150mm						
- granular fill	0.12	0.67	1.61	0.34	m2	2.62
- sand	0.14	0.78	1.27	0.31	m2	2.36
- hardcore	0.18	1.00	1.73	0.41	m2	3.14

BEDS AND BASES	Labour hours	Nett labour £	Nett material £	O'heads /profit £	Unit	Total £
Beds and bases, compacting in layers where necessary, grading thickness contd.;				—		
Average 200mm						
- granular fill	0.15	0.83	2.15	0.45	m2	3.43
- sand	0.17	0.94	1.69	0.40	m2	3.03
- hardcore	0.20	1.11	2.31	0.51	m2	3.93
PATHS AND PAVINGS						
Ready mix concrete mix B in beds, thickness						
- not exceeding 100mm	2.10	11.66	57.78	10.42	m3	79.86
- 100 - 150mm	1.70	9.44	57.78	10.08	m3	77.30
Trowelling surfaces of concrete to falls	0.23	1.28	-	0.19	m2	1.47
'Korkpak' fibre joint filler 10mm thick x 78mm wide in paths	0.05	0.28	1.42	0.26	m	1.96
Wrought formwork to sides of concrete paths not exceeding 250mm high	0.75	4.16	1.70	0.88	m	6.74
Steel fabric reinforcement B.S.4483, laid in concrete beds (A142)	0.12	0.67	1.52	0.33	m	2.52
Labour rate £6.44 per hour						
Precast concrete paving flags (B.S.368), spot bedded in cement lime mortar (1:1:6), size						
Natural colour						
- 600 x 600 x 50mm	0.60	3.86	6.61	1.57	m2	12.04
- 750 x 600 x 50mm	0.50	3.22	6.50	1.46	m2	11.18
- 900 x 600 x 50mm	0.45	2.90	5.30	1.23	m2	9.43

PATHS AND PAVINGS Labour rate £6.44 per hour	Labour hours	Nett labour £	Nett material £	O'heads /profit £	Unit	Total £
Precast concrete paving flags (B.S.368), spot bedded in cement lime mortar (1:1:6), size contd.;						
Coloured, size						
- 600 x 600 x 50mm	0.60	3.86	8.00	1.78	m2	13.64
- 750 x 600 x 50mm	0.50	3.22	7.80	1.65	m2	12.67
- 900 x 900 x 50mm	0.45	2.90	6.50	1.41	m2	10.81
'Pennine' precast concrete paving, spot bedded in cement lime mortar buff, brown or red 38mm thick, size						
- 225 x 450mm	1.00	6.44	11.50	2.69	m2	20.63
- 450 x 450mm	0.80	5.15	11.20	2.45	m2	18.80
- 675 x 450mm	0.65	4.19	10.30	2.17	m2	16.66
Charcon 'Europa' precast concrete blocks size 200 x 100mm laid on sand bed 50mm thick, laid flat, thickness						
- 65mm	1.30	8.37	8.55	2.54	m2	19.46
- 80mm	1.50	9.66	8.40	2.71	m2	20.77
<u>Edgings</u>						
Precast concrete edgings to paths, bedding and pointing in cement mortar, haunched with site mixed concrete mix A, size						
- 50 x 150mm flat top	0.35	2.25	3.45	0.86	m	6.56
- 50 x 150mm round top	0.35	2.25	3.50	0.86	m	6.61
- 50 x 150mm bullnosed	0.35	2.25	3.50	0.86	m	6.61

The following composite rates
have been built up from
information given earlier in this
chapter. The rates have been
rounded off for ease of use and
should be helpful when assessing
approximate values of
construction work. It should be
noted that some trades do not
have an entry because the related
item descriptions are given in
the preceding prices and do not
lend themselves to composite
descriptions.

EARTHWORKS

Excavate by hand for trench
including supports and sides,
level and ram bottom, part return
fill and ram, part load into
skip, average width 600mm,
average depth

- 0.75m	m	22.00
- 1.00m	m	25.00
- 1.50m	m	32.00

Excavate by machine for
foundation trench including
supports to sides, level and ram
bottom, part return fill and ram,
part load into skip, average
width 600mm, average depth

- 0.75m	m	13.00
- 1.00m	m	18.00
- 1.50m	m	24.00

CONCRETE WORK

Plain concrete (1:3:6) in foundations 600mm wide x 225mm deep	m	10.20
Plain concrete (1:3:6) in foundations 750mm wide x 225mm deep	m	12.75

366

CONCRETE WORK	Unit	Approximate Prices £
Reinforced concrete (1:2:4) in bed with A252 reinforcement thickness		
- 100mm	m2	12.30
- 150mm	m2	16.25
Reinforced concrete (1:2:4) in wall including wrought formwork both sides and bar reinforcement, thickness		
- 150mm	m2	87.00
- 225mm	m2	105.00

BRICKWORK

	Unit	Approximate Prices £
Cavity wall in gauged mortar including forming cavity and wall ties between half brick wall in common and		
- 100mm blockwork	m2	50.00
- half brick wall in common	m2	56.00
- half brick fair faced wall	m2	60.00
- half brick wall in facings	m2	77.00
Cavity wall in gauged mortar including forming cavity and wall ties between 100mm blockwork and		
- half brick fair faced wall	m2	57.00
- half brick wall in facings	m2	71.00

ROOFING

	Unit	Approximate Prices £
Natural Welsh blue slates on battens and felt	m2	47.00
Marley Modern concrete tiles on battens and felt	m2	17.35
Woodwool slabs 50mm thick and two layers built up roofing felt	m2	29.00
Reinforced woodwool slabs 75mm thick and three layers built up roofing felt	m2	38.00

WOODWORK	Unit	Approximate Prices
19mm thick tongued and grooved boarding to joists size		£
- 50 x 100mm	m2	24.00
- 50 x 125mm	m2	26.50
- 75 x 125mm	m2	27.50
Stud partition thickness		
- 75mm	m2	12.00
- 100mm	m2	13.00
Standard flush door hardboard both sides including frame, architrave both sides, fixing only ironmongery, size		
- 686 x 1981 x 35mm	nr	87.50
- 726 x 2040 x 40mm	nr	108.00
Standard flush door plywood faced both sides including frame, architrave both sides, fixing only ironmongery, size		
- 762 x 1981 x 35mm	nr	94.00
- 826 x 2040 x 40mm	nr	115.00
Standard flush door teak faced both sides including frame, architrave both sides, fixing only ironmongery, size		
- 686 x 1981 x 35mm	nr	120.00
- 726 x 2040 x 40mm	nr	165.00

PLUMBING

RAINWATER INSTALLATION

Rainwater installation complete including gutters, pipes and connections to drains

uPVC; 112mm half round gutter; 75mm diameter pipe
- terraced house ... 125.00
- semi-detached house with gable end ... 134.00
- semi-detached house with pitched end ... 165.00
- detached house with gable ends ... 135.00
- detached house with pitched ends ... 205.00

HOT AND COLD WATER INSTALLATION

Approximate
Prices
£

Hot and cold water installation complete; plastic
storage cistern; indirect copper cylinder with
immersion heater; feed to ground floor sink, first
floor W.C., washbasin and bath; lagging to cistern,
cylinder and pipes in roof space

- copper pipework   840.00

    Add for servicing additional fittings
     - W.C's   20.00
     - washbasins   40.00

CENTRAL HEATING INSTALLATION

Central heating installation complete; floor mounted
gas boiler with pump; copper distribution pipework;
expansion tank; connection to indirect cylinder;
stove primed steel radiators

- three bed terraced house   1650.00
- three bed semi-detached house   1700.00
- four bed detached house   1850.00

SOIL AND WASTE INSTALLATION

Soil and waste installation complete; serving ground
floor sink and first floor bath, washbasin and W.C.

- uPVC pipework   165.00

    Add for servicing additional fittings
     - washbasin   25.00

- cast iron pipework   410.00

    Add for servicing additional fittings
     - washbasin   70.00

APPROXIMATE ESTIMATING

SANITARY APPLIANCES	Approximate Prices
	£

Washbasin and pedestal complete; vitreous china;
chromium plated pillar taps, waste and chain; plastic
plug and traps

Size 560 x 430mm
  - white 90.00
Size 660 x 565mm
  - white 145.00
  - coloured 150.00

Bath complete; chromium plated pillar taps, waste
and chain; plastic plug and trap with overflow; bath
panel to side and end

3mm acrylic
  - white 165.00
  - coloured 168.00

5mm acrylic
  - white 185.00
  - coloured 190.00

1.6mm pressed steel
  - white 180.00
  - coloured 190.00

2.5mm pressed steel
  - white 230.00
  - coloured 250.00

Cast iron
  - white 270.00
  - coloured 290.00

Close coupled W.C. complete; 19mm overflow
pipework through wall; plastic seat·

White

  - washdown type 140.00
  - syphonic type 245.00

Coloured
  - washdown type 170.00
  - syphonic type 270.00

APPROXIMATE ESTIMATING

FLOOR WALL AND CEILING FINISHINGS

Approximate
Prices
£

11mm two coat plaster; browning and finish to walls; 12.5mm plasterboard and skim to ceiling; individual rooms

Floor to ceiling height 2.4m;
floor area
- 9m2   244.00
- 12m2 298.00
- 15m2 350.00
- 18m2 400.00
- 21m2 450.00
- 24m2 500.00
- 27m2 545.00
- 30m2 590.00

50mm granolithic to floors; 19mm thick 175mm high skirting; individual rooms

Floor area
- 9m2   155.00
- 122   195.00
- 15m2 240.00
- 18m2 285.00
- 21m2 325.00
- 24m2 365.00
- 27m2 410.00
- 30m2 450.00

25mm thick quarry floor tiles bedded in 12mm mortar; 12.5mm thick x 150mm high skirting: individual rooms

Floor area
- 9m2   290.00
- 12m2 375.00
- 15m2 460.00
- 18m2 555.00
- 21m2 630.00
- 24m2 715.00
- 27m2 800.00
- 30m2 880.00

APPROXIMATE ESTIMATING

2.5mm thick Econoflex series 4 vinyl tiles; 100mm high matching vinyl skirting; individual rooms		Approximate Prices £
Floor area		
- 9m2		85.00
- 12m2		105.00
- 15m2		130.00
- 18m2		150.00
- 21m2		170.00
- 24m2		195.00
- 27m2		215.00
- 30m2		235.00

Woodblock Mahogany flooring, 25mm thick
tongued & grooved, herringbone
pattern, fixed with adhesive,
sanding.

Floor area		
- 9m2		325.00
- 12m2		430.00
- 15m2		540.00
- 18m2		645.00
- 21m2		750.00
- 24m2		860.00
- 27m2		965.00
- 30m2		1075.00

PAINTING

Two coats emulsion
paint on

- plastered walls	m2	2.10
- plastered ceilings	m2	2.70

Knot prime stop, two undercoats
and one coat gloss on

- wood general surfaces	m2	6.30
- metal general surfaces	m2	6.50

EXTERNAL WORKS		Approximate Prices £
Prepare existing ground, apply fertilizer and grass seed	m2	3.20
Prepare existing ground and lay turf	m2	6.70
Excavate to reduce levels, lay sand or hardcore bed 100mm thick and lay path in		
- insitu concrete 100mm thick	m2	12.00
- precast concrete flags	m2	17.00

DRAINAGE

Hand excavation

Excavate trench, granular bed and benching, lay 100mm Hepseal pipe, backfill and remove surplus, average depth of trench

- 1.00m	m	28.00
- 2.00m	m	52.00
- 3.00m	m	88.00

Excavate trench, granular bed and benching, lay 150mm Hepseal pipe, backfill and remove surplus, average depth of trench

- 1.00m	m	31.00
- 2.00m	m	55.00
- 3.00m	m	91.00

Excavate trench, granular bed and benching, lay 225mm Hepseal pipe, backfill and remove surplus, average depth of trench

- 1.00m	m	43.00
- 2.00m	m	69.00
- 3.00m	m	108.00

Excavate trench, concrete bed and benching, lay 100mm Hepseal pipe, backfill and remove surplus, average depth of trench 1m

	m	32.00

DRAINAGE

		Approximate Prices £
Excavate trench, concrete bed and benching, lay 150mm Hepseal pipe, backfill and remove surplus, average depth of trench 1m	m	38.00
Excavate trench, concrete bed and benching, lay 225mm Hepseal pipe, backfill and remove surplus, average depth of trench 1m	m	53.00

Machine excavation

Excavate trench, granular bed and benching, lay 100mm Hepseal pipe, backfill and remove surplus, average depth of trench		
- 1.00m	m	22.00
- 2.00m	m	31.00
- 3.00m	m	39.00
Excavate trench, granular bed and benching, lay 150mm Hepseal pipe, backfill and remove surplus, average depth of trench		
- 1.00m	m	26.00
- 2.00m	m	34.00
- 3.00m	m	42.00
Excavate trench, granular bed and benching, lay 225mm Hepseal pipe, backfill and remove surplus, average depth of trench		
- 1.00m	m	36.00
- 2.00m	m	45.00
- 3.00m	m	55.00
Excavate trench, concrete bed and benching, lay 100mm Hepseal pipe, backfill and remove surplus, average depth of trench 1m	m	27.00
Excavate trench, concrete bed and benching, lay 150mm Hepseal pipe, backfill and remove surplus, average depth of trench 1m	m	33.00

DRAINAGE

		Approximate Prices £
Excavate trench, concrete bed and benching, lay 225mm Hepseal pipe, backfill and remove surplus, average depth of trench 1m	m	47.00
Manhole including excavation, concrete base and benching Class 'B' engineering brick walls, 150mm straight main channel, two three quarter section bends, light duty cover and frame, depth to invert		
- 1.00m	nr	325.00
- 1.50m	nr	375.00
- 2.00m	nr	440.00

Chapter 13: General Data

Mensuration

Circumference or Perimeters of Planes

Circle   3.1416 x Diameter

Ellipse   3.1416 x $\frac{1}{2}$ (major axis + minor axis)

Sector   <u>Radius x Degrees in Arc</u> + 2r
                           57.3

Surface Areas of Planes and Solids

Circle   Pi (3.1416) x Radius^2 or 0.7854 x Diameter^2

Cone $\frac{1}{2}$ Circumference x Slant Height + Area of Base

Frustum of
Cone   Pi (3.1416) x Slant Height x (radius at top + radius at
                base) + Area of Top and Base

Cylinder   Circumference x Length + Area of two ends

Ellipse
(approx)   Product of Axes x 0.7854

Parallelo-
gram   Base x Height

Pyramid $\frac{1}{2}$ Base Perimeter x Slant Height + Area of Base

Sector of
Circle   <u>3.1416 x Degrees in Arc x Radius^2</u> = <u>$\frac{1}{2}r^2$ x degrees in arc</u>
                              360   57.3

Sphere   Diameter2 x 3.1416

Triangle   Half Base x Perpendicular Height

Volumes

Cone   Area of Base x $\frac{1}{2}$ Perpendicular Height

Cylinder   3.1416 x Radius^2 x Height

Pyramid   Area of Base x $\frac{1}{4}$ Perpendicular Height

376

General Data

Capacity

1 fl oz	= 28.4ml		1ml	= 0.0352 fl oz
1 pt	= 0.568 ltr		1dl	= 3.52 fl oz
1 gallon	= 4.546 ltr		1 ltr	= 1.7598 pt

Weight

1 oz	= 28.35g		1g	= 0.035 oz
1 lb	= 0.4536kg		1kg	= 35.274 oz
1 st	= 6.35kg		1t	= 2204.6 lb
1 ton	= 1.016t		1t	= 0.9842 ton

Temperature equivalents

In order to convert Fahrenheit to Centigrade deduct 32 and multiply by 5/9. To convert Centigrade to Fahrenheit multiply by 9/5 and add 32.

Fahrenheit	Centigrade
230	110.0
220	104.4
210	98.9
200	93.3
190	87.8
180	82.2
170	76.7
160	71.1
150	65.6
140	60.0
130	54.4
120	48.9
110	43.3
90	32.2
80	26.7
70	21.1
60	15.6
50	10.0
40	4.4
30	-1.1
20	-6.7
10	-12.2
0	-17.8

General Data

Equivalents

| **Imperial** | **Metric** |

Length

12 inches	= 1 foot	10 millimetres	= 1 centimetre
3 feet	= 1 yard	100 centimetres	= 1 metre
22 yards	= 1 chain	1000 metres	= 1 kilometre
10 chains	= 1 furlong		
8 furlongs	= 1 mile		
6080 feet	= 1 nautical mile		
6 feet	= 1 fathom		

Area

| 4840 square yards | = 1 acre | 10,000 square | |
| 640 acres | = 1 square mile | metres | = 1 hectare |

Volume

20 fluid ounces	= 1 pint	10 millilitres	= 1 centilitre
2 pints	= 1 quart	100 centilitres	= 1 litre
4 quarts	= 1 gallon	1 litre	= 1 cubic decimetre
		1000 cubic	
		decimetres	= 1 cubic metre

Mass

16 ounces	= 1 pound	1000 grammes	= 1 kilogramme
14 pounds	= 1 stone	1000 kilogrammes	= 1 tonne
2 stones	= 1 quarter		
4 quarters	= 1 hundredweight		
20 hundredweights	= 1 ton		

Imperial/Metric Convertion

Imperial to Metric - multiply by factor

Metric to Imperial - divide by factor

Length

	Factor
Miles into kilometres	1.60934
Yards into metres	0.9144
Feet into metres	0.3048
Inches into millimetres	25.4
Inches into centimetres	2.54

General Data

AREA

Square miles into square kilometres	2.58999
Square miles into hectares	258.999
Acres into square metres	4046.86
Acres into hectares	0.404686
Square yards into square metres	0.836127
Square feet into square metres	0.92903
Square inches into square centimetres	929.03
Square inches into square millimetres	645.16
Square inches into square centimetres	6.4516

Volume

Cubic yards into cubic metres	0.764555
Cubic feet into cubic metres	0.0283168
Cubic inches into cubic decimetres	28.3168
Cubic inches into cubic centimetres	16.3871

Capacity

Bushels into cubic metres	0.0363687
Pecks into cubic decimetres	9.09218
Gallons into litres	4.54609
US gallons into litres	3.785
Quarts into litres	1.137
Pints into litres	0.568
Gills into litres	0.142
Fluid ounces into cubic centimetres	28.4131

Velocity

Miles per hour into kilometres per hour	1.60934
Feet per second into metres per second	0.3048
Feet per minute into metres per second	0.00508
Feet per minute into metres per minute	0.3048
Inches per second into millimetres per second	25.4
Inches per minute into millimetres per second	0.423333
Inches per minute into centimetres per minute	2.54

Mass

Tons into kilogrammes	1016.05
Tons into tonnes	1.01605
Hundredweights into kilogrammes	50.8023
Quarters into kilogrammes	12.7006
Stones into kilogrammes	6.35029
Pounds into kilogrammes	0.45359237

Index